D1594240

ORDER FORM

PANTHER PUBLISHING
P.O. Box 181
Wales, MA 01081
(413) 245-6655

Please send ( ) copies of the book **The Pond Dwellers** by Kelly Savage to:

Name____________________________

Street____________________________

City or Town_______________________

State______________ Zip ___________

For each book ordered, include a check or money order made out to Panther Publishing for: $16.95 plus 5.0 percent sales tax (Mass. residents) and $2 for shipping. Allow 4-6 weeks for delivery.

Thank you for your order.

THE POND DWELLERS

KELLY SAVAGE

SECOND EDITION

PANTHER PUBLISHING

THE POND DWELLERS

By Kelly Savage

Published by:

PANTHER PUBLISHING
P.O. Box 181
Wales, MA 01081

First Printing 1996
Second Printing 1996
First Revised Printing 1997

Library of Congress Catalog Number: 96-68639

ISBN 1-57502-191-9

Printed in the USA by

Morris Publishing
3212 E. Hwy 30
Kearney, NE 68847
800-650-7888

TABLE OF CONTENTS

TABLE OF CONTENTS -2

MAJOR MASSACHUSETTS RIVERS, 1600s

a

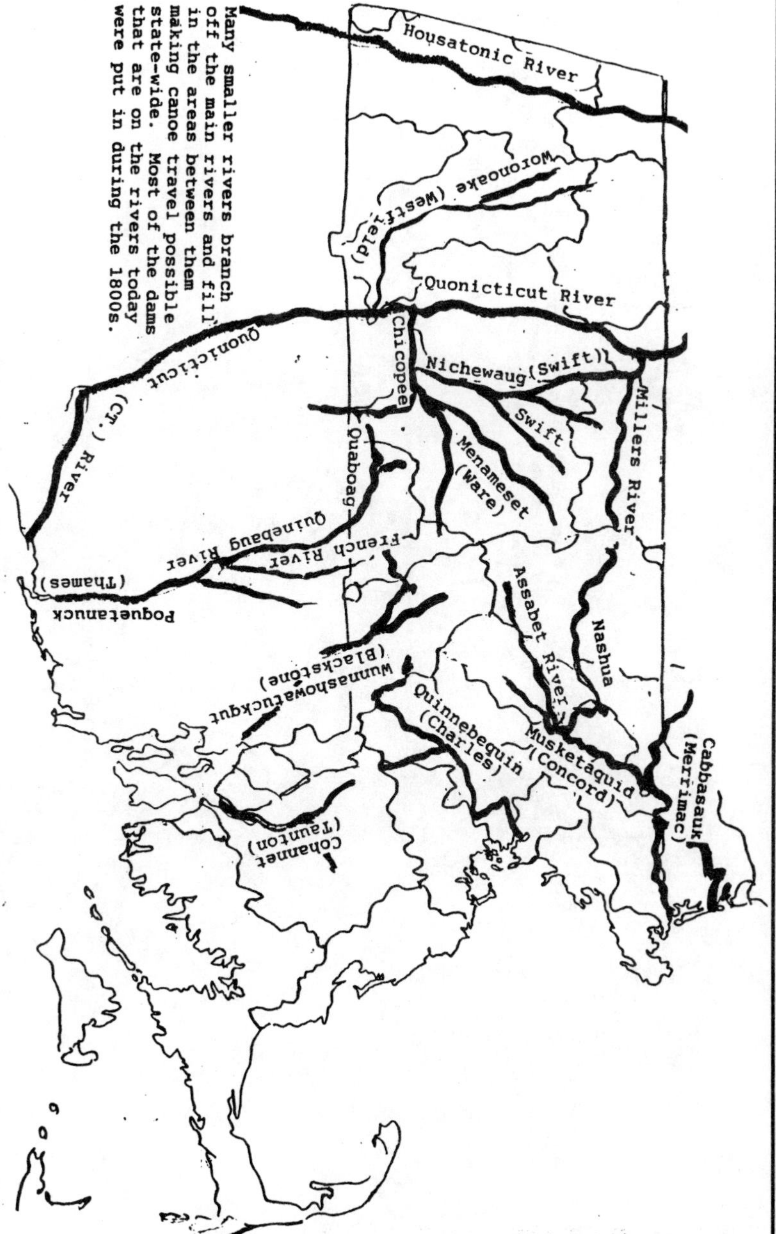

Many smaller rivers branch off the main rivers and fill in the areas between them making canoe travel possible state-wide. Most of the dams that are on the rivers today were put in during the 1800s.

Housatonic River
Woronoake (Westfield)
Quonicticut River
Quonicticut (CT.) River
Chicopee
Nichewaug (Swift)
Swift
Millers River
Quaboag
Menameset (Ware)
Quinebaug River
French River
(Thames)
Poquetanuck
Assabet River
Nashua
Wunnashowatuckqut (Blackstone)
Quinnebequin (Charles)
Musketaquid (Concord)
Cabbasauk (Merrimac)
Cohannet (Taunton)

TRIBAL RIVER BASINS, 1600s

b

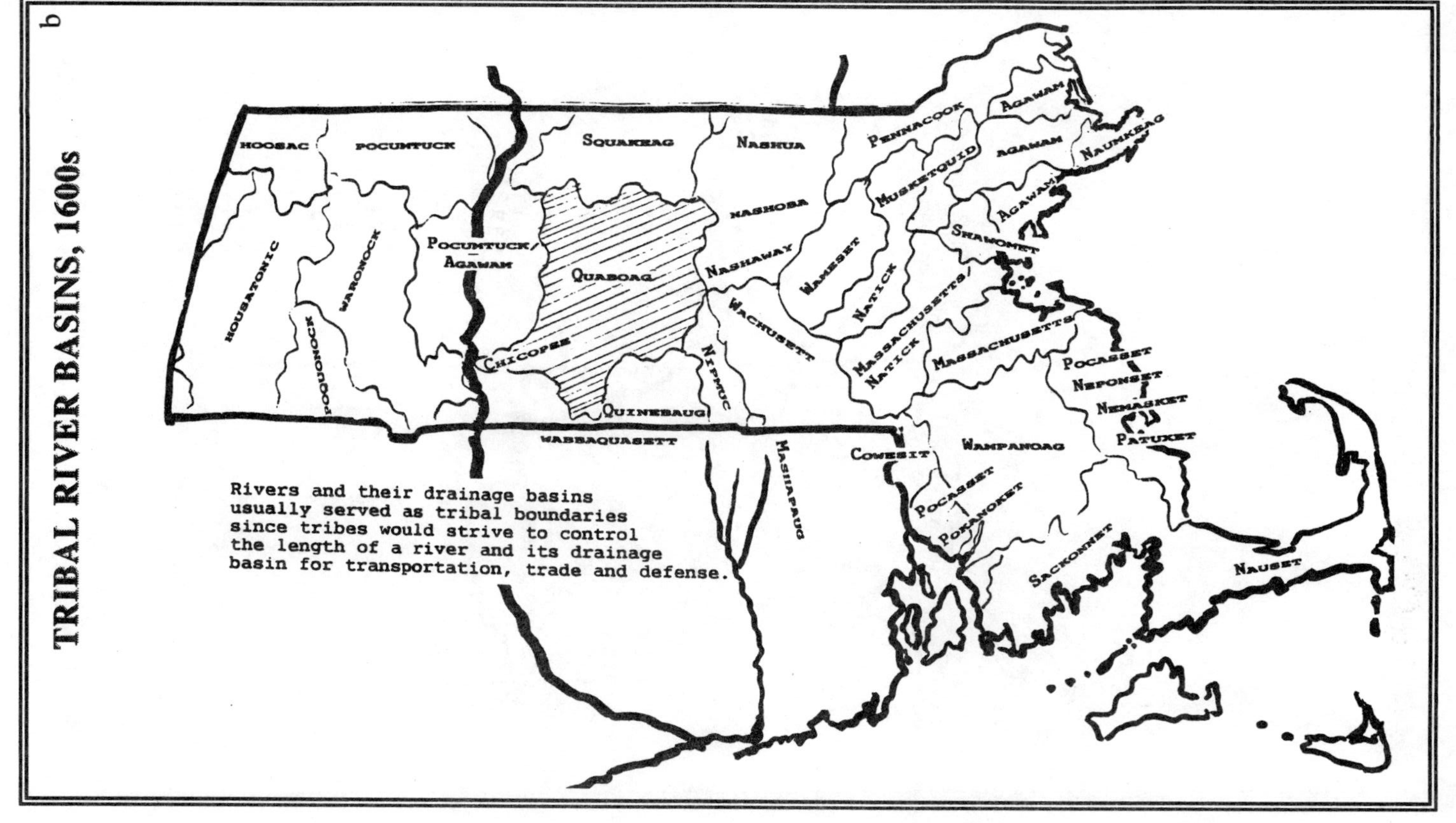

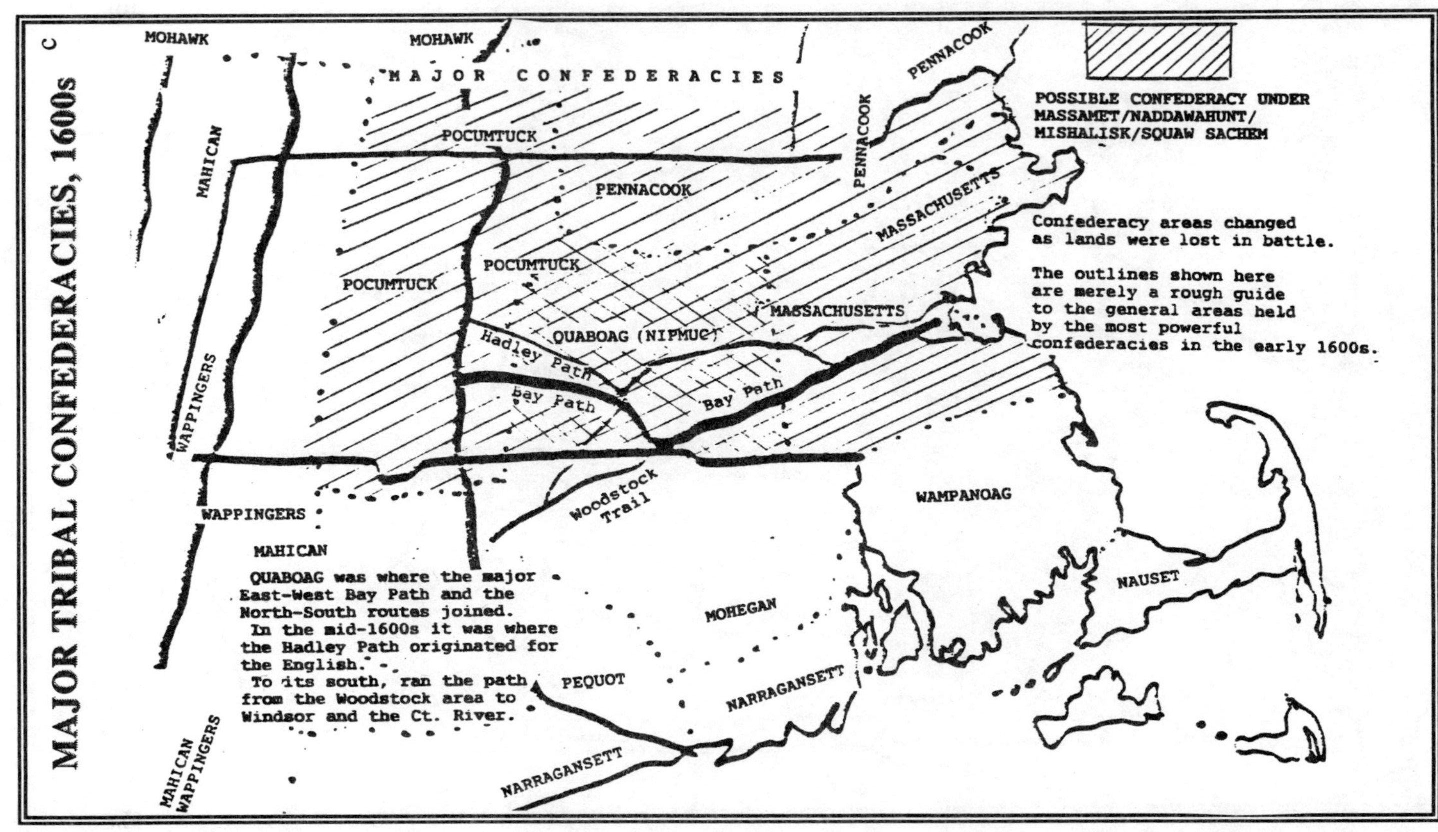

MAJOR TRIBAL CONFEDERACIES, 1600s
C
MAJOR CONFEDERACIES
POSSIBLE CONFEDERACY UNDER MASSAMET/NADDAWAHUNT/MISHALISK/SQUAW SACHEM
Confederacy areas changed as lands were lost in battle.
The outlines shown here are merely a rough guide to the general areas held by the most powerful confederacies in the early 1600s.
QUABOAG was where the major East-West Bay Path and the North-South routes joined.
In the mid-1600s it was where the Hadley Path originated for the English.
To its south, ran the path from the Woodstock area to Windsor and the Ct. River.
MOHAWK
MOHAWK
MAHICAN
WAPPINGERS
WAPPINGERS
MAHICAN
MAHICAN WAPPINGERS
POCUMTUCK
POCUMTUCK
POCUMTUCK
PENNACOOK
PENNACOOK
PENNACOOK
MASSACHUSETTS
MASSACHUSETTS
QUABOAG (NIPMUC)
Hadley Path
Bay Path
Bay Path
Woodstock Trail
WAMPANOAG
NAUSET
MOHEGAN
PEQUOT
NARRAGANSETT
NARRAGANSETT

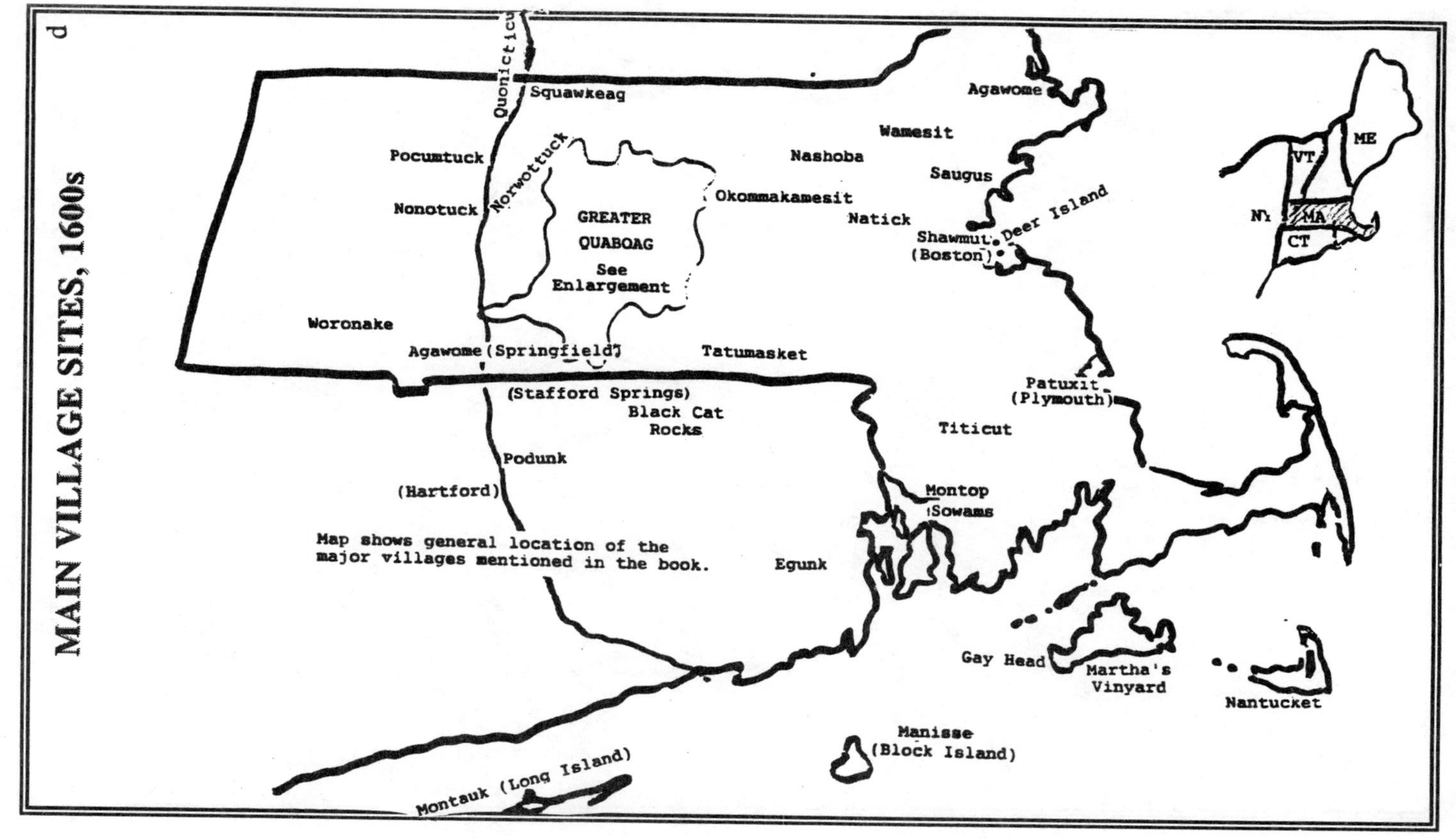

MAIN VILLAGE SITES, 1600s
d
Quonicticu
Squawkeag
Agawome
Wamesit
Nashoba
Saugus
Pocumtuck
Norwottuck
Okommakamesit
Nonotuck
GREATER QUABOAG
See Enlargement
Natick
Shawmut (Boston)
Deer Island
ME
VT
NY
MA
CT
Woronake
Agawome (Springfield)
Tatumasket
Patuxit (Plymouth)
(Stafford Springs)
Black Cat Rocks
Titicut
Podunk
(Hartford)
Montop Sowams
Map shows general location of the major villages mentioned in the book.
Egunk
Gay Head
Martha's Vinyard
Nantucket
Manisse (Block Island)
Montauk (Long Island)

THE GREATER QUABOAG/QUANSIK AREA [e]

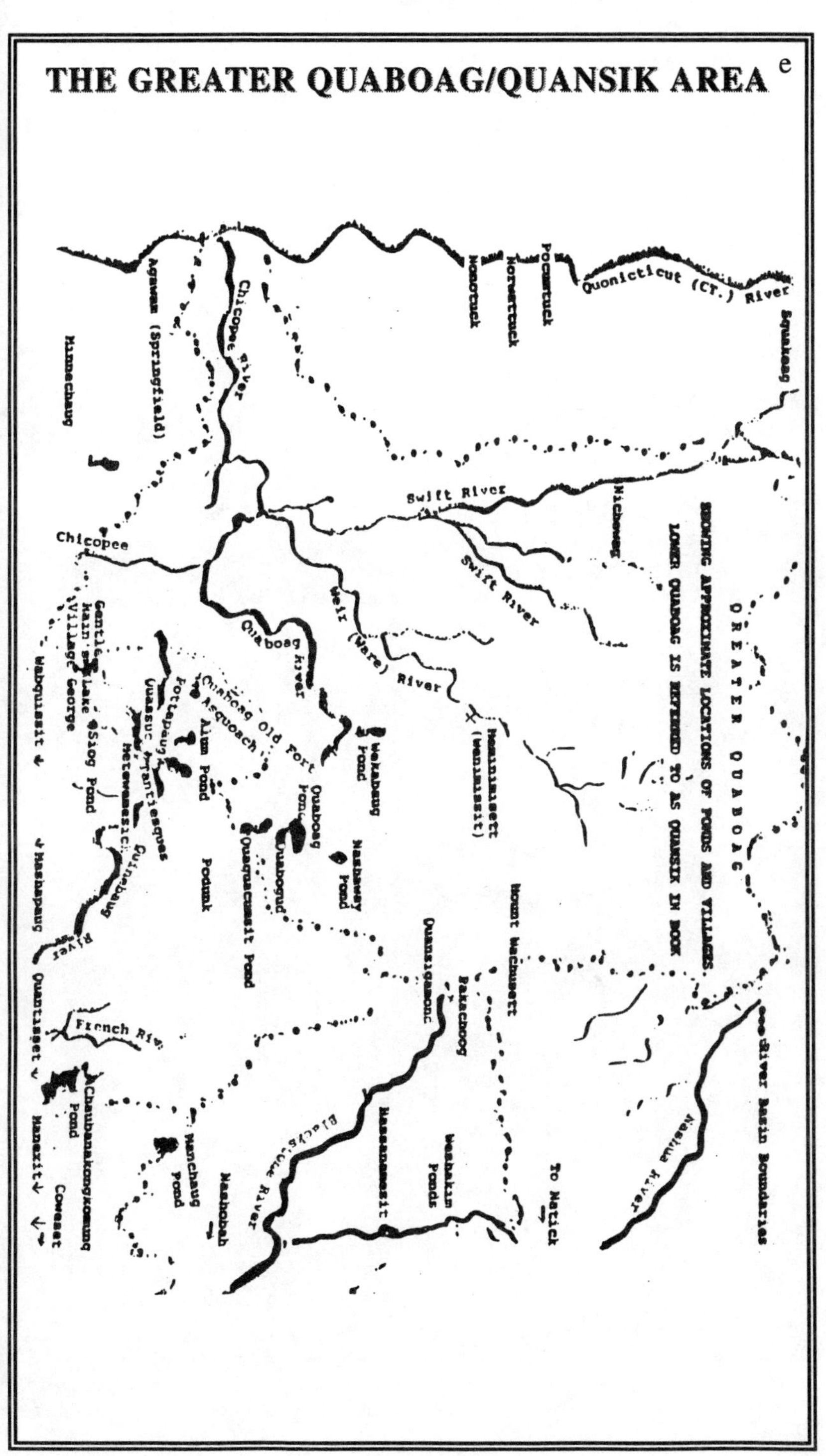

I

ACKNOWLEDGEMENT

I would like to thank all the people who generously shared their time and knowledge with me as I conducted research for what proved to be an ever-growing project.

I would especially like to thank the Nipmuck Sachem Wise Owl and the Nipmuck Medicine Man Little Turtle (and posthumously thank the Nipmuck tribal member Gentle Moose) for all their assistance in helping me learn the ways of their people.

I would also like to thank the Massachusetts Cultural Councils in Wales, Brimfield, Holland, Sturbridge, Monson and Palmer for grants which helped defray some of the research expenses.

And, last but not least, I wish to thank my mother for all her help and encouragement over the years.

FOREWORD

This book is primarily based on written Puritan accounts from 1620-1676; scholarly works from the seventeenth to twentieth centuries about all aspects of the New England Native American people/culture and interviews and hands-on activities with modern Nipmuc tribal leaders and New England Native Americans. Using a wide variety of data, I have attempted to retell early American history from the perspective of the seventeenth-century Central Massachusetts Native Peoples from the area I refer to as Quansik, most of which is now called called Nipmuck.

There are many Native American names and words in this book. Against expert advice, I have chosen to leave them in because I feel the spirit of the book is to show their foreign culture. Readers can gloss over them and not worry about their pronunciations or spellings, for there are many variations in the records. In general, the Nipmuc people did not pronounce the "n" sound, instead substituting a (flat) "l" sound. Other tribes substituted a "s"or "r" sound so the word for dog would be pronounced by the Nipmucks as Alum and by the Massachusetts as Anum, the northern tribes as Arum and the Mohegans as Asum. I have chosen to use the "n" sounds in the words since that is how most people will recognize them. In addition, newer research questions the use of the word "squaw" for "female". I have used it because authors of books about the New England Native American languages (written from the1600s-1962) list it as an accepted word for female. It is based on the Natick/Nipmuck word *esqua.*

Because in certain cases big pieces of history are missing about these Native American tribes, I have made educated guesses about alliances and familial relationships based on years of work with the data. Controversies over how to interpret certain data from the 1600s will continue until all the missing links are discovered.

Although I attempted to be as complete and thorough as possible, this book is not intended to be a genealogical reference or to answer all questions: its purpose is to make people aware of how the Pilgrims/Puritans might have been viewed by the other side.

The reader is asked to keep this in mind while reading this book. In these pages you will meet a people who existed one way in 1620, but within two generations of contact with Europeans, almost ceased to exist at all. Their pain and bitterness fill these pages and it is to them and their descendents that I dedicate this book.

Chapter 1

The glacier was the first to lay claim to the long valley the people called *quansik.*

Everywhere, swept clean by the massive blades of ice, the thin soil shivered in the shadows of gigantic glacial outcroppings. In the furrows made by the glacier's violent ice plow, stands of oak, maple, chestnut and pine grew tall. Hemlocks, elms and hickories rambled over the drumlins and down into jagged gashes which were strewn with a debris of large, grey boulders and slate.

For thousands of years Mother Earth patiently nurtured each precious seed dropped by chipmunks and crows, each seed in turn providing many more as it grew into a tall tree. With the return of the ice bridge in winter, each twirling maple seed danced a circular dance to Creator before it gently laid its body over the ravaged earth. Its sacrifice was joined by others as each tree shed its leaves to weave a blanket of red and gold for their mother. And each year's blanket of leaves grew until a soft padding of brown and red flesh covered Mother Earth's bones.

Jealous of her growing beauty, the powerful spirits of the sky were not always kind to their sister's young body. They sometimes sent frosts too early or too late, killing the soft plants. They sometimes poured rain and hail down over her fragile layer of earthskin and they sometimes withheld all rain under a hot, blue stare. But the thing that had done the most damage - the thing that could wipe out centuries of slow growth - was the lightning. Wherever the lightning god licked, all turned black and died beneath its fiery tongue.

This was the thing the people feared now, huddled in bear hides inside their fragile dwellings in the snow-filled ravine. As the lightning lit up the snow-filled night sky, their oily red-brown faces shone with fear in the firelight.

The pond dwellers had a name for lightning. They called it *Cutshausha* - the far-away sharp broken thing. They were used to it coming during the summer, but when it flashed during a blizzard, their shamans said could it only mean one thing: the gods of fire and ice were at war.

To take their minds off it and to pass the long winter's night, the elders told stories.

Winter, 1697-8

The interior of an Oneida longhouse in Eastern New York.

A winter storm howls outside as Native American children and young adults, ranging in age from four to twenty winters huddle on and under thick bearskins around the longhouse's four fires.

Smoke curls from the long-handled pipe a shaman solemnly offers to the four directions. He puffs and hands it to the other elders seated at the fire circle near the eastern door.

Sap boils out of the burning pine branches and pops loudly as a very old man slowly rises, his gnarled hands curved around a long stick painted with yellow, red, white and black designs. Attached to it by beaded leather thongs are turkey, hawk and bluejay feathers. As the old man clears his throat, he shakes the talking stick, winging a flock of shadows over the children and young adults. The longhouse grows silent, a hundred pairs of black eyes on the elder. The speaker's voice, once clear and strong, now is a raspy growl.

"I am Many Winters Bear. You know me as the Keeper of the Stories. Every winter when the ice bridge covers the land, I tell you the old stories[1] about how our people came to be.

"This winter, I am joined by the other elders for a ceremony of Memory and Passing. They have many stories to tell you, the children of Quansick.

"All of you have been born here, in the land of our brothers the Oneida, the younger brother of the Mohawks. Many have only one parent from the land of your grandfathers. But many winters past there was a time when your parents and elders lived free, not as adopted children of another nation. We once lived on many ponds and along many rivers and the numbers of our people were as great as the kernels of corn in our fields. But that was a very long time ago."

He pauses and points the talking stick in the direction of Nopatin, the eastern wind, and continues:

"There, beyond quonicticut (the Connecticut - the place of the long river) our lands lie. Our feet walked the land and our canoes floated down the rivers between the long man and *Wechekum* (the great sea). We were happy there until the white man came."

"We tell the stories now, when the *Djo-geh-oh* (the little people) are asleep in the woods, for we do not want them listening in. They send Brother *askug* (the snake) to the wetus of those who tell stories between *Neepunnakeeswush* (the Strawberry Moon) and *Taquonckeeswush* (the Moon of Falling Leaves). The plants might stop growing or animals might stop eating and get lost while listening to our stories. And if a hunter should brag about the number of animals he caught, they could overhear and become angry and leave forever. So now, while the animals and plants are asleep, we tell the stories.

" The animals are our brothers and sisters and once roamed the earth as men do now, able to speak to men and each other. Our brother *Musquash* (muskrat) taught our grandfathers how to build round houses and brother *Tummock* (the flooder, beaver) showed them where to catch the salmon that spawn in the spring. Brother *Awasoos* (bear) and brother *Muckquashim* (wolf) taught them how to follow a trail and brother *Alum* (dog) taught them how to be patient and watchful. Brother *Pussough* (the wild cat) showed them how to hide in the trees and how to jump out and surprise their enemies. And brothers *Pequawus* and *Mishquashim* (the grey and red fox) taught them how to be clever and cunning.

"For many winters all creatures lived in harmony. But then our grandfathers thought they were better than all the other creatures. They began to steal the beaver's logs to make boats and paddles shaped like his tail. They fished in his private streams and even began to use his fur so they, too, could be warm. Brother beaver's heart began to turn against his human brothers.

"The bears and wolves also became unhappy as our grandfathers learned to hide their mocassin prints from them so animal humans killed could not be feasted upon by all creatures. When our grandfathers took the honey from the trees, brother bear's heart began to turn against his human brothers. When young braves began killing wolves to give their beautiful pelts as presents to their brides, the wolves' hearts began to run against their human brothers. The dog and panther were unhappy as the humans became even better at watching, waiting and hiding than they. Brother raccoon stopped climbing high trees and went deep into the woods to brood when our grandfathers could climb even higher. And brother fox was unhappy as our grandfathers had learned how to outsmart him.

“Finally, the animals could stand it no longer and they called a secret council. They held it without a fire at night after our grandfathers had gone to sleep.

"Brother Wolf spoke first,

“We must go now and kill them all in their sleep!” he said.

" Beaver argued that they should wait until winter and then sneak in and chew up all their wetus so they would freeze to death but Bear spoke up and said these were not dignified means.

“We must send them a challenge to war,” he said and then sat down with a thump on his large hind end.

"Brother Raccoon, who came from a very old and respected family, said he agreed with Beaver’s plan but Fox said they should just pretend to be friends while the sun shone but at night dig into their corn stores and untie their boats and nets so they would starve.

“After all had spoken, Dog came forward. “This is the first time we have not invited our human brothers to sit in council." He looked at the others and continued," In winter when snow covers everything, my human brothers have fed me and taken me into their beds. What they take from us is very little compared to all that *Cautantowwit* has given us. They have treated me with kindness. I will not harm them, instead I will go into their villages and warn them of what you plan to do.”

“The other animals began snarling and growling at dog. They called him a traitor and they threatened to kill him. But just then *Cautantowwit* stepped into the circle, moonlight glowing all around him.

“I have heard all your words,” the Great Spirit said.

“I had planned for all to live together peacefully, but now see that the peace has been broken. I will go into the village and tell the humans what everyone has said.”

“Creator then said to Wolf and Panther, “From now on, you they will think of as their most dangerous enemies and they will kill you whenever you come near their villages.” He turned to Bear and said, “Humans will not hunt you, but if you try to harm them, they will fight you bravely unto death. And once they taste your fat, they will crave it forever.

“To Beaver and Raccoon he said,” Because of your deceitful plans to destroy the humans, you shall be hunted and forced to give up your furs whenever humans need them for warmth. And you, Fox, shall be mistrusted and called a thief."

"Then Creator turned to Alum and said, "You shall remain friendly with humans, but because you came to this war council you shall be punished. You will continue to understand the tongue of your human brothers, but your speech is now taken away. From now on, barks and and whines will come from your throat when you try to talk to them."

"I have spoken," Creator said and vanished.

"And ever since, man and animals have had to follow these rules."

The wind howls louder, throwing a spatter of ice rain against the dry bark shingles. It runs down the longhouse's sides, sounding like a tribe of mice scurrying down into the deep snow.

Many Winters Bear clears his throat with a sip of hot sassafras tea and continues,

"Before our grandfathers came to live on Mother Earth, all was water. One day Creator looked down and saw *Torup*, Giant Turtle, swimming in the waters. On his back were *Wompissacuk* (Eagle), *Kokookehom* (Owl), *Kaukont* (Crow), *Attuck* (Deer), *Quashim* (Fox), *Neyhom* (Turkey), Muskrat and Beaver. Creator came down in the shape of a *taggamut* (hare) and sent Crow to search for brown earth to make an island with. Crow flew off but as the sun was setting, he returned without any earth. One by one, Creator sent the others in search, but all returned at the end of the day with nothing.

"Finally, he sent Muskrat. Muskrat dove deep down and after a very long time, returned with a little bit of mud in his paws. Creator took this and placed it on turtle's back. As it grew, Turtle was able to slip out from under it. It continued to grow and grow until it became all the land you see.

"Afterwards, Creator rewarded Muskrat by telling him he could live anywhere he wanted. First, Muskrat chose the deep, blue lakes. But soon he got sick of all that water and he asked Creator for a new home in the grassy meadows. Creator granted his wish, but soon Muskrat realized he had plenty of grass but nowhere to swim so he again asked Creator for a new home. Creator said, "Muskrat, one day you ask to be in the lakes and the next in the meadows. You do not know what you want, so I will choose for you. From now on, your home will be in the marsh where it is neither dry land or open water."

"This was what Muskrat really wanted and so he continues to live in marshy places and builds his home in the shape of a turtle's back from the mud and reeds. In the winter, he eats the grass on the inner walls of his house. But because of his favor with Creator, the minks, snapping turtles, hawks and eagles are jealous of Muskrat and seek to do him harm every chance they get."

Within the longhouse all turns quiet as Many Winters Bear pauses. An owl hoots outside and the shaman shakes his deer hoof rattle to warn it away.

"As turtle island was being created, the great sachem in the sky decided to take a maiden called Mature Petals for his wife. In his village there was a great magical tree with four long white roots that went in each direction. As soon as the sachem married Mature Petals, he noticed she was with child, her pregnancy caused from his breath when he had kissed her before marriage. He became so upset he decided to uproot the great tree. All the village worked on it until the tree was gone, replaced by a huge hole. Mature Petals went to the edge of the hole to see what had lain beneath the great tree and her husband, still angry, pushed her down. She fell, and as she fell she passed a white fire serpent who gave her a mortar, pestle, an ear of corn and a marrow bone. He told her she would need these to live below. Duck-like spirits caught the maiden and deposited her on the back of the growing turtle island. There, she spilled seeds out of her soft doeskin apron and a great tree immediately grew up surrounded by other green trees and plants.

"Soon after, Mature Petals gave birth to a daughter.

"For many winters the mother and daughter lived with the animals. When the daughter became a woman she was very beautiful and all the male creatures wanted to marry her. But her mother said no to all who called at their witu with their gifts until *Waupi* (Grandfather Wind) asked for permission to marry her.

"After they were married, *Waupi* visited her and left two arrows near her side, one pointed with flint, the other unpointed. Shortly afterwards, the daughter gave birth to twins. The first one was born the normal way, but the second was in such a hurry to come out, he came through her armpit and killed her.

"The grandmother called the first one Sapling and he was full of goodness. He planted new trees and plants on the earth and learned his lessons well. Everywhere he went, animals and plants flourished. The other, called Flint, was full of evil and only delighted in tearing things down. The snakes and reptiles were his animals and poisonous or thorny plants grew where he trod. After many, many winters, Sapling grew old and died, but he is reborn each spring in new trees.

"The brothers had many battles during their time on Turtle Island together. And they still battle, with Flint trying to harm anything good and gentle. Flint is hard and good for fighting and hunting, though, which is why we use it for our arrowheads.

"After the boys had grown up, the grandmother flew to the sky and became *Munnannock* (Grandmother Moon).

"And in the sky at night we also see the *Oot-kwa-tah* (the dancing children or Pleiades). These were formed many winters ago in the days of our grandfathers.

"At that time, a hunting party went a long way in the woods to where there was a lake a beautiful as *chaubongumamug*, our people's sacred lake. The waters were full of *aumachick* (fish); the shores of the lake were full of *attuck* (deer) drinking and amongst the beech and chestnut trees were *mishannekequock* (squirrels) and bears.

"The hunters gave thanks for the bounty and set to making a winter camp. After it was made, eight children in the group took to dancing to pass the time. One day while they were dancing their joy dance near the river, an old man, dressed all in white with silver hair, came to them and told them they must stop dancing at once and not dance again or great evil would come to them.

"But they did not pay attention to him and continued to dance each day. Their parents refused to give them any more food to take into the woods and they wouldn't sit with their families, preferring to dance instead. Again and again the old man appeared, but each time they ignored his warning.

"Then, one day, after they had gone some sleeps without food, they started to get dizzy and they began rising into the air as they danced. One looked back to earth as they rose and he became a shooting star. The rest reached the sky and there they continue to dance and dance and dance.

"There is in the night sky another set of stars called *Paukunnawaw* (the Great Bear). One night, in the days of our grandfathers, a taggamut (runner) appeared in a village where four brave brothers known for their skill in hunting lived. He said he had been sent from a village nearby to ask for their help in driving away a great monster bear that had suddenly appeared, frightening the village.

"The brothers immediately took up their spears and called to their small dog to join them in their pursuit. As they traveled deeper and deeper into the forest they noticed all the animals and birds had fled. There were great scratch marks so high on the trees that the braves could not touch them. "It is Paukunawaw, the monster bear," said one. His brother said he remembered the elders telling about such a creature and about how it couldn't chase a hunter who had found its tracks. They had said if a hunter found Paukunawaw's tracks it would have to run from him.

"When they reached the village they noticed that everyone was hiding and there was no food or fire. The runner's uncle told them that every day they went out to track the bear but the tracks would disappear whenever they tried to follow them. Yet every morning the tracks were closer and closer to the village, he said.

"The second brother patted the head of their little dog, who had black spots above its eyes. "*Nattawunnash* (Four Eyes) can track anything," he said and the four brothers started off.

"After a while the laziest and fattest brother began complaining that he wanted to rest and eat but the other brothers said they must not stop or they would become the hunted ones. So he opened his *pemmican* pouch to eat while they walked, but instead of pemmican, white worms squirmed out. The bear's magic had changed the food into worms!

"That made the fattest one angry and he determined to find the bear. Just then Four Eyes began to sniff and bark at something in the woods. They had found the trail. Then the bear began to run and they chased it through the woods, up hills, down valleys and over mountains. Soon the fattest one pretended to fall and hurt his ankle so the others had to carry him and his spear. Grandfather Sun went west and Grandmother Moon rose as they tracked the bear.

"As they got close, the little dog began nipping at Paukunnawaw's heels and the fattest hunter asked his brothers to set him down because his ankle felt better. As soon as they did he took off fast after the bear, for he was rested and his brothers were very tired. By the time they caught up to him, he had killed the great bear and was roasting it over a great fire. They all ate until they could eat no more and then the first hunter looked down at his feet. “Brothers,” he shouted, “look below us!”

"There below the four hunters were thousands of sparkling lights in the darkness. “We aren’t on a mountain at all,” said one, “we are in the sky!”

“And so they were. Paukunawaw was indeed magical and had taken them up into the sky. Then, as they looked, their little dog yipped and they saw the great bear alive again, rising up from its bones.

“Follow me!” said the first and they took up their spears to give chase again. Now every year as the nights turn cold you can see them chasing it across the night sky and when they kill it, the bear turns upside down and its blood falls to earth to change the maple leaves scarlet. And the grease from cooking it falls to turn the grass white."

From the dark behind the aged teller of the stories comes a faint chanting. The ends of the long logs are pushed farther into the fires, creating small volcanoes of embers.

“When the earth was young, evil spirits unleashed a terrible flood. Some of the animals survived by fleeing to a mountaintop in the southwest. This was the home of Cautantowwit. Because they lived there with him certain birds and beasts are sacred.

“Cautantowwit remade the mud-soaked earth and then made a man and woman from stone. He was not happy with them, so broke them into little pieces. Then he took clay, or Mother Earth, and fashioned a new pair of humans. These he gave immortal souls to. He put them on the earth with the animals, who became their teachers. When we die, we go to the land of Cautantowwit in the southwest. There, it is beautiful and all creatures live in harmony. But if you are a bad person you will not be allowed to enter, for Cautantowwit will see your heart as a black cloud and you will have to thunder around outside forever.”

“Yet, many winters ago, in the time of our grandfathers, the weather was warm and pleasant all year long. But humans were not happy. They complained all the time. It was too hot or it was raining.

"After listening to their complaints, Creator decided to let the sun travel further and further each day from their villages. The days grew shorter and colder. They had to hunt and trap for furs to cover themselves and had to add bark to the mats covering their wetus. Many humans died from the cold.

"Afraid, the people called upon Creator to send the sun back to them. Creator took pity on their suffering and sent it back, but each year there is a season of short days and cold weather to remind the people of how they were not grateful for what they had.

"Poisonous plants grew from the bodies of those who had been rebellious and not called upon Creator as a reminder that he provided everything good and it was not appreciated.

"And that is why we now give thanks to Creator for everything, always."

Winters Bear's eyes fall on the hempen bags and baskets of beans and on the dried ears of corn hanging over the many sleeping platforms on either side of the longhouse.

"Cautanowwit also gave us the plants we grow in our gardens: the three sisters *weatchunnubbeasgm* (corn), *tuppuhqquammash*, (beans), *asquoash* (squash)) and *wuttammaug* (tobacco).

"Many winters ago, our people depended on hunting and what they could gather in the fields and woods for their food. One winter when the food supply was scarce and many people were starving, a man had a vision in which wise crow, Konkontu, told him about three foods that grew in Cautantowwit's garden. The young man asked how he might find this garden, but Konkontu said it was a very long distance and a man could not walk it.

"A few sleeps later, the man was walking in the woods when he heard Konkontu call him. He looked up and saw the crow watching him from a tree branch. It flew to his shoulder and told him to put out his hand. Rubbing his head in the hand, three seeds dropped out of Konkontu's ears: corn, beans and squash. The three sisters. Konkontu told the man how to plant the seeds and how to prepare the hills with gifts of fish for Mother Earth.

"Now every year when the *weatchiminnochohtek* (fields) are planted at the Moon of *Nahmoskeeswush* (catching fish), when the oak leaves are the size of misheanequs (squirrel) ears, and when it is harvested, Konkontu's relatives come to visit, to take their share. However, Creator knows how greedy they can be, so he sends *quanunon*, the hawk, to keep them from taking it all."

The elders smoke their pipes in silence for a while and then Many Winters Bear continues,

"In the time of our grandfathers when there was much warmaking, a wise and peace-loving elder traveled to the different tribes to get them to lay down their war clubs and bows.

"This man lived to be very old, even older than I, Many Winters Bear. When it was his time to go to the garden of Cautantowwit in the southwest, he called a council meeting around a great fire and sachems, sagamores and elders from all the different tribes came to listen to what he had to say.

"He told them he must leave them soon, but that he would return in a new form to remind them of the peaceful brotherhood they should share.

"A short while after he died, a new plant sprouted from his grave. This plant was tobacco and is has been used ever since in ceremonies to symbolize unity, peace and honesty. The rising smoke from this sacred plant reminds us that our thoughts and prayers go upward through the skies to Creator."

"Another plant Creator sent to remind us of peace is the strawberry. Many winters ago in the time of our ancient grandfathers, there was a brother and sister who were always fighting. One day they had a terrible fight and the sister wandered off in the woods.

"After a while she forgot about the fight and laid down to rest in the meadow. When she woke up she saw a little red heart-shaped berry near her head. She looked around and there was a whole field of them. She tasted them and found them to be delicious. After eating many, she decided to gather some to take to her little brother.

"When she got back to the village she found that her brother had been very sad for he thought she was lost. She gave him the berries and after he ate them he asked if he could go with her to the meadow to pick some more.

"From that day on, the brother and sister lived in peace.

"This is why the strawberry festival every year is a time to make peace with those you are angry or fighting with. Strawberries are shaped like our hearts, so they symbolize making our hearts good through forgiveness and friendship."

A s a young brave shifts his position, his head dips into the fire-light. Many Winters Bear catches a glimpse of the sheen of the snake-skin tying the brave's long locks at the nape of his neck.

"Our Iroquois brothers tell us that many winters ago there lived a young brave named *Djisdaah* who did not treat animals with respect. He enjoyed torturing any creature he killed. He would laugh at its pain and suffering, which is not Creator's wish. Many of the tribe's elders and his parents talked to him about this, but he did not change.

"One day this boy attacked a snake. As the sun went down, he watched it squirm and moan in death agony while he laughed. Just before it died, it stared at Djisdaah, remembering his face forever.

"The next morning one of the men in his village went out to the woods to hunt. In a huge tree he saw all the snakes gathering for a war council. He crept up and listened to their hissing.

"That brave Djisdaah has challenged us," said one, "so in four days time we will go to their village and destroy them all." All the snakes hissed their approval. The man ran back to his village and warned the people of the snakes' war plans.

"The village's sachem sent another warrior and yet another out to listen to confirm the terrible news. They all said the same thing, that the snakes were going to war with their people. So the sachem gathered everyone together and told them to cut down many trees and stack them tight together in a circle around the village. A distance in from the stakes he told them to build rows of stakes to keep the snakes out.

"In four days time the sachem ordered the pallisade set afire. Just as they did, they heard a terrible noise like the hissing of a great wind. Snakes came from everywhere, straight towards the fire. Normally snakes will run from fire, but these snakes were on the warpath and did not turn back. They kept coming, crawling over the bodies of their slain comrades as they advanced towards the village. It was a terrible sight to see!

"When they got near the inner row of stakes, the sachem ordered that it be fired. Again the snakes kept coming and the people began battling with them. The first to be killed was Djisdaah. As more people died, the sachem stepped forward and yelled,

"Hear me, brother snakes. We offer peace to you and all are sorry for the bad thing our brother did to one of your people. Since he is dead, we ask you to stop this war of vengeance. Please have mercy on us."

"The army of snakes stopped and the villagers and snakes stared at each other for a long space. Then there was a terrible rumbling and the earth shook. Just in front of the humans the ground opened up and the giant snake who lives at the center of the earth came out.

"The huge snake looked at the sachem and frightened people.

"I am the great sachem of all the snakes," he said. " We will go from here and leave you in peace if you agree to two things. "

"The sachem said his people would agree and the snake continued, "First, you must always treat my people with respect. And second, you must never name another man Djisdaah."

"So it was done and to this day, we treat our snake brothers with respect."

"Not all stories are so serious. Our animal brothers did many strange things in our ancient grandfathers' time. Our brothers the birds had agreed with the land animals that the birds would live in the treetops and the others could live down below. But the land animals made so much noise every morning and night that it disturbed the birds, who couldn't outshout the growls and roars of the huge animals. The birds met in council and said, "We feel it is disrepectful to greet the sun with animal noises. We think songs should be sung to it as it rises and sets."

"All agreed, but none knew how to sing a pretty song. Finally, they decided to send a bird to Cautanowwit's place in the southwest, where there were many beautiful songs. They asked *honck* (the goose) to fly there, but after he got up very high, he became frightened and returned. Next, they asked crow, but crow said he only flew low. Finally, brother eagle said he would try, for he flew the highest and was able to speak to Creator so he knew how to get to the land of Cautanowwit.

"As eagle set out, a little brown bird, the hermit thrush, settled on his back for a nap. While eagle flew higher and higher, challenging the clouds, the bird rested. Soon eagle began to descend, for he had tired himself out playing with the clouds. The thrush, however, was not tired and flew off eagle's back to search for the magic land. It was not long before she came to a beautiful place, more beautiful than ever imagined. She found a wonderful high tree to perch in, and, resting, heard many lovely songs. She listened and listened and finally found the song she thought was the most beautiful. She sang it over and over to memorize it and then flew home to her brothers and sisters.

"But on her way home she began to worry. What if brother eagle was angry that she had ridden on his back? What if the others were jealous of her beautiful song?

"So when she returned, she didn't go back to her tree. Instead, she found a secluded spot in the thicket in heavy forest and there, each morning and evening, sang her song of thanks to Creator."

"At first, all the animals lived together in one area, but as it became more and more crowded, the little animals found that they were not getting a chance to find food. So *Annequasanequussuck* (chipmunk) called a council and said, "My brothers, I propose that we all go out to the land beyond the mounatins where there is plenty of water, grass and trees to support us all. Each can claim a certain place for our own."

" All the animals thought this was a good idea and immediately lept up and ran off to claim their new areas. But chipmunk, in his excitement, didn't leave the council fire until all the others had gone. Once there, he found all the good homes were taken, so he scurried and scampered amongst the leaves until he decided to dig himself a burrow. And ever since, that has been his home.

"Our animal brothers were always having contests to see who was the strongest, the smartest, and so on. And so it was that the little chipmunk and the bear got to arguing one day. The bear, who got hot from his heavy coat when the sun came out, wanted only night and no day. Brother chipmunk wanted daylight so he could see the nuts under the leaves.

"Bear boasted that, because he was the biggest animal, he had the most power. Chipmunk challenged him to prove it and bear bragged that he was so powerful could prevent the sun from rising.

All the animals gathered to watch as bear sat down and faced the direction of the rising sun. All night they waited. The sun did not come and still more time passed and the sun did not rise. They began to speak amongst themselves, "Maybe brother Bear is as powerful as he says." Then, all of a sudden, the rays of the sun shot through the thick mist and the sun shone brightly overhead.

"The animals laughed at bear, who became very angry and began chasing them to kill them. All escaped except for chipmunk, who was caught under bear's paw. As he struggled to escape into his burrow, the bear's claws tore three lines down his back. And to this day, Brother Chipmunk wears the bear's mark to remind us to be humble."

"Brother Bear once had a fine, long, full tail, even longer and bushier than brother Fox's. But brother Fox was clever and one day he saw a group of otters playing on the ice. They disappeared down their hole and Fox licked his lips, thinking that he would love to have one of those big, fat tasty creatures for dinner. But he knew the only way to catch them was to fish for them. He looked at his tail and then down into the hole and knew it wasn't long enough to reach.

So, still drooling from the thought of otter dinner, he trotted off into the forest.

"A little ways in he found brother Bear looking for honey. "With a tail as long as his, I could catch many otters," fox thought. "Brother Bear," he said, "How can you live on just honey and nuts?" The bear replied that the honey was sweet and the nuts nourishing. Then fox told him about the fine otter meat they could enjoy and bear began to lick his lips. He followed the fox to the pond and listened as fox told him to go over to the hole, drop his tail in, and when he felt a nibble, lift it out, throwing the otter over to the fox.

"As you know, Brother Bear is very patient. He sat for some time, just staring at his reflection in the hole. Then he felt a nibble and pulled his tail out to see a strange black creature attached to the end. He threw it over to fox, who greedily devoured it. Again and again Bear caught otters and threw them over to brother Fox, who kept eating them.

"Bear was so intent on catching otter that he did not notice the sky growing darker or *Paponetin* (grandfather west wind) warning him. Soon snow began to fall and the otter, sensing a change in weather, settled deeper into their pond. Yet bear waited. He called over to fox to tell him there were no more nibbles, but fox had a mouth full of otter meat and couldn't reply. So bear sat on and on.

"Finally, after much snow, the bear decided he would leave off fishing, gather his honey and nuts and go home. But when he tried to pull his tail out, it was very heavy. "It must be full of otters," bear thought, and pulled harder. Then he pulled with all his might. But instead of the weight of all the otters, his tail felt lighter. He looked behind him and saw that he no longer had a tail! It was frozen in the ice. And brother Fox was long gone, his belly full of otter meat.

"Bear wandered back to his forest home, muttering to himself about how fox had tricked him. And from that day on, the bear had no tail."

As the laughter of the children quiets down, the old man stops, his voice now very low.

"I am old. I can talk no more now. Creator willing, I will tell you more tales at another time. I, Many Winters Bear, have spoken."

---

[1]Notes on legends: The original tellers of these of legends are unkown since legends have been handed down orally from generation to generation. Most of the legends used in this chapter and elsewhere in this book are based on ones written in the following books or tapes:

Voices in the Wind, Margot Edmonds and Ella Clark, Facts on File Publishing, *Iroquois Stories*, Joseph Bruhac, The Crossing Press, *The World's Rim*, Clyde Kluckhorn, Univ. of Nebraska Press, Bison Books, *Story Telling Stone*, ed., intro Susan Feldman, Dell, *Legends of the Longhouse*, Jesse J. Cornplanter, intro., Carl Carmer, Empire Stare Historical Society, *Tales of the Eastern Woodlands and More Tales of the Eastern Woodlands*, cassette tapes by Medicine Story, Story Stone Co., *Indian Tales* retold by Joseph and Edith Raskin, Random House, *Mythology of North America*, John Bierhorst, William Morrow & Co., *Tales of Native American Indians*, Stith Thompson, ed., Indiana Univ. Press and *Native North Amerian Spirituality of the Eastern Woodlands*, Elisabeth Tooker, ed., Paulist Press. If you are interested in myths, please refer to any of the above for many more stories and legends of the Native American peoples.

Chapter 2
(A re-telling of events in 1620)

The voices in the longhouse become silent as an old man in soft buckskins draped with wampum strands takes the stick. He does not rise, but his voice carries well to the children, touching them with its authority. This is their sachem. When he speaks all listen.

"I was shot (sachem of) the place of the long-tailed black cats. We called it *quoquinnamoqck*. I called myself Lone Hawk and Fighting Hawk but my old man name is Firehawk. When I signed deeds with the white man I called myself *Shatookquis* (mark of he who rules), *Nommoshot* (sachem of far away heaved up rock place), *Sheat, Namesowhat* or *Nokin*. All these were just titles saying I was sachem of the place being deeded. As you know, we do not use our real names with each other. Even my name Firehawk is not the name Cautantowwit knows me by. Many of our people took English first names in time but inside they kept their spirit names.

"If someone had told me that one day I would live to see my people removed from *Quansick*, I would have laughed in their face. We had survived many invasions over time and felt we could defend our lands forever.

"In the time of my grandfather Massamet, chief sachem of the great confederacy of all the tribes of the Pocumtucks, the Mohawks waged a war on their neighbors the Mahicans, driving them into our lands.

"The Mohawks were part of a five-nation confederacy that included the Oneidas, the Onondagas, the Senecas and the Cayugas.

"They were united by the great peace-maker *Dekanahwida* in the time of our grandfathers. He began the peace talk then departed, covering himself with bark, when the Seneca chief sachem Hiawatha took over. According to Iroquois stories, the Great Spirit in the sky was so pleased with the peace that he gave gifts to the people: to the

Mohawks he gave corn, to the Oneidas, nuts and fruits from trees, to the Seneas the beans, to the Cayugas the roots of plants and to the Onondagas the grapes, squashes and tobacco.

"So long before the white man came to our shores, the Mohawks and our western neighbors were united: united against us and the Mahicans!

"Many of the fiercest battles with the Mahicans were over the lands belonging to my grandmother's people, the Quansuk, who controlled all the land east of the great quonicticut river below the Schatecook's land and to the long pond on the quanapaug river where the Cowesits, then friends of the Narragansetts, lived.

"The Pocumtuck territory was split into four sections. My grandparents controlled the far north lands and their three children controlled the rest. Since land rights are through the females, my oldest aunt, known simply as Awonunsk, or squaw sachem, controlled the southern part of the quonicticut river and east through Wabbaquasett to the quinebaug river basin then north to mount wachuset. She controlled the waterways of the river the English call Blackstone. We called it wunnashowatuckqut (pigeon territory for the large amount of pigeons there that fed on the acorns and chestnuts). She controlled the upper quinebaug and the lower nashua river. When she married the Massachusett chief sachem Nanepashemet her children, my cousins, controlled all the coastal Massachusetts lands in the quinnebequin (Charles) river basin.

"Her brother Naddawahunt, my father, ruled all of the northern nashua river basin and southern cabbasauk (Merrimac) river, which was known for its sturgeon fish. His lands continued west to the lakes at weshakim and then south into quaboag to where it bordered squaw sachem's lands on the south and east. With their younger sister Mishalisk, he ruled the quaboag river system and the chicopee river systems. Through marriage to the daughter of Sagamore John of Pentucket, his children controlled the assabet river basin.

"Mishalisk also ruled the upper quonicticut and baquag (Miller's) river basin.

"Between the three, they ruled all of the land and waterways from the housatonic river in the west, to the shore of wechakum (the sea); from the southern cabbasauk to shawnsheen to the coast at pawtucket in Cowesit north of Wampanoag and to podunk (Windsor, Ct.) on the west.

"When the Mahicans were forced out of their lands, many went to live in Narragansett and Woronoco. There were constant raids into our border lands, so Massamet called a great council and invited Commucke, chief of the Mahicans, and Punham, chief of the Cowesits, to smoke the peace pipe with our people. Mishalisk gave Commucke's people permission to settle in the lands between the northern quonicticut and housatonic rivers and in squakeag.

"While in Cowesit, Commucke had married Punham's sister. Their son Wrutherna married Mishalisk to consolidate the alliance. Through this marriage, her children obtained land rights in Cowesit and along the southern quinebaug river basin.

"With peace, our crops once again grew on the hillsides and our hooks and spears fished the *nippamaug*, the fresh waters.

"Massemet had many wives and many chidren. Massepetoat was his eldest son and because he was from a Pocumtuck wife, he would become the chief sachem of the Pocumtucks after his father died.

"Mishalisk's children through her marriage to Wrutherna were Etowomp, who would later be father to two daughters- one was called Hester - and Aguntus Ponham, also called Hyems or Black James, later father to Simon and Benjamin; Wetolechen, later father to Wascomos (Wequagan), also called Chickwallump or Allumps, who was father to Squompe (Willomachin) or Noas, and Mesea, father to a daughter, Pomate Kenio, also called Kenix. Hyems and his children went to live in their grandmother's lands in quinebaug. Allumps went south to Wabbaquasett and Mesea remained in the northern part of the quonicticut.

"Squaw sachem and Nanepashemet had three boys- John Romneymarsh(Wonohaquaham),JamesRomneymarsh (Montowompate) and George Romneymarsh (Winnepurkitt) - and two daughters - Yawata and Abigail.

"John and James died before reaching adulthood but Yawata's son John Romneymarsh married Aguntus' daughter Mary Ponham. After Passaconnaway's daughter died, Hyem's other daughter Ahawyetsqune became the second wife of George Romneymarsh, the only surviving son of Squaw sachem and Nanepashement.

"Naddewahunt settled near Nashaway but often traveled and stayed in the villages in his territory, as did all the chief sachems. He married Sagamore John's daughter. His children by her were

Nassowanno, John and Sam. She divorced him to marry John Oonomog. Our half-brother through that marriage was John Tahotooner and our half-sister was Nanashquaw. Naddawahunt then married my mother, the daughter of the dead chief sachem of the Quaboag pond area. This marriage produced me, Andrew, David and three sisters. One sister married the Pigwackett chief Konkowasco, Tasnunsquaw married Waban and the other, Nawwashawsuck, married Massasoit the year the English came to live in Pautuxit.

"My first wife, Gentle Rain, and I had a son, who took the name Konkowasco, after my sister's husband. When I married Singing Water (Keems -Mattaquallenatt's sister), I had more children, including another son who took the name Coggerynossets. For a while I went to live in her mother's village in Podunk south of the Congomond lakes when the English began moving into the Quanik territory. My grandchildren included Mishnosques, daughter of Coggerynossets and his wife Quashabuck.

"Nassowanno's children were Lawrence and Unquirim. Lawrence's son was Edwmund. Unquirim's son was Toto.

"Sam's children were Sam Nawont and Matthew.

"The marriages happened about the same time and so during my youth there were many children to play with when our families gathered.

"As we got older, Nassowanno became sachem of the coast called agawam then moved inland to quansik, James and John became sachems of saugus and massebequash (Marblehead). George became chief sachem after Nanepashemet died. He married Passaconnaway's daughter, thereby giving his children rights to the Pennacook land. He later also married Poquanum, daughter of Hyems, one of the sachems of Cowesit and wunnashowtuckett on the quinabaug river.

"All these things I tell you before I begin so you can see how great and powerful my family was. Through my grandfather and grandmother, my father and my aunts we controlled all the lands below the Penobscot, MicMac, Sokokois and Mohawks and all of Quansik into Narragansett. Through my cousin we had title to Pennacook lands and through my other cousin, we had land rights and trading rights along the quinebequin river and through Wabbaquasset to the quinebaug and wunnashowtuckett rivers. Our federation was greater even than that of the Narragansetts or of Massasoit's federation of coastal tribes.

"Our neighbors north and in the direction of wampanucket (the rising sun) and the Pennacooks often traded with us for the corn that grew so well on our hillsides. They had the great sea and all its wonderful fish and its access to traders, but they also had the Tarrantines, who kept coming down from the far north, trying to overrun them and take their lands.

"For many winters my people lived unmolested, but then the Pequots began to move in, first taking some of the Narragansetts' land. At first our southern neighbors weren't too hard on these people, for they had been driven out of their lands in the south due to the white man's trade with the Iroquois confederacy. But later, the Pequots became aggressive and took more and more lands and we all came to think of them as truly what their name meant: grey foxes, clever and cunning. Because of the Pequots, my people stopped traveling south to the shores of the Niantics every year in the time of the Burning Moon (July- August). It was no longer safe to travel the path that led along the great river and so we began to go east, through hassanamesit (the place of many stones) and along the path that led to the land of the Pokanokets.

"Later, when the Cowesits, Pequots and then the Mohegans began fighting over our lands along the quinebaug, we even stopped going to sowams. But I get ahead of my story.

"Many winters ago Creator became angry with his people. He sent many MicMac warriors from Abnaki on the other shore of the Saco river down upon us.

"We had grown to one great nation. Our leader Nanepashemet (Moon Walker) was a great powwow (shaman). He had a vision of all our people living together in peace and went from tribe to tribe to speak the good words of friendship. These were good years and even though I was young, I remember Nanepashemet and his councillors visiting my village.

"His words were music that we couldn't hear enough."

"When he talked to my people of peace he held up a single arrow and passed it to our chief sachem Massamet, my grandfather, asking him to break it. He easily snapped it on his knee and Nanepashmet said, "You see, alone we are like that arrow - easily broken." Then he passed a bundle of arrows tied in a snakeskin around, asking all to try to break them and when they couldn't he said, "See this, my brothers: if we join together we are like that bundle. We can't be defeated by our enemies."

"And so the tribes from the Connecticut to Wechekum, from the lower Merrimac to the Quinebaug joined Nanepashemet and his people, the Massachusetts, to create one great confederacy.

"However, the Pennacooks and Abnakis refused to join, despite speeches by my sister's future husband, Cogawasco (Konkowasco), chief sachem of the Pigwacketts. Challenging Nanepashement, Konkowasko's brother Somerset, chief of the southern Abnakis, began sending raiding parties down every fall to collect tribute by force from the bands living north and east of Quaboag and many were killed or taken captive to the north.

"Then a new people rode on the back of Wechekum. These people were from three tribes - the English, French and Dutch. When they began arriving on our shores the tribes warred with each other because each white tribe wanted our people to trade only with them for the wonderful goods they brought in their huge bird ships.

"And what wonders these thing were! They had fine, brightly dyed coats of a light, soft fur called wool, gold and copper chains and silver jewelry with many beautiful stones we had never seen before. They had tortoiseshell combs and looking glasses in which we could see ourselves. But better than all these, they brought the metal called steel. Their steel knives cut through thick hides like bear grease and their steel hatchets cut the trees we had to girdle and char to bring down. We used their steel to shape our arrow shafts and then melted their metal called brass and tipped our arrows with it. We were able to hunt better and do our work faster - and to fight off our enemies better. They had a stone they called a lodestone that made the steel magical. If it were rubbed on the steel, anything metal that came close was grabbed by an invisible spirit and stuck onto the steel.

"We liked this metal steel so much we called the English Chauquanock (the knife men). We could not get enough of it and when their ships sat in our bays word spread and we would hurry to the coast to give them furs, corn and wampumpeag in exchange for it.

"But the day came when they wanted more than this and they began taking our braves. We no longer eagerly paddled out when we saw their ships.

"It was after a group of young braves were kidnapped off the shores of nauset that Nanepashemet had a great vision. He called the sachems of the many tribes together and told them the white men were a trick being played on us by the great rabbit-trickster. He said they gave us things that shone like the sun while stealing our sun. He said he learned in his vision that first they would steal our people and then our lands. He said Trickster was having a joke on us and we were like moths, drawn to the shining light of the white man's steel.

"Many of the sachems near the coast, especially Corbitant and Obbatinnua, disagreed with Nanepashement for they were blinded by the spell of Trickster's light.

"Then Nanepashemet did the thing that began all our troubles (for Trickster was better at playing games than we people were).

"Nanepashemet's braves drove a Francois ship away from the coast during a storm. It crashed apart on the rocks and Nanepashemet ordered his people to let the sailors die, to let their bodies be a sacrifice to Wechakum so it would listen to us and eat the foreign wooden ships before they arrived at our shores.

"But Obbatinnua and Corbitant sent warriors out and rescued five of the sailors.

"When he heard of this, Nanepashemet sent word to these sachems that they were to surrender the five or his nation would war on their tribes. They refused and there were skirmishes as the Francois were moved from one village to another. Then Massasoit, Pokanoket sachem of the Wampanoag confederacy, intervened saying his tribe would be the woman and so could claim the right to ransom the five.

"But Trickster was not done yet. Some of the Francois were very sick and soon many, many people began to die - first in the villages where the Francois had stayed and then in Nanepashemet's villages.

"The sickness spread so fast that whole villages died. We called it the yellow death for the eyes and skin of the people would turn the color of the butternut leaf in the time of the falling leaves. The devil responsible for this sickness worked from the inside out - their insides turned yellow and they vomited and passed yellow from every opening until they died, empty inside.

"Nanepashemet called it the metal disease and said it came from touching the Francois sailors' brass buttons.

"All the people were frightened and many fled away from the

coast, towards Wachusett, to avoid catching it. No ships were allowed to stop along Nanepashemet's shores but the Narragansetts to our south and the Penobscots and Abnakis to our north allowed the white man to come ashore.

"This made Nanepashement very angry and he sent a bundle of arrows wrapped in a snakeskin to the Abnakis with a message that if they didn't kill the white man and help drive him away, Nanepashemet's nation, as represented by the bundle, would war on them.

"The Abnakis were blinded by the white man's magic and sent their reply in the form of a great army of warriors.

"I remember that time well for my family fled to the fort at wachuset to avoid the yellow metal death and the slaughter by the Tarrantines. Blood spilled over the land as the river of war brought the fighting west, towards the quonicticut and even south to the great bay of the Narragansetts and Wampanoags.

"There was so much dying that our eyes dried up from the crying. Some of the sachems cried out for peace at any cost but Nanepashemet refused to listen. He said his vision was right and we would not make peace unless the other tribes joined his nation in sending the white men away forever.

"For many winters the fighting went on, the Abnakis helped by spirit warriors who killed with invisible arrows dipped in plague.

"Nanepashemet had built a strong double pallisade inland and was not afraid of the Abnakis. There was only one way to get into it and its location was a secret. But, as is often the case, his Massachusett brothers Corbitant and Obbatinnua, tired of the dying and fighting, betrayed Nanepashemet by going in secret to the Abnaki war captains and offered to lead them into Nanepashemet's fort in exchange for peace.

"By night the Abnakis came down the cabassauk (Merrimac) and shawnsheen rivers, portaged to the mystic river and, while Grandmother Moon watched, they carried their war canoes overland and used them to scale the high pallisade walls.

"During the battle, my aunt, Nanepashement's wife, escaped to Wachusett. There, she planned a counterattack with Naddawahunt but before they could rally, Cogawasco appeared, offering to let his nation be the woman and make peace. He said his brother had returned north and would bother us no more. He told his children that making war on Obbatinnua and Corbitant would only cause more bloodshed. He said it was time to return to our villages and grow strong once again.

"He spoke so well that Naddawahunt, Mettacomen (Passaconnaway), Mishalisk and Montowompe of Agawam agreed to peace. Now they would all be brothers, they said, equal and no longer tribute-payers. Two confederacies were created then: the first was made up of the river tribes under Naddawahunt to the south, Passaconnaway to the north and my grandfather Massamet to the northwest. The other was the Wampanoag confederacy under Massasoit and his brother Quadequina. In between lay a few bands of Massachusetts who refused to join either confederacy.

"But our peace was short-lived, for no sooner had the hatchet been buried in the tree of peace to our east than the Mahicans invaded Massamet's territory on the quonicticut.

"Again this was because of the Francois white man. The Mahicans had been friends to the Dutch white men and had let them attach their ropes to the shores along the housatonic. But when they let them build a fort at schagticoke (Albany) the Mohawks, friends of the Francois tribe to the north, drove the Mahicans east so the Mohawks could control the beaver trade from Quebec to montauk, the long island in the sea.

"How the Mahicans came to stay in our lands, I have already told you. Their warriors helped to keep the Pequots from attacking Pocumtuck and in Squakeag they helped keep the Mohawks away.

"The Pequots, or foxes, had come from the west in the time of my grandfather's boyhood. They were agressive and fierce fighters and they were feared almost as much as the Mohawks, the wolves.

"All tribes feared the Mohawks the most. They were Moquahs-man-eaters- and would capture people just to roast them like game on their spits. They would force captives to watch as they ate their kinsmen and families, cutting off strips of flesh while their victims were still alive. They were like poisonous snakes - so silent and yet so deadly when they attacked.

"No one blamed the Mahicans for fleeing from them. We knew we would have done the same.

"In time, the Mohawks let the Mahicans have most of their lands back - as nephews, paying tribute to the Mohawks - but many remained in Quansik and along the Connecticut.

"I have told you these things to show you how Trickster played a bad game with our people.

"Now I will tell you how it was with me after the fighting ended.

"As a boy, I grew up in my mother's village, Quabogud, on the northern shore of Quaboag pond. I had many brothers and sisters because my father Naddawahunt (like his father) had three wives. When the white men came, they called us royalty, for we were like the families of their kings. But we never felt any different from the other children. We swam together in the pond, hunted small birds with blowpipes together, ran foot races and fished in the weirs of Wemaskit together at the time of the sequan (spring) moon. Only when we became older and married were we aware of a difference.

""Whereas the other braves could choose whomever they wanted to marry, as long as their clans were not the same, we and our sisters had to marry other members of the sachem class. Ours were marriages of tribes. Our parents would usually arrange for us to meet the son or daughter of a sachem in another area and at the spring fishing camps at the great falls on the quonicticut or chicopee, sachems often performed the marriages. When both the maiden and brave were of high royalty they would live in her village sometimes and in his village sometimes. When commoners married, the brave would live in the woman's village for the rest of his life.

"We had not gone to the shore at niantic for many summers because the Tarrantines had attacked as far south as Pautuxit. The yellow plague had killed everyone except a handful in Pautuxit. Massasoit's entire family was killed- all his wives and children. Traders who came through our territory told us whole villages died with no one left to bury the dead. They said there were piles of bird-cleaned bones all over the ground in such places and it was best to stay away, for who knew what their spirits would do.

"But the summer of my sister's mariage to Masasoit our village packed up and headed east to the cool, fish-laden shores near Sowams. We left those who were unable to travel due to monthly seclusion, illness or heaviness with child behind, along with the old men and women who would tend the growing corn, squash and beans.

"At the shore we would fish in the great waves, dig clams and cook them under seaweed in huge pits. Our women would dry fish so we could take some home with us, but mostly we just ate and ate and ate. We also did a lot of dancing and singing and played games with the Wampanoags. Usually there were Pokonets, Sackonnets and Nausets at these gatherings, and sometimes some of the Massachusetts tribes would come.

"The sachems and their councillors would spend most of their time in the longhouses or in a circle away from the rest on the shore, discussing matters of concern to their tribes. In such a way, it was decided that my sister Nawwash-awsuck, who was younger than I, was to marry Massasoit.

"I had undergone the adulthood ceremony several winters past and was now ready to marry. I was courting Gentle Rain, the daughter of the Wabbaquasett sachem in a very small village directly south of ours on the north-south trail. We were to marry upon my return to quabogud. Although the marriage was to solidify our position to prevent the Pequots from spreading north, I was blessed in that Gentle Rain and I truly loved each other.

"On our journey to the great sea our group had stopped at chabungungamong lake and our medicine men performed a blessing ceremony using the sacred waters of that beautiful lake.

"The lake was a boundary place between the Cowesits, who were part of the Narragansett federation, and of the Quinebaugs. While we were there we heard the old story of the battle between the Wabbaquasetts and the Narragansetts at acquiunk, the place where the quinebaug and assawago rivers joined.

"Many winters ago, in the time of the ancient ones, the Narragansetts invited the Wabbaquasetts to a feast of shellfish at the shore. After the feast, which was enjoyed by all, the Wabbaquasetts invited their Narragansett neighbors to feast with them at acquiunk.

"There, they served many delicious, fat eels to their guests, but the Narragansetts weren't used to eating eels and took offense, thinking that their neighbors were insulting them. They began taunting their hosts and a battle ensued in which most of the unarmed Narragansetts were killed. The Narragansetts sent a large war party to avenge the death of their kinsmen, but the Wabbaquasetts had a stronghold on the other side of the river and from there kept the Narragansetts from crossing. After many days of fighting, the Narragansetts withdrew and the Wabbaquasetts buried their dead in pits near the river. For many years afterwards an uneasy truce existed between the two tribes. Only the area near chabunakongkomaug remained neutral.

"While we were at the neutral boundary place, members of the Hassaminisco tribe joined our party and together we continued on, stopping often at the villages along the way. In each village we were all fed and usually we stayed up very late singing and eating around a large fire circle. We knew that our party probably ate everything the people had, for this was our own way to entertain visitors, but we did not feel bad because it was a time of plenty and more could be gathered or caught to replace what we ate. It was considered an embarassment to not be able to feast your guests and more than once the braves would be hastily assembled to go out and do some hunting when a group of visitors arrived. We could usually catch large, fat eels in our rivers and streams and some crayfish, but larger game were not always in the mood to be caught. In summer, we did not hunt the deer, for they had babies to care for and we did not want to kill the mothers and leave their fawns to die of starvation. The deer spirits would not like that and would make our fall hunt a failure. So mostly we hunted smaller game in the summer and ate much fresh fish, berries and vegetables.

"When we arrived at the shore that summer we saw the braves of Chickataubet's tribe making something on the beach. Chickataubet was sachem of a tribe of Massachusetts that lived between Nanepashemet and Massasoit. He was under the protection of the Narragansetts, which most of us hated, and so didn't usually come to these gatherings. Along with Corbitant, he was one of the sachems who had betrayed Nanepashemet so my aunt was his bitter enemy. His name meant "house afire" because he was responsible for burning the villages of the dead.

"We went over and watched as they tied hand-made twine around a ball of dry hay and then poured whale oil over it. They were making a fireball, we were told, for Chickataubet's mother was very ill and they were going to perform the fireball ceremony that night on the beach in order to appease the spirit making her ill.

""Later, all the powwows gathered together in a sacred circle on the beach and began chanting and singing, shaking their turtleshell rattles and banging their drums. They made a frightful wailing noise as the ball was lit and then kicked, first in one direction and then in another as two groups of warriors vied to kick it towards a tall torch on either end.

"We were impressed by the fact that they didn't burn their feet, even though the ball was red hot. But we knew it was all part of the spell being cast by the shamans in their circle, for their spirits were running with the men. Suddenly the ball went out and everyone made an unhappy sound. This was a bad sign. Chickataubet's mother would not get well.

"The powwows said it had to do with the four comets they had seen in the sky the summer before. Such a sight meant much trouble for the people. Already there had been the plague, they said. A Nauset powow said it was because a white man still lived amongst them. The Nauset sachem Epanow said he would be glad to kill the Francois man, and his half-Francois child, but Massasoit said he had given them permission to live with his people and if anyone killed them, he would claim vengeance.

"We had seen the Francois before, soon after they were shipwrecked off the cape. Most had been killed in the storm or on the beach , but five were spared and given out to surrounding sachems so they could be studied and some of their ways learned. This had been Massasoit's decision, for Epanow hated them for kidnapping him and his fellow sachem Coneconam and taking them to their country. Epanow said they had been treated like slaves, dragged around in chains and displayed like captured wild animals until they were sold to a captain named Hunt. While amongst the white men, they learned that they valued the metal called gold more than anything else and so Epanow and another captive, Assacumet , made up a story about gold on cappawack (Martha's Vineyard). Hunt believed their story and sailed back. As soon as they were in sight of the colored rocks (Gay Head), the two Nausets hailed their friends, jumped off ship and swam ashore. Ever since, they had sworn themselves to avenge the wrongs done to their people by the white men.

"That night on the beach Epanow bragged of how he had led an attack on Captain Dermer's ship two moons past as Dermer was sailing away with two prisoners he had ransomed. He knew his eagle-talon-tipped arrow had struck Dermer a fatal blow and said they would never see another white man's ship again in their harbors. He said the white men brought the plague that had killed so many, but Massasoit refused to believe him and would not give up the Francois. He said the French sailor had asked to remain with the Pokanokets instead of going back with Captain Dermer.

"A few sleeps later we heard that Epanow had gone to a powwow to cast a spell on the white man and his child to poison them. But by then Epanow and his people had returned to Gay Head and could not tell us if it were true.

"The powwows were very upset with Epanow, for they said his actions were sure to lead to a flock of the white man's birds to our shores to seek vengeance. Massasoit's powwows told of dreams and of Mitark's vision of a great white whale coming to them in the powow pond off the coast of Martha's Vineyard. Of course, these things were told in confidence to Massasoit and the other sachems in the longhouse, but being of royal blood I was allowed to sit in.

"Massasoit said he would put a stop to such talk and he ordered all the people at the shore to assemble on the flatlands below monthop, where his village stood. He then brought the Francois man out and said to him, "I am a powerful man. I rule more than thirty tribes." Massasoit then named each tribe and said that they had the powerful protection of 37 gods. The Francois man said that his one god was more powerful, which made Massasoit angry and he told the Francois man to take his child and leave his village. He wouldn't let the man's wife and child leave with him, but after dark she snuck out of camp, aware that her act of defiance would lead to execution. A short while later all three were found dead and Massasoit ordered them buried in two pits- one for the Pokonoket and another for the white man and his half-breed child.

"Such events dampened the fun a little, but we soon forgot about them and enjoyed spearing blue fish, cod and sea bass off the shores. I loved going out in the sturdy hollow-log canoes the cape dwellers had and loved the smell of the salt water and the cries of the sea gulls overhead. I loved walking in the soft, white sand and sitting amongst the tall grasses and eating the juicy plums and tart rosehips that grew all over the place. The only thing I liked better in Quabogud was the temperature of our pond water. The water of Wechakum was like winter water, even when the sun shone hottest. It never got warm and I was not one of those who loved to stand in it and cast nets or catch crabs or small fishes with my bare hands. Even with extra fish grease on my feet, they would hurt when I stood in it. This thing I tell you now, but at the time I would not have dreamt of telling anyone, for we were taught not to show weakness or pain. A warrior's way was to keep the expression on his face unchanged when exposed to pain or if he were afraid. To show hurt or cry out was to bring shame on oneself and one's family and tribe.

"During our stay, Massasoit married my sister and gave my father a beautiful wampum belt with much blue wampum hens (beads) in it to commemorate the event and to seal our nations together. My family gave Massasoit many fine gifts, and, because my father had met Samoset, a sachem-trader from Monhegan, he was able to obtain a steel knife to give to Massasoit. This knife, which all desired, cost my father many furs, but it made Massasoit very happy.

"At this time the Wamesits, Nashobas and Squakeags renewed their friendship with Massasoit. Other friendly bands included the Massachusetts, Nashaways, Wachusetts, Quaboags and all of the inland tribes plus the coastal and island tribes. The only inland tribes that had refused to declare open friendship were squaw sachem's Wabbaquasetts and the Quinebaugs. They were constantly being attacked by the Pequots and so they paid tribute to the Narragansetts after they took Aquidneck island from the Wampanoags. They needed protection from the strongest ally and felt the Narragansetts were going to keep warring and annihilate Massasoit's friends the way the Tarrantines had slaughtered Nanepashemet's allies.

"When the marriage was over, Massasoit declared himself brother to my father and my uncle. The two chief sachems had been born at the same time and had always been great friends. He knew how precious the gift of my sister was.

"Massasoit's brother Quadequina also married into our family at this time - to a squaw from my mother's people- the Quans, just south of us and bordering Wabbaquasett. She lived in Tantiesques, near the place of the black rocks. I think Massasoit thought this was a good alliance, for it would place his brother in a position to talk to the Wabbaquasetts and get them to join the federation.

"We were happy for Nawwashawsuck, for we knew she had married a fine, kind man. Not only was Massasoit much respected among the people, but he was tall and broad chested and very strong for his years.

"Such was my last happy visit to Sowams. Whole families of white men came and stayed that winter and when my father and I visited in the time of the Falling Leaves Moon, we could see that things had begun to change forever along the shore.

"But for me and my wife's village, the change came sooner."

Firehawk smokes for a while as a pot of succotash with venison in it is brought in and the children take turns eating. After all eat, he clears his throat and continues,

"I first saw Gentle Rain when I was a boy of 11 winters. My father and I were hunting and had followed one of the Waddaquadducks to the mountain called pussough (Mt. Pisgah). This was named for the big cats that denned on it. We would often hear their screams in the woods at night. They liked to hunt from the trees, jumping down on their prey, so we were always careful when hunting in their area.

"That summer the thunderbird was holding back rain, so we went to drink at a place where there was a spring in the rock that flowed year-round. It was in a swamp, which that year was not very wet. As we neared it, we heard a girl cry out and turned to see a mother bear about to charge the girl, who had become separated from her older sister, Gentle Rain. My father pulled an arrow from his quiver and aimed straight for the bear's eye. He knew his arrows were not strong enough to kill the bear if fired into its chest, so he had to go for its eye, which would lead to its brain. The bear bellowed a great cry of pain as it fell, almost on top of the little girl.

"Gentle Rain ran over to her sister and hugged her tight, then looked up at us to thank us. As her soft brown eyes met mine, something happened in my chest and I knew this was the girl I would marry. I remember hearing the skrill of brother Hawk above as we walked back to her village, where the men decided that my father could have the bear since he hadn't been actually hunting it inside their territory. When we returned to the site, we found its cub trying to rouse it and I was allowed to adopt it as a pet.

"The women cut up the bear and carried it back to Gentle Rain's village where my father presented a good portion of the meat to them. We had a fine feast and later my father and I returned to our village with lots of bear fat and choice pieces of meat, as well as with a very fine bearskin.

"The little bear cub became very tame and soon I had to build a pen for it as it kept getting into my mother's food supplies. As it got bigger, it became mean and one day I had to lead it out into the woods, far away from any villages, and let it go. I said a prayer to

Creator when I parted with my bear brother. I prayed that Creator would protect him and teach him how to be afraid of people so he wouldn't get killed.

"While I was out in the woods with him, I had a vision and knew my family had bear magic. This is very powerful magic for the bears are the teachers - they taught our grandfathers in the long ago how to fish for salmon, how to use the acorn, and which plants to use for medicines.

"When we got older, Gentle Rain and I began to make excuses to accompany travelers to our villages and soon I began courting her properly, sitting outside her village and playing my flute to get her to come for a walk at dusk. We would walk to the other side of the pond her village overlooked and sit by the shores, watching the circles the fish left in the moonlight and the bats swooping over the water to catch mosquitoes and other insects. Sometimes I would bring her a present of a nice fat eel or an animal I had killed and she would giggle as she accepted it. She also made me presents- a nice buckskin pouch with sweetgrass flowers sewn into it and a small bark container with her teeth-mark designs on it.

"We would sit side-by-side on the shore and I would play my flute or we would sing together softly. Her eyes were the most beautiful in all of Quaboag and I would lose track of all time looking into them. Many nights I had to sleep over in her father's wetu because I lingered too long to make the trip home before the sun rose.

"When we decided to marry, I chose a spot on the edge of her village of quoquonset where there was a group of saplings. I chose the six I needed and chopped the rest away with my stone-headed hatchet, then used my prized obsidian knife to cut the rest of their trunks out beneath the surface of the ground. Our obisidian knives were as sharp as the white man's steel knives, but they would break if dropped on something hard, whereas the white man's would only get a little knick in it. This was the only thing the English had that we in Quansik admired - until they showed us the thundersticks.

"After I had the area cleared, I bent the saplings over to make a dome-shaped frame. Then I went into the woods and began stripping bark from trees to cover the frame with. While I was doing this, my wife-to-be was busy gathering reeds from the large meadow of reeds, which wasn't far from her village. She dried them and then used her tall weaving frame to make mats to line the inside of the frame with.

"After the mats were tied in place with strips of basswood rope, the bark was layered to create a wetu that would withstand the winter snows. I was to move to her village and live amongst them as co-sachem with her father. Even though her father was a sachem, my direct descent from Naddawahunt's blood made me automatically co-sachem of any village I married into. This helped to strengthen their ties to Quaboag and loosen their ties to Narragansett.

"The marriage took place a few sleeps after we returned from the seashore. Her family prepared a great feast and my village plus people from the village between us, Asquoash, came to the feast. There, Naddawahunt reminded them of his agreement with Massasoit. Gentle Rain's father was worried, for the Narragansetts had been after his village to do as the other Wabbaquasetts had done and pay tribute to them in exchange for protection from the Pequots. My father told them that as long as I lived amongst them, they would be his children and subject to his will. This was said as uncle to nephew. Everyone loved my father and trusted his judgment so Gentle Rain's father put aside his worries and we sang and danced until the stars went to bed.

"In those times our tribes were bodies - flesh and blood with hands, feet and heads. We were all related in some way. Our grand-parents were the Delawares, far to our south and the Hurons far to the north. Our legends said we had come from these people. We would have given a member of these tribes honor in our circles but were not obligated to follow orders from them. Fathers we did not have, for a father cannot command his children, but later we learned the white man's sachem called us his children so we called him father.

"Our uncles were tribes that had invaded us and then left us to do as we would. As nephews we offered gifts to them every year and in return they looked out for us, offering protection if we were attacked.

"Our brothers were equals. Often a small tribe was called a younger brother by its bigger brothers. In a sense, Quaboag was a younger brother to Nashoba but Squakeag was equal to Nashoba. But, as brothers, we all had equal say and independence. Our older brothers would offer advice and guidance but we were not obligated to follow it. And the older brother was usually the one who sat in council with the older brothers of other tribes. So for us, Naddawahunt would sit in council with Massasoit.

"We also had tribes who would call themselves the women so they could negotiate peace treaties when the men were too proud to see reason and stop fighting. This was not a weak station, for our females had the land and carried the royal lines. Massasoit had been very wise when he took on this role, for he earned much respect from all the tribes.

"So my marriage to the Wabbaquasetts created a family between my wife's village and Quobogud. The Quaboags were now uncles to Gentle Rain's people and would protect them if attacked.

"Following the ceremony, I took Gentle Rain's hand and we went into our new home, which was furnished with things made by her family and friends. I gave her a fine pale wolf skin as my wedding present.

"By the first moon after our marriage, Gentle Rain was carrying our son and I began to hunt more often, for her appetite began to grow to that of two webcowits (married squaws).

"I made new friends easily in her village and soon hunted often with a large brave called He Who Roars Like Bear. We called him Bear-Roarer. We went with the other men to the minnechaug (Wilbraham) hills that autumn to hunt deer. We tried to bring down moosic (big shoulders- moose), but they were too fast for us.

"Later that winter, a trader by the name of Waban, from Natick, came through our village. He told us the knife men had come back and this time they were living on shore, away from their floating island.

"Waban said Passaconaway and other powwows gathered in the swamps to drive them away, like they had done before, but this time the white man's magic was very powerful and they stayed. He told us that the Nauset sachem Aspinet had led a party of men to war on them, but even though they used special harts-horn, brass and eagle-tipped arrows, they didn't kill them. Instead, Aspinet was wounded from the thunder they carried in long sticks. He told us Massasoit had asked Samoset to spy on them, for he knew the knife man's ways from trading with them in Monhegan. Samoset said he would go into their camp, but only if he could be protected from their magic, so Massasoit's powows prepared two arrows for him to carry - one Flint, the other He Who Grasps the Sky. These would make him immune from their spells.

"Waban said the sickness had returned and many people in the villages to the east were again sick or dying from it.

"Following his visit, I had a vision and the Bear spirit told me how to cure the sickness by herbs and sweating but I did not get a chance to tell it to anyone.

A terrible shudder of pain sweeps across Firehawk's face and he falters, wiping at his eyes with the edge of his woolen blanket.

"I wanted to travel to Quobogud to talk to my father about these things, but Bear Roarer wanted to hunt moose, so we traveled with Waban on the south path to the Skipmunks territory, where Bear Roarer got a moose-hunting party together to go out to moose meadow. This was the best time to get moose, we knew, for they couldn't run fast in deep snow.

"We brought down two large moose and would have returned home within two handfuls of sleeps but Bear Roarer gambled away our meat and hides in Scitico and so we had to go back, just the two of us and another brave from our village, Running Deer.

"Running Deer was as old as my father, yet thin and tough, like a hide that had been cured too long. He kept up with Roaring Bear and myself and soon we were back in Moose Meadow, back in the cave that served as our winter camp.

"Before we could go out to hunt, we had to cleanse all human scent from our bodies, so we built a wetu near the pond, heated rocks and made a sweat lodge. Then we rubbed ourselves with bear fat strongly scented with sweetgrass. Finally, we smudged ourselves with the smoke from sweetgrass and set out to the meadow.

"It wasn't long before we spotted a large buck, but it took a full day before we were able to track him near the woods. Once he was near the trees, Roaring Bear stood up on top of the rock outcropping we were hiding behind and let out a loud shout. This startled the moose, who saw me on one side and Running Deer on the other and it headed into the woods. Once there, it tangled its large antlers in the underbrush and Roaring Bear finished him off with well-placed arrows.

"As any who have hunted moose knows, it can be very tricky. If the moose had rushed for either Running Deer or myself, we would have had a hard time outrunning it. Even though the deep snow slowed the moose down, it also slowed us in our snowshoes, down. If the moose had gotten free after being wounded with only one arrow, it could have led us on a chase deep into the woods or up the mountain. This could have taken days, for moose are strong and have great endurance. However, Creator was kind to us that day and we were able to go to the moose before the sun went to the land of the southwest.

"Roaring Bear first said a prayer of thanks to the *moosamuttuck* spirit, then cut out its tongue, heart, sinews and left hoof to offer back to Mother Earth. Then he cut off its lip and presented it with thanks to Running Deer and myself for helping with the chase. This was an honor for usually the lip went to the village sachem.

"Afterwards, we carved up the meat, wrapping the choicest parts in its hide. By then it was dark so we had to bury the rest in snow to defend it against predators who would steal it from us. We took the hide and put it on our sled, then took the entrails and other pieces of meat and cooked them for our meal back at the cave. In the morning we would return for the hairpipes and antlers plus any other pieces of meat we could carry on our backs. Normally, our squaws would carry the meat, but we had left them at home this time for Gentle Rain was very heavy with child and Running Deer's wife was nursing Roaring Bear's wife, who had come down with a sickness that made her bleed from her nose and mouth if she exerted herself.

"Once back at the village his wife would only have to carry it from the outside of the village in, to show that it belonged to her. Otherwise, Roaring Bear's clan could claim it and she might not be allowed to eat any of it or to have its hide.

"At the cave, we heated rocks, then put them and snow in a green bark container and added nokehick to the hot water. Some of the meat was laid on frames over the fire to dry out a little before our journey.

"That night Running Deer had a dream. It bothered him so much he woke before the rest of us and urged us to forget the antlers and return home immediately.

"He said he dreamt that grey wolves were surrounding our village, standing on their back legs like men. Their eyes burned yellow then the whole village began to burn in yellow flames.

"I became worried that his dream meant the Pequots, those sly grey foxes, had attacked the village. But we had many fine warriors to defend it, so I followed Roaring Bear to the carcass, which had been dug up and chewed on by wolves during the night. We worked quickly to get the antlers and bones. Later, in his wetu, he would make ornaments and decorate different articles with the things he had carved from them.

"As we worked, Running Bear remembered more of his dream. He said there were no ashes after the fire, nothing. It was as if the village had never been. He said instead there were strange brown beasts roaming over the corn fields, beasts that looked a little like moose, but were smaller and rounder, with white splotches on their sides.

"The journey back took us in a circle away from the Tantiesques trail, for Running Deer wanted to bring some of the healing waters from the spring in Shenipsit to his wife, Little Leaf, whose eyes were bothering her.

"We followed a narrow hunting path around the great hollow of the Mashapaug to where it met the trail to the black rocks. This area was full of wild cats so we were on the lookout for footprints and looked up often as we walked through the woods.

"Where a tree had been felled, we crossed the Weamantuck, our mocassins slipping on the icy log. The river was slow-moving; the color of the insides of the black rocks near Tantiesques. The shadowy areas along its banks were lined with ice and so we moved slowly, cautiously.

"The medicine springs were a short distance beyond the river in a cedar swamp, whose ground was thawed and mushy beneath our snowshoes. We looked for a large maple tree, and at its base found the springs, covered with matted leaves. Running Deer pushed the leaves aside and steam rose through the cold air.

"Deer reached for his pouch of kinnikinnick (tobacco mixture), which hung on a thong attached to his belt, along with his pipe. He squatted and took some pooke (tobacco) out of his pouch and put in in his clay pipe. He puffed and offered it to the four directions, saying,

"Nopatin, Wind of the Rising Sun, I praise you for the warmth you send to my people and for the life you give to our crops.

"Paponetin, Wind of the Thunder Beings, I praise you and thank you for the rain you bring to the people.

"Sowwaniu, wind of the Southwest, I praise you for the pleasant breezes you send during the time of the burning moon.

"Wind my face is directed into, I praise you for breathing on me as I walk and sleep. I praise you for taking my words to the eagle, who carries them to Manitoo."

"Grandfather, I call on you to listen to my prayers. My squaw is sick, she suffers and calls out. I pray that you will infuse this water with powerful medicine to cure her, if she is still sick upon my return."

"Deer then laid a pinch of tobacco on the earth and opened a small birch bark container attached to a thong. From the red-bottomed spring he scooped some water, then he went to the spring that smelled of rotten things and added its waters to the first, tying the whole in a secure bundle with hemp twine. Afterwards we all dipped our hands into the rotten-smelling waters and rubbed our eyes with it, for our people often came to this place during Moonesquanimok, the Strawberry Moon, to do this for our eyes after being in smokey wetus all winter. Deer said when his village used to travel to this place they would catch fish at the place where the river dropped and feast with the Wabbaquasetts and Skungamungs. But they had not come in some time because of the Pequots.

"As we began down the path, I heard Deer yell "Ah yhee!" We grabbed our bows but found him looking at a white owl in the tree above him. It had flown up in front of him, he said. This made us all anxious, for a white animal is a bad omen, especially after a bad dream. Our snowshoes quickly padded up the inclining narrow path as dusk began to descend. We could hear our breathing as we hurried past the ponds and through the swamps and woods back to the great pond where our village lay.

"With the shadows growing longer, we heard the familiar sounds of the blue jays near our village and could see the outline of the wetu tops on the rise above the pond. A golden yellow sunset dripped over the pond. Further above, the sky looked like one of Gentle Rain's mats, woven with bands of gold and pink. A large grey huron swooped down to the pond's black surface and flew off as a flurry of bats came out of the pine trees.

"All seemed well and at peace. But it was too quiet. There were no sounds of children playing or men and women talking.

"In the silence I smelled old smoke.

"Suddenly, a rush of panic flooded my body and I remembered how Mohawks would burn their victims alive, roasting little children like turkeys on sticks over the fire.

"I dropped my grip on the sled and ran towards the village yelling, "Gentle Rain, Gentle Rain!" Then I shouted, "Mohawks!" as I raised my tomahawk and rushed into the village, the blood pounding hard inside my head.

Note: Some marriages and confederacies mentioned in this chapter are based on the author's "educated guess" and are not documented in other sources. They are not intended to be used for genealogical purposes.

Chapter 3
(A re-telling of events in 1620)

The sachem pauses for what seems like a very long time. No one speaks; no one moves. All are hanging onto his story, waiting for him to finish. When he speaks his voice seems far away, in another world:

"Munnannock, Grandmother Moon, lay like a huge white shell gorget against the black breast of the sky. Below, Mother Earth reflected its light in the deep, black eye that was our pond. A siog (pickeral) surfaced then disappeared into its cold depths, leaving behind gently expanding circlets of silver.

"How long I had been sitting there, I don't know. It was cold, but I was numb and felt nothing but my grief. In the darkness, the world of cheepi, the silent army of cattails stood sentinel over the small village across the pond. The podless stalks spoke to each other in the small hours before papisha (dawn). I heard them ask why there were no fires, why there was no people noise, why this human sat weeping in their midst.

"I slowly raised my eyes and saw the small dugout canoes on the edge of the iceless pond. I could not look directly at the village, but instead looked above it at the forest and beyond to the hills between it and my father's village. I was aware of Roaring Bear and Deer and aware of the little bundle sleeping in my lap, but I was like a spirit - seeing everything but not as one living in the world.

"I don't know when it happened, but I had a vision while I sat on the edge of the pond.

"I saw first one member of my village then another become very ill, turn wet with sweat, turn yellow, then die. Nishkeneunk, Gentle Rain, was the last to die. She had barely given birth to our son when the fever struck her. I saw her resting on the pale wolf fur, her fingers trembling as she tried to suckle our son. I heard her moan and call out, but there was no one to tend to her, no one to sing the songs for her.

"I saw the dogs outside become tense, sniffing the air. Then, like something fired from a bow, the wolves shot out of the forest and killed the weak dogs. Our dog was the last to go. It fought bravely, like a warrior. He locked eyes with the leader of the wolf pack and stiffly circled in the dance of death. But the wolf was bigger and its fangs sunk into the dog I called sampum, for his color was like ground corn.

"The odor of blood from his convulsing body urged the other wolves on and the shores of the pond became agitated, full of slushy red snow and mud as the wolves ravaged the dogs.

"Nishkeneunk heard this battle from where she was lying on the fur and mats of the sleeping platform inside our wetu. There was no fire, but she was drenched with sweat. I heard her whisper to our son in the cradleboard next to her, "Poor nippapoos." I could feel her heart beating faster as she heard the sound of paws scuffling amongst the cold firestones in a wetu nearby. She spoke to the wolves in her mind, reminding them that she was a sister of the wolf clan.

"As the growls grew louder, she touched the medicine inscription on the slate pendant hanging around her neck. She sighed a deep, exhausted sigh of sorrow for the infant she had brought forth. Shaking, she pulled herself up on the platform. She picked up our son and tried to run, but a blizzard began in her head, turning everything white behind her eyes.

"Suddenly the night was no more, the witu was no more. It was a brilliant blue day and the clouds in the sky formed like eyelids around the blue. In one instant, she knew that Mother Earth was only one organ in Creator's body and that she was the smallest particle of cornmeal on Cautantowwit's tongue. The blood in her body merged with the blood of the universe: beating. All was one, all was whole.

"My son awakened when he felt her cold hand fall across his face. He tried to nuzzle her breast beneath her damp deerskin mantle. The *non anese* felt something was different and began to fret quietly.

"Outside the witu there came a yelp as one of the wolves pulled a pot of cold aupuminea-naw-saump (cornmeal) from a pole over a dead firepit and was hit by the clay pot. By now the noises of the late winter night had changed. There was a new sound, a sinister, dark sound that said death had taken over. Its voice was the throaty howl we had heard so often from the mountain to our north. But now it was ten-times louder and a hundred times more frightening.

"My son could hear scuffles as wolf fought wolf for the half-frozen bodies scattered inside or outside the witus. The crunch of bones silenced the owls above as they watched the wolves feasting on the flesh of their human brothers and sisters. Yet, as they watched, they waited, their sharp, round eyes greedily claiming the bits left by the shaggy grey wolves.

"Suddenly, the mat flap covering our witu's western entrance was shoved in by a bloody, saliva-covered muzzle and cold, yellow eyes stared into my son's home.

"No strong braves jumped off the platforms and grabbed their bows or spears. No grandmother screamed. The witu was deathly silent and naked of life, save for the tiny babe in the flower-decorated cradleboard.

"My nipapoose felt hot, bloody breath on his mother's neck and then felt her being tugged away, off the platform to the hard earth beneath. In the total darkness, his tiny brown eyes could not see her but he heard the snarl and snap of bone as its bloody haunches disappeared through the flap, dragging Gentle Rain's body from its jaws.

"Through glimpses of moonlight he saw her bare foot flop from side to side, half inside and half outside the witu. The mats trembled as the wolf strugged to hold its prize and lick her still-warm, sweet blood. Another head, smaller and darker, looked inside the witu from the eastern flap and my boy felt a hot, sweaty warmth near his head. The wolf stood with its paws on the low, lashed-wood platform and then knocked the cradleboard to the earth. Under the beaver skins, down the length of his tiny spine, my son felt a tingle tighten his greased and sooted skin. The leathery nose nudged the cradleboard, trying to turn it over. It pulled the board side to side as it chewed on the rawhide thongs lacing it tight. Then, with a whine it backed away, the strong urine odor from days of unchanged moss burning the wolf's eyes. It prodded the cradleboard gingerly, then turned its attention to Gentle Rain.

"My son's face was turned sideways against Mother Earth. A flea crawled over his eyes and he blinked, but did not cry. He laid there listening while the knife of pain in his small stomach buried its blade deeper. He worked his fist to his mouth and began to suck, but no warm, sweet milk tickled his throat and quieted the searing pain in his middle.

"In the shadows of the wetu there appeared to be another creature watching, a black panther with yellow eyes. Unlike the wolves, it wasn't there to kill. It looked more like a mother protecting her cub.

"As my son dozed, the owls became silent and the blue jays began to sing in the trees beyond the witus. The menacing creatures disappeared back into the underbrush and the hawks and crows jockied with each other, feeding in the grey time between night and day.

" And so my vision ended.

"Nippawas (Grandfather Sun) felt his way through the treetops and woke me with a touch on my eyelids. I heard a scream echo across the pond and was aware that it had come from my own throat. The ducks and crows took flight as I stumbled down the hill into the village. Roaring Bear was rocking back and forth on his knees amongst the scattered remains of his squaw and children. He moaned and clawed his face and chest.

"Running Deer could not find his family, but their witu had been taken down, so he knew they had died before the wolves and had received a proper burial. The three of us had never felt so alone in all our lives. Even when we were out camping, or when we had undergone the winter survival, we knew we were part of a family, our blood beat with that of our friends and relatives. We did not exist alone, we were one of a people. But now, our village, our people, our identity was lost for a moment.

"Mourning with us, Grandfather Sun covered his face and hid the bloated, mauled bodies littering our once neat village. As the sun's warmth grew, so did the stench. Through my blurred eyes I glared at a crow that did not want to leave its meal - a squaw's blood-clotted eye socket. The murder in my eyes scared it more than my waving tomahawk and it flew up to the tall pines with an angry, gutteral taunt of "ha, ha!"

"All of a sudden, Roaring Bear jumped up and began running towards the pond. "The yellow death!" he shouted over and over as he tried to wash it off him. I picked up my son and ran after him and Deer followed. Bear was crazy and fought us off as we tried to drag him out of the water. He finally quieted down, but then he saw the cradleboard and its tiny occupant and he grabbed it and threw my son into the ice-cold water.

"I jumped in after it and he fought me, shouting that my son carried the yellow death, but I was able to grab the cradleboard as Deer grabbed Roaring Bear. I quickly cut the thongs, which were drawing tight from the water, and pulled my son free. As I did, a hawk, my totem, flew close over the water. My son was struggling and fighting for life. I bundled him against my chest under my tunic and could feel him searching for his mother's milk. As I rose to take him to my father's village Asquoach, which was a few fingers walk against the sun, I saw Roaring Bear setting fire to the witus.

"As if in a trance, I rose through the acrid smoke and walked to my witu, my anguish touching the ghosts roaming through the smoke. Through the snakes of smoke I could see the face of my father-in-law. He raised his square hand in greeting and smiled gently, his eyes warm. I could see Gentle Rain's grandmother, her brown hands outstretched and the shells on her cape clinking in rhythm to her graceful dancing. I pulled open the flap to our witu and saw Gentle Rain sitting by the fire, her soft brown eyes and small face full of love and concern for me and our baby. Before I ran away, I took one last look at the witu. The flames were licking Gentle Rain's quill-embroidered boxes and the clothes she had lovingly sewn and embroidered.

"The witus were close together with piles of firewood in front, so it only took seconds for the flames to rush from one to the other. Within minutes, they exploded, flinging bark and wood everywhere.

"The smoke alerted my father's village and we were met on the north-south path by a group of their fastest runners.

"I was numb. My heart had died in that village and all that walked the path was an empty shell.

"I dimly remember being led to their winter fort nestled between ridges on the mountainside. I remember my mother and her sister taking the nipapoose and clucking as they saw how starved and cold he was. I remember many people stroking my soot-covered cheek and head and saying, "*Kutchimmoke* (be of good cheer), *netop*." And then I remember falling into a black sleep, a sleep without visions or dreams, a sleep that was as deep as the great sea.

"Later, I found out I had slept for two days. When I awoke in my father's large witu, I saw my father and other brothers sitting with him near the fire. Their voices were raised, they were discussing what had happened to my village with the shaman from asquoach.

"Massasoit's brother Quadequina, who had been living in

asquoash and its winter village of quaboag old fort, sat facing me, his deeply-lined face glowing from the small firelight. Next to him on one side sat my aunt Mishalisk's son Wetolechen, sachem in Tantiesques. My father Tahattawan (Naddawahunt), sachem of Nashoba, was not there, but we knew he would come soon.

"Roaring Bear and Deer also sat with the men and I heard Quadequina say, "My sons and my brothers, my heart is filled with sorrow for our loss. The hills cry out to Creator, asking him to drive this devil plague from our people.

"For many moons this plague has snuck amongst the peoples of our land, lying in wait to ambush us when our manitoo is weak.

"We grieve together, my brothers, we draw blood in our loss and we ask 'What terrible thing we have done to make the gods so angry with us?' Is it because we have not been keeping the give-away of goods and have been careless in burying our dead? Our brothers the Narragansetts have kept these rituals and have been spared the yellow death."

"I heard the sound of a rattle and drum as aa shaman entered the witu. He smudged each of the men with a torch of burning sweet-grass and chanted a spell of protection.

"People began to gather at the door flap and peer in. From where I lay all I could see was their mocassins and a few flakes of snow lazily running along the frozen ground.

"This is a bad thing that has come to our people," the shaman said as he offered smoke to the four directions and then joined the others in smoking their pipes.

"I think we have done something that has made our gods angry with us. I had a dream and saw that man there -" he pointed his rattle at Roaring Bear - "and his wife. Then I saw him take another wife, and she is the cause of our troubles."

"Roaring Bear stopped staring at the coals and looked up, "You speak of Yellow Leaf's sister. Her village died from the sickness and that is how she came to live with us. Could it be that she brought the anger of the gods for her village with her?"

"The shamans looked at him. Then one spoke, "What robes did she bring with her to your village?"

"Roaring Bear lowered his eyes, for he knew she had brought her dead husband's fine bear robe and not her own old bear robe.

"It is true, brothers. I knew she buried the wrong bear robe with her husband. I had never seen so large and fine a bearskin before and wanted it for my own."

"They started to chastise him and I broke in, 'Brothers, don't judge Roaring Bear too harshly. He travelled all the way to the land of the Massachusetts to bring his sister's wife to her new home. She was a big eater and he knew he would have to hunt twice as hard to feed her and her children. The robe is gone now, as is all of the village and all of the goods in it. Is that not enough of a sacrifice for our gods? What more can they want?'

"The shaman shook his ochre-painted head and said they wanted more. He and the elders then began to make plans for a huge give-away and burning of goods ceremony.

"I fell back to sleep and later when I woke up, the sachem's mother and my aunt, now the wife of Quadequina, were in the witu with my son.

"Their round, motherly bodies were clothed in long mantles of deerskin, the fur from each mantle's two hides turned inward. The ragged mantle edges dragged on the hard ground as they moved around the fire. They were almost identical, each with a thick black braid tied in a club-shaped knot at the back of her neck and soft, rabbit-lined mocassins on their feet. Across their shoulders were short pelts for added warmth for the day was bitter cold.

"The older webcowit was holding the baby, making clucking noises as she held up a string of shells, but the boy's eyes were turned inward on its pain and he did not smile.

"They noticed I was awake and brought me a wooden bowl of soup. I was too weak to hold it so my aunt held the maplewood spoon and gently fed me, like one would feed an old man.

"Our women were our strength, for they were the care-givers. They completed our lives. They were the ones who sang at our weddings, who baked apoon (little sweet cakes) for our children, who teased the boys when they caught their first tiny fish, but bragged afterwards about their skills as fishermen. They cradled the babes, nursed the sick and again cradled us when we were old and like children. Creator gave men the kind of strength it took to hunt and fight, but he gave women a quieter strength, one that never became tired. And he also gave them a fierceness that few men liked to see, for we knew that it was the kind Creator gave to all mothers so they could fight to keep their offspring safe.

"Little Petals, the squaw nursing my boy, picked a bone out of the coals and threw it to the brown and black dogs lying across the doorway. She was singing a soft song to my son as she gently rocked back and forth. Her own papoose lay against the side of the witu, snug in its cradleboard.

"I said to the women, "Last year, when we were at the seashore, a sachem-trader from Monhegan named Samoset said the plague had come over on the floating islands of the knife men. Do you think this is so?"

"My aunt gave me a sharp look, her face serious, "It is not good for us to talk of the knife man's magic. Sleep now," she said, gently taking the bowl and pouring what was left back into the pot simmering over the small fire.

"But as I laid back on the wooden platform and let the soft furs close over me, Samoset's words kept coming back and I felt my first hatred for the knife men."

Chapter 4
(A re-telling of the first meeting in Plymouth, 1621)

An old man with long, stringy, grey-streaked hair stands up. He is very thin and his back is bent. His nose seems unusally large because his face has shrunken in where his teeth had been. Unlike Firehawk, who had the voice of a taupawau (a wiseman used to talking to people), his voice is rusty and squeaks when he runs out of air.

"I am Tuophen, He Who Crossed the River. In my younger days I was called Kullaggulleuteg, Big Eel Pot, for I was a good fisherman and the best at catching eels in Tantiesques.

"Because I loved to fish, I always went to the seashore in the winter when our ponds were frozen over. I was staying in Old Watuspaquin's village near pautuxet the winter before Firehawk's village was destroyed.

"Despite the fireball ceremony, Chickataubet's mother had died. So had the Francois man and his child. I knew these things, although no one would mention any of these people by name, for we don't speak of our dead. I knew them because the white men who had decided to stay in pautuxit had desecrated their graves. This was unthinkable and so there was much whispered talk about it.

"So I was with the Nemaskets when Massasoit and about sixty Wampanoags camped in the meadow near nammassakeeset. I heard of the plan to send Samoset to them to spy on them for they were still taking strange things off the floating island. These things were very heavy and they had to drag them out of the small boat and up to the top of the hill. Samoset said they were cannon and that ships usually had some on their decks. He said they made a great thunder and spat out large metal stones. Samoset was sent to spy on them to learn if they were planning to attack the Nemaskets, Pocassets or Pokanokets.

"I was not a warrior, netops, although I would raise my tomahawk to defend my people. I was a fisherman, and so I did not pay much attention to the talk of the white men and their warrior party. The weather had turned warm and I was busy trying to catch anish, osacontuck (haddock and cod), kauposhshauog (sturgeon) and missukekekequock (bass) off the coast of the Conohassets. Bass we especially loved for its brains and fat are sweet. I had learned from my first fishing trip to the sea that the little stone sinkers we used in quansik and the small bird-bone hooks wouldn't do for the large fish in the sea. I made sinkers the size of a woman's breasts and tied rawhide thongs around the curve of their middles. I made hockamock (fish hooks) as big as a man's hand out of the antlers of a moose. And I had a spear tipped with a barbed point carved from the tusk of a sea creature far to the north.

"Even though I was a fine fisherman in quansik, I had much to learn from my coastal brothers, who often laughed at my clumsy attempts to catch the large tatackommauog (porpoises) they speared.

"They even speared potoppauog (whales), but only if they were in shallow waters, for a dying whale would take the man attached to it right to the sea's bottom and never bring him back up again. Mostly we just watched our brother whale, marvelling at his size and power, at the waterfall he could spit out of the top of his head. Once, when I was younger, I saw a family of whales dying on the beach off Nauset. We helped Epannow's people cut them up and I carried much fat home to my squaw, who said it was better than bear grease. Epannow's people believed the whales were sent by a spirit, who sang a song from shore that they couldn't resist, even when they knew they were giving up their lives.

"Although the wind turned warmer, the waves were very rough, so I had to put off fishing. While waiting, I went with some of the Namassakeesetts to a hill on the other side of a ravine which had a brook running through it. On the other hill stood the strange thunder things. We learned from the people camping on our side that Samoset had gone into the white man's camp the day before and had just come back. Over his fringed loincloth he wore a red knifeman coat, long in the back but split in two. Everyone wanted to see it, to touch it. He said the white men wanted to trade, so a handful of sachems sent braves to their villages for furs, which the white men always liked.

"I watched the next day as the five sachems of the area each carried a beaver skin and followed Samoset down the ravine, over the brook then up the other bank where they were met by a man whose skin was so light it shone like their knives. This time the white men were rude and said they could not trade, because their god said it was not a good day to trade. The sachems came back but Samoset pretended to be sick so he could stay and learn of their plans.

"A short while later Samoset returned and told Massasoit that they would not be in danger if they went into the white man's camp. Massasoit wanted to make sure, so he sent another man who knew the white man's tongue back with Samoset. This was Squanto, or Tisquantum, who had been captured by the whites and returned after most his whole village died of plague. He was taken in by Massasoit at sowams, but later, when the chief sachem learned Squanto was trying to get his relatives living in Pokanoket to go back to pautuxit and live under his sachemship, he wanted to kill him. Massasoit's councillors had told him that a man who knew the white man's tongue could be valuable, so instead of killing him he made him his slave. As such, Squanto was ordered to accompany Samoset. Three pnieses, or great warriors, accompanied them. Squanto, who was a good friend of mine, carried some mishaumsuogsuk (red herrings) he had just caught and a few skins into the knife man's camp, which was where his people's village used to stand.

"As Squanto was talking to the knife men, Massasoit and his brother Quadequina, who had been summoned from Asquoach, walked to the top of the hill, along with about 60 warriors. A short man with a beard, clothed in dark woolskins with a large-brimmed hat shadowing his face, came down the hill to the brook, a sword-knife poking out from beneath the cape that flapped like wings around him.

"He stopped suddenly when he saw how many of us there were, but Massasoit stood still and then raised his hand in greeting. The man reached into a pouch and our warriors started to reach for their bows, but relaxed as he pulled out a long copper chain with a bright red stone in it. He handed it to Massasoit, then reached in and pulled out two knives, one with a wooden handle and the other with an ivory handle. These were very fine gifts and Massasoit was pleased. The man then gave Quadaquina a metal pendant with a blue stone in it to hang in his ear.

"Then this dirty, unshaven, red-faced man with thin hair on his upper lip and down the middle of his chin said their great sachem, King James, from across the great sea, wanted to treat for peace between the knife men and Massasoit's people. He said the great sachem's sagamore, Carver, would speak for the king in this matter.

"Massasoit was wary. The thunder-cannons made him nervous, so he told the man, who was called Winsnow (Winslow- some inland tribes don't pronounce the letter 'l'), that he would only go into the village if he remained behind, with us. Winsnow immediately agreed and Massasoit and his chief councillors went up the hill. They were met by the knife men, who asked them to leave their bows and knives with a warrior just outside the village. We saw Massasoit trying to explain that a warrior never parted with his weapons, but finally, we saw each man hand over his bows, tomahawks and knives to a brave. This made Quadaquina, who had stayed with us, very anxious. Why did they want them disarmed? Was there an ambush planned? Fear of that had made him and Massasoit agree that only one of the royal sachems would go in at a time.

"I was curious about the white men, for I had only caught glimpses of them in their floating islands offshore before. I moved closer to where the white man sat on a rock. His sword-knife was poking up from the ground near his leg. He smiled often, showing crooked, yellow teeth.

"Quadaquina sat on a bearskin across from him, smiling back. He lit his redstone calumet pipe, offered a smoke to the four directions, then gave it to Winsnow, who tried it and coughed like a boy. He handed it back and Quadaquina and his councillors continued to smoke in silence, observing the strange being Creator had floated to our shores.

"One warrior touched Winsnow's large hat and made a joke that it was big enough to live in. Many reached over and touched the material that covered him from head to toe. Some admired the steel-colored buttons down his dark coat front and the tassels at his throat under his large white collar. Although it was the beginning of sequan and still cold, most of us wore only a loincloth. The thick coating of beargrease kept us from feeling the wind. This man did not have grease on him, but he stunk of unwashed human odor. His clothes stunk of smoke and sweat and old grease. We didn't get too close, for the scent was offensive to us.

"Winsnow tried to ask questions using his hands and gestures, but we understood little and so he just continued to smile at us.

"Quadaquina was shorter and thinner than his older brother,

Massasoit. He had been on the path to his wife's village in quansik when the messengers arrived to tell them the white man wanted a meeting. He was dressed officially for the occasion, with a crown of three eagle feathers on the front of his head. Like many of our people, his hair was plucked with clamshells or singed with hot stones except for a scalplock. He wore his wealth - several long strings of white and purple wampum - around his neck. In their midst hung his medicine pouch, into which he placed the jewel Winsnow had given him, for he felt his magic would neutralize any spell the white man had put on the jewel. Like most of the Pokanokets who had accompanied him and Massasoit from Sowams, he was painted red to show that they had come in friendship. Had it been the time of the burning moon, the red would have meant nothing, for we all painted ourselves with the red ochre throughout the summer to keep the mosquitoes and gnats from biting us.

"Quadaquina also wore a spotted wildcat skin down his left arm. This was the mark of a sachem or highly-respected sagamore, for most of us only wore deerskin tunics in the bitterest cold and no other covering otherwise. Also across Quadequina's chest was the thong carrying his pipe and tobacco bag, which we all carried. He carried a talking stick like Massasoit's, carved and bearing the color of each direction, plus turkey feathers. Its tip was knob-shaped and Quadequina used it when walking.

"I tell you of all these things, for Quadequina was second only to Massasoit in rank and also because we saw the white man drinking in each of these details, memorizing them the way a brave memorizes the features of an animal he is stalking.

"The sun moved closer to the west as many of the braves played games, throwing their knives and tomahawks into a target. I had nothing to gamble, so I went in search of crabs in the saltwater marshes near the camp.

" Then Masasoit and a knife man appeared at the top of the hill. The white man embraced Massasoit and then he came over and talked to Quadequina, who gathered another group of sagamores and councillors together and they went into the white man's village. Masssoit ordered Squanto to remain behind, so he could coverse with Winsnow.

"Massasoit was tall and very broad across the chest. He wore his hair long, parted in the middle with a single yellow feather at the back of his head. Around his neck he wore a white bone necklace made of long bones and bone beads. Beneath it now hung the reddish-brown chain with its fire stone. His doeskin tobacco pouch was slung over his right shouder, which was hidden by the fine turkey-feather cape his attendants placed over his shoulders. All around the cape were eagle feathers, standing straight up. Only the most royal sachems possessed such a robe and it was sign of great rank and wealth.

"Masssoit seemed very pleased with his visit to the white man's village and gathered everyone around. He told us he had promised their sachem across the sea that neither he nor any of his people would injure or hurt any of the knife men and that if any of his people did, he, Massasoit, would send them to the knife men for punishment. This we thought most strange, for it was the way of our people to allow only the great sachem to punish offenders. This made us very much afraid. It was one thing to die honorably at the hand of one's sachem, but to die in the hands of the enemy, who would torture us to death, was the worst death. So we knew that Massasoit was deadly serious. In my heart I began to wonder if that chain had been bewitched, if Massasoit was under some kind of magic spell.

"Massasoit said they had given him fire water to drink and it made him sweat like in a sweat lodge. He described their wetus. He said they were straight on four sides, not round, and that they sat on wool hides the color of grass.

"Our sachem said he told the knifemen that if anything were taken from them, such as the tools the Nemaskets had taken, he, Massasoit, would make them give the things back. He said they agreed to return anything to Massasoit's people their people took, such as the corn they had dug up.

"Massasoit said he told their sagamore Carver that if any of the tribes made war on the knifemen without reason, he, Massasoit, would gather warriors and help the knife men. The English said they would do likewise and help Massasoit's people if any tribes warred on them without reason.

"Massasoit said he had also promised that any time one of his people entered their village, they would leave their weapons outside.

"After he spoke, Massasoit said the fire water had made him sleepy, so he went into the temporary shelter his attendants had made. He invited Winsnow to accompany him while he rested.

"Now the sun was one finger from the treetops. Quadequina and his group appeared on the top of the hill and joined the rest of us huddling around the fires. Massasoit ordered both Squanto and Samoset to accompany Winsnow back and to stay overnight to learn of their plans.

"Quadaquina told of the strange food he had eaten, of how salty it was. He, too, had tasted the fire water and sat on their green furs. He described how they made things out of wood to sit on, how they ate off wooden things and the metal things they served their food on. He said he had asked them to also put their weapons outside the village but they had refused. This made him very suspicious and he told us they were to be watched.

"The shamans listened carefully, smudging all who had gone into the white man's camp. The fire water intrigued them- how could the knifeman put fire in water? This was a great mystery and they said it was great medicine.

"It was very late before all the talking quieted down and we slept. Even I had stopped thinking about fish. My head was full of these strange things and they kept swimming around, like a school of fish before the fisherman's net.

"The following sunrise Squanto and I went to the river to catch eels and dig ssickissuog (clams). We returned to camp to find the man in the knife-colored suit (Standish) and another knifeman eating breakfast with Massasoit, Quadequina and Old Tuspaquin. Massasoit told them the Wampanoags planned to plant corn near their village.

"Afterwards, Squanto took some of the eels and accompanied the two men back to the village. Samoset and some of the squaws also went with them, for Massasoit told them they were to show the knife men how to plant corn. Old Watuspaquin's people had seen the knifemen trying to plant seeds earlier, none of which sprouted, for they did not know to wait until the oak leaf was a big as a mouse's ear before planting and to offer fish to Mother Earth in their fields.

"Massasoit and his people broke camp and returned to sowams and I returned to quansik with Quadequina and his group, for the mishquammauquock (salmon) would be running in the weirs to our north and at the falls to our west.

"Quadequina reported all this to Naddawahunt, who held many councils with his sachems that sequan to tell them to trade only with the knifemen called English."

Chapter 5
(A re-telling of the kidnapping of Massasoit and first treaty with the knifemen, 1621)

Firehawk again rises.

"I was the next to see the knifeman. My spirit was not right and I was making others unhappy so my father asked me to accompany him and a group of his councillors to the council fire at sowams. My sister had given birth to a son she and Massasoit called Mooanum.

"We went during *kikkikizoos* (the Earth-cultivating Moon-June). Most of the way to sowams we were drenched with rain and when we stopped in villages along the way the people welcomed their chief sachem with great feasting and warm fires.

"When we arrived in sowams Massasoit asked my father to go with him to Corbitant's village, for that sachem had been speaking against Massasoit's treaty with the knifemen and Massasoit wanted to make peace with him. Afterwards, we were to go duck hunting in the fowling ponds near cohannet, Massasoit's summer camp.

"When asked about the Englishmen, Massasoit told my father, 'I think the English will not survive. Half of them are already dead. Mother Earth has not opened up her storehouses for them or else they are blind to her goodness. Even with Hobbomock and his wife showing them how to plant the three sisters I think they will starve. But they say they have a great sachem across the sea. He must be our cousin, I think.'

"I was a young brave and hadn't learned the wisdom of a still tongue. I told Massasoit, 'I think they lie! I think they were cast out of their sachem's land and they will have to pay him tribute to live here.' Massasoit forgave me my outburst as he said, 'Time will tell what kind of men these are.' I replied, 'I hope the truth does not burn like a sunbeam into our chests!'

"We had no sooner set out when a brave from Massasoit's village came after us to tell us that two knifemen from pautuxit (Plymouth) were in sowams to see Massasoit. We returned and Massasoit found the man Winsnow and another named Hopkins waiting in his longhouse.

"I had not seen such knifemen before. They were not hairy and loud like the Francois sailors. These white men were stiff. They smiled but did not laugh out loud.

"Squanto, whom Massasoit had ordered to live with the English, was with them and he interpreted as they exchanged greetings. Massasoit sent a messenger to Quadequina telling him to come but later he sent back word that he was in bed with the chest sickness. He had traveled throughout much of quansik to bring the others to council, but with all the walking in the cold, he had taken ill.

"Massasoit was greatly embarrassed that a feast had not been made and he spent some time telling my sister and the other squaws to prepare food for his guests. They told him that most of the men were at the fowling ponds or ocean and there was no fresh meat in camp. This made Massasoit very angry and he sat glaring at them as they served the white men a meatless soup.

"Then the man Winsnow reached into the big bag he was carrying and pulled out a red coat like the one they had given to Samoset. This was their main garment so we often called the English wautacone "coat men". Massasoit smiled big and put it on, admiring along with us its bright red color, the fine cloth and bright buttons with colored piping. From listening to my father talk about how his people in the north traded with the sailors, I knew the red cloth was most valued. They also gave him a suit of clothing which the women began inspecting. They made clucking noises as they saw how fine the white man's thread was and how tiny the stiches were. They asked how the cloth was made, where it came from and other questions but Massasoit silenced them when they kept asking more and more questions about the plant the English called flax.

"Winsnow then gave Massasoit a thick copper chain and said that if Massasoit wanted to send a message to the English, he should give this chain to his messenger so they would know the message came from Massasoit. They told him that they had recently received a visit from one who said he came from the Narragansett sachem

Canonicus and that they didn't want to get confused about who the messages came from.

"At the mention of Narragansetts, Massasoit snorted and made a scornful remark about how the two tribes could never be confused with each other. He took the chain and put it on over this coat then turned to my father and the other councillors to discuss the Narragansetts with them.

"He said if the Naragansetts were to become friendly with the English they might get them to war on Massasoit's people, for they were enemies. And the Narragansetts were already friendly with the Francois, who did not like the English. Massasoit said his people should do something to make the English like them the best. They talked for some time about what the English valued most and then Massasoit turned to Winsnow and said,

"I will tell all my people - and he named all the inland tribes and bands from the Connecticut and up and down the coast - that they will only trade their furs with the English only. They will not trade with the Francois."

"This pleased Winsnow and Hopkins very much. But it did not please my father for his father's people to the north traded much with the Francois. It was not a new order, however, for Quadequina had been telling the people of quansik this for many moons.

"Following the trade treaty we sat outside around the fire while the people in camp danced and sang for the English. Massasoit shared his long, carved soapstone pipe with them and the Englishmen learned how to pull in the smoke, how to hold it briefly, then let it out. The squaws served cornmeal cakes and fresh berries, which the knifemen liked, but Massasoit was still embarassed because there was little food for his guests. We learned that the knifemen were short of food, also, and they asked that only Massasoit or his representative visit their village for they could not feed large groups. Their confession made us all feel very superior, for no real person would ever admit to such a thing. (After their visit Winsnow and Hopkins returned a basket of corn their people had found earlier in a storage hole at pokanoket and asked for corn seed to plant. Massasoit was pleased that they were showing his people honor by returning what they had stolen and gave them a whole basketful of seed corn). My father and I exchanged words over this corn, for I felt the English were returning the stolen corn just to get better corn.

"That night Massasoit invited the two white men to sleep with him and my sister in his longhouse, where my father and I also slept. The knifemen and my father shared Massasoit's large bed but the others, including myself, slept along the sides on the sleeping platforms. As was our way at night, we sang and sang until the stars faded from view in the smokehole overhead. Any of us would have felt honored to share the chief sachem's bed, but the Englishmen tossed and scratched, complaining under their breath about lice and fleas in the thick furs covering the boards. They didn't know how to smudge themselves or apply a thick layer of grease and ochre to make their soft, pale flesh less appetizing to the insects.

"The next day Massasoit went to the fowling ponds and speared two large fish which the women immediately put in the pots to boil. Then Massasoit relaxed and joined in the singing and dancing. My aunt looked happy and played with the moon-old nippamoos in his cradleboard. Seeing her joy, I was cut in two with pain for Gentle Rain and for my own poor little one who would never again know the warmth of his mother against his cheek.

"The coatmen stayed another night and then left the next day. Massasoit enjoyed Winsnow's company very much for he said he made him laugh with his strange questions. My father and I weren't very impressed, but we liked their nice gifts.

"No sooner had they left then a messenger from pautuxit came running into camp with news that the Nausets had captured a white boy who had gotten lost in the woods. Massasoit sent a message to Aspinet, the sachem in possession of the boy, that he was to return him unharmed to the coatmen. He then sent a message to pautuxit to tell the knifemen where they could find the boy. After he learned the boy had been returned safely to their war captain, a man called Standish, Massasoit and the rest of our party prepared to leave for the fowling ponds to enjoy the fine hunting and fishing there. Some of the knifemen remained with Iyanough's people to fish in the sea and all seemed at peace.

"A handful of sleeps later as we were packing up camp, a war party of Narragansetts suddenly appeared and before our braves could grab our bows, the Narragansett warriors surrounded Massasoit, their bows pointed at his chest. I heard them say something about Corbitant and then saw them forcing Massasoit to leave with them.

The great sachem yelled for us to hold our bows, that he would settle the matter with Corbitant himself.

"My father called a hasty war council and we decided to follow at a distance so as not to be seen.

"The squaws were all wailing and crying for Massasoit as we quickly painted our faces for war and readied our weapons.

"Then Hobbomock, Massasoit's war captain, or pniese, came running into the camp. He said he had been captured along with Squanto and another man friendly to the English in pautuxit. He said Caunbitant (Corbitant) had a great gathering of people in his village and was talking of declaring war on all the white men and on Massasoit's people, because of their treaty with the English. Hobbomock said the Narragansetts, friends of Caunbitant's, had Massasoit. We knew this was true for it was known that Caunbitant had wanted to become chief sachem of the federation after Nanepashemet's death.

"Hobbomock paused only long enough to tell us this for he was on his way to Nauset, where Standish was fishing, to get the knife men to come with their thundersticks.

"We were divided then, for some did not want to risk their lives saving Squanto. He was not respected by many. Some disliked him for trying to take his fellow Pautuxits away from Massasoit's villages to resettle their own village. This had been considered an act of treason and Massasoit had enslaved him for it. Others disliked him because they thought he lied. He told them he knew where the white men buried the box containing the plague. This he said in order to make himself appear more powerful than Hobbomock, who had also been ordered by Massasoit to live with and watch the English. However, it was agreed that we would set our feelings for Squanto aside and go after Massasoit. One of the warriors made a speech that I still remember. He said, ' Squanto is our brother. Are we to let him be fed to the wolves so we may live? What kind of people are we? If one of our brothers or sisters is in trouble, do not we all feel their pain? If we let Caunbitant take one of our brothers, will he and his wolves keep coming back and nipping away at the rest, at the younger and weaker? The only thing wolves respect are stronger wolves! Without Massasoit, are we stronger wolves?'

"We went on to Caunbitant's village but found it deserted. As we searched through the empty wetus with the still-warm fires, the metal-clad Standish and a group of his warriors rushed into camp. They shouted and pointed their thundersticks at us but Hobbomock called out we were friends. They searched and then left, not wanting us to join them. But we caught up with them later that night at nemasket. They snuck into a wetu outside the village and pointed their thundersticks into it, ordering the squaws start a fire so they could see if Squanto and Corbitant were hidden there. Hobbomock then jumped on the roof and began yelling Squanto's name until he came running towards him from a wetu in the village. He was chased by many Nemaskets with their bows raised. But when Standish, flanked by Hobbomock and Tokemmehamon, fired his thunderstick into the air, the villagers went wild with fear. In their panic, some of their boys, seeing how Standish's men didn't hurt the squaws, yelled 'Neensquas! Neensquas!' You see, the sound of the thunderstick so frightened them that they forgot the Nemasket way of the warrior. Many of us felt this fear the first time we heard the loud roar of the thunderstick. We thought it was the most powerful medicine of all to be able to put thunder in a stick and point it at someone.

"The English were able to recapture Squanto and the other brave but not Massasoit or Caunbitant, who had escaped by tearing the shingles off the side of the wetu he was inside of. After everyone had settled down on both sides, Standish accepted tobacco and food from the Nemaskets and told them to tell Caunbitant that if he did not return Massasoit he would be overthrown.

"Then a squaw and a brave injured in the ambush returned with Standish to Pautuxit to receive treatment for thunderstick wounds.

"Meanwhile, a large war party began to gather in Pokanoket and we went back to sowams to join it. But before we could organize a raid, Massasoit suddenly appeared on the path outside the village.

"He said when the metalman Standish had recaptured Squanto, he had sent a message back to Caunbitant that if Massasoit were harmed, the English would kill every man, woman and child of the tribe responsible. This was a terrible threat and Caunbitant had immediately released Massasoit.

"We gathered in council to discuss going to war anyway to avenge the wrong done to our chief but Massasoit wouldn't hear of it. He said Caunbitant was not our enemy, that he had warred because he was afraid of the white man. Caunbitant thought they could bewitch him. He said his heart was at peace with Caunbitant and if any of us warred on him or Canonicus, chief sachem of the Narragansetts, that he, Massasoit, would kill us personally.

"Much strong words passed that day, first from the English and then from our sachem. That night when we went to bed, they kept sounding in our ears and we sang very little.

"Our party remained in Cohannet for the rest of the summer for my sister became ill and Quadequina was so ill Massasoit asked me to travel back and forth to sowams to check on him and matters there. I also visited other sachems in the area to ask them to meet with Massasoit about the treaty he had signed with the white men a few moons past. He wanted to know how many felt as Caunbitant did and also wanted to have them come together to go to the white man's village called Plymouth and have them sign a new treaty together. Massasoit was very wise in this, for the sachems felt respected and most agreed to go. Epanow and Caunbitant he visited personally for he learned they were plotting to kill the white men while they slept. They told Massasoit that there were few white men now and they should kill them all before their bird came back across the sea with more. Massasoit said they were our brothers and sisters and that Creator had made room for them by killing off so many of our people.

"So it was, in the time of tauonck, the harvest moon, that I went into the white man's village with my father, Naddawahunt, Massasoit, Quadequina, Canacum, sachem of Manomet, the village closest to Pautuxit, and Epanow. Caunbitant went with us but the English didn't want to see him for they felt he was Massasoit's enemy. Massasoit told them he had forgiven Caunbitant and insisted he also sign the treaty with the magic feather that leaked black blood.

"Obbatienewat, sachem of Shamut, refused to go to the meeting in the strange square wooden house because he was still angry about the way they desecrated his mother's grave before they desecrated Corbitant's mother's grave. But five sleeps later the English visited him and, after they promised to be his ally and fight off the Tarrantines with their thundersticks if they came down from the north again and raided his villages, he signed their treaty.

"Obbatienwat then accompanied them to Squaw sachem's place but she refused to meet with them for she was Obbatienwat's enemy. Her messenger said she had heard the English spent a night in Nanepashemet's pallisade, an unthinkable taboo, and had forced the squaws they met on the way to trade their doeskin breast mantles for pieces of jewelry. She refused to meet with any in their party.

"On our way back to Quansik we also stopped briefly at Wachusett and found many warriors defending the base of the mountain. Even vision seekers were not allowed to ascend, they said. Squaw sachem was angry with all the tribes who signed the treaty with her enemy so my father didn't see his sister on that journey.

"That winter we learned that the Narragansetts had sent a bundle of arrows (nanequoxet) wrapped in snakeskin to Standish and that he had returned their war challenge with a snakeskin full of gunpowder.

"After that, we heard little of the knife men or talk of war for awhile."

Chapter 6
(Konkowasco's brush with death, 1623-4)

A man in his mid-seventies rises. Unlike the others, he is still in the prime of his life. His chest is wide, his eyes bright and his hair thick and as black as raven's feathers. His black brows meet in the middle of his forehead and form a permanent, intense frown. He clears his throat and jabs his deep voice into the silence:

"Many of you have never seen me before. My title now is Wawanwejagtuck- the sachem of the hollow people. I live in Pennacook on the Malamake river, in Panukkog, the village my Pigwackett uncle Konkowasco came from. My name, too, was Konkowasco. I am Firehawk's firstborn son. I was the nipamoos in the burning wetu.

"When I was little, I was called Strong One. Later I took the name Konkowasco, Dove of Peace. I am no longer a peace-lover. I will tell you why at another time, but now I will you of how it was in Quansik when I was a very little boy.

"I remember well the spring following my third winter.

"I remember waking up one morning and smelling the sap running in the maples. The birds were returning from Cautantowwit's garden in the Southwest and were calling to each other in the trees. I remember that before we fell alseep, my father said the plague had been let out of the box and was running like sap through the veins of the tribes to the east. I didn't understand his words, but when I looked at the trees that morning, I wondered about them.

"I was always the first one awake in our one-fire wetu. My cousin, Little Sky Dancer, was still sleeping on the mats when the cheerful singing of the phoebes and robins came in with the faint light through the hole above the cold fire circle.

"I could smell the plants growing and new life all around. It was a wild, exciting odor, an indication that the ice bridge was melting and falling into the sea. I could smell the black dog sleeping on my feet and, as I shifted, it raised its head and got up, following me out the eastern kuppuhhou (door flap).

"I pulled the fox fur tightly around my thin shoulders and walked up the ravine. Below, in our winter camp at Asquoach, the wetus lay in silent rows. The dog and I felt all alone in the mist as we climbed to the top of the big boulder the men used when sending fire signals to the observation sites on the surrounding hills. My bare feet felt the cold, charred embers and gritty soot as I stood on the lichen-covered red-grey rock and waited to greet the sun in the east.

"That morning was like many I had known on that boulder. At first all I could see was the nishkenan (morning mist) and a few tall, dark tree shapes. Then the treeline of the waddaquadducks (long mountains) and the ledge tops rose out of the mist and I could see the ravines below and the silhouette of the booming rock and its stone cavern a short distance away.

"As the pink tongue of dawn licked the hilltops in the distance, I could see the black outline of the pond and, as the sun rose higher, glints, like quartz arrowhead chippings, strewn all over its surface.

"With the full sunrise the spell was broken and my communion interrupted as the village awakened and the girls and women rose to get wuttuck (firewood) and wattuppa (to draw water).

"I remember this morning well because after breakfast we were leaving to go to Quabogud for the fishing and maple sugar thanksgiving celebration. I loved these gatherings, I loved to play along the shores with the other children and practice shooting the dull arrows from the bow my father had made for me. I loved the music, the dancing and all the eating. But I was afraid of the medicine men and their strange masks.

"Strong One!" my father called and I jumped off the boulder and ran through the low blueberry bushes to the ravine which now smelled of pukat (smoke) and apoon (corn cakes).

"As I saw my father I suddenly remembered that at the ceremony he was going to get married to She who Sings at the Water. I wasn't sure if I wanted a new mother, for my aunt had been my mother, but when my father spent time with Singing Water, he did not frown or look sad.

"My father grabbed me as I ran to him and he swung me up into the air. He scolded me for wandering off and my aunt came out of the wetu and said, 'These woods are full of danger, papoose! There are Mohawks, who will roast you on a spit and eat you. There are pussough and mukkoes that could eat you and cheepies (bad spirits) who steal little children.' I had heard all this before - all the children had heard this - but it never stopped us. She handed me a barkskin bucket and asked me to fill it with water from the spring. Soon this would be a chore done only by the girls but I was still young enough to help the women.

"As I approached the cool, dark punkgunnup (pool), I saw Doe Eyes, a papeesh about my age. She was standing on one of the flat stones overhanging the clear pool, her bare feet delicately perched on the edge as she bent forward and dipped her bucket into the water. Unlike the boys who wore their hair long and wild, the squashees wore their hair short. She also wore a little apron with dainty floral designs embroidered on it but we boys ran buck naked.

"I'm going to see my grandparents at the weirs," I told her as I hoisted my bucket up. She smiled at me and then pulled her bucket up as she said, 'Race you back!' Our laughter over the race was cut short by my aunt when she saw how much water my running had cost me. I was sent back down because she needed more water than usual that morning. We had to drown each wetu fire before leaving. This was done every spring. At the end of the maple sugar thanksgiving ceremony we would all take home a new fire, lit from the council fire. My father said it reminded them that they were all were bound together every time they blew on the morning sparks. "

Konkowasco's eyes narrowed. He sighed deeply and said,

"This is no longer done by my people. We have few ceremonies for now everytime we meet the English accuse us of conspiring against them.

"We all didn't leave the village. A very old squaw we called Grandmother Grey Wood stayed behind. Her body was bent like an old tree and she supported herself on an old grey wooden staff on which were carvings of animals and birds.

"She watched as the women and girls took the mats from the inside walls and tied them to the woven tumplines that would go around their foreheads so they could carry the mats on their backs. We children tied the door flaps from inside the wetus and then climbed up the smokehole flap's pole. This would keep the wild animals out of our homes while we were gone.

"A handful of others stayed behind, including a family who stayed with a squaw in her last days of pregnancy. I remember hearing my aunt sigh as she left behind a very fine deerskin she had spent the winter chewing to a delicate softness. She said that sometimes when they went away the Narragansetts came and demanded tribute from those left in the village and if they didn't get anything good they would kill the people left behind.

"I knew from the faces of those waving goodbye that they wanted to go to the weirs also. I looked back from my father's shoulders until the path descended and I could see their faces no longer.

"The path took us up the hill and across our corn fields. Some of the fish we brought back would be planted in the mounds of corn, beans and squash as a gift to Mother Earth. In the distance, near the trees, were the small wooden platforms we sat on while watching the fields to keep the crows away. This was the only garden work for men - that is, for boys and old men.

"During the growing season I would see little of my mother, for the women went out to work in the fields every day. From the platform I would hear them sing and see the clamshell hoes rise and fall but my job was to watch for birds.

"We would shoot our little arrows at the chogeneuck (blackbirds) but were told to never kill a kaukont (crow) because Brother Crow had brought us our seeds. Besides, wompissackog (eagles), crows and wushowwunnaneuck (hawks) were meat-eaters and that made them sacred.

"For the duration of the growing season our village would be down near the pond. The mats would be rolled up and carried down the hill to the bluff overlooking the pond where the wetu frames stood. Chestnut bark mats or hides would go on the outside to keep the rain out.

"I always looked forward to the move because I loved to fish and swim in the pond and sleep in less flea-ridden quarters.

"We left the clearing and my father lifted me down from his shoulders. He told me to stay on the path for the rattlesnake lived in the tall grasses on either side. As we crossed a brook I saw a fat, green frog (chickawallop) jump off a stone and heard a loud whirring noise like that of the bullroarer toy my father made for me.

"A group of the older boys left the path, tracking something downstream. They returned a while later, their pointed sticks loaded with big, fat black eels.

"About half-way (nas) between asquoash and wekapaug, we stopped at a small village. It, too, was deserted save a few people. A very old woman with no teeth greeted us and, with her daughter helping, began roasting the eels. Some of the young braves added pigeons they had shot along the way and another placed a dead tummock (beaver) on the ground for the women to clean.

"We all gathered around the beaver as the men asked the brave why he had shot it. He said he heard the knifemen traded knives, guns, kettles, needles and cloth for beaver skins and he was going to get enough to trade for a gun.

"I poked the still-warm carcass. Its huge teeth were bare and its tongue hung slightly out one side of its mouth. I felt strange touching this thing that had no living spirit in it and I wondered if its spirit was still nearby, waiting to jump into a young child's body. I felt relieved when they left it behind after our meal.

"When we travelled along our paths, we often stopped and put small, flat rocks on a *tcipai* along the way. When we did this we said a little prayer to the ancestors or asked for a wish and for the blessings of the spirits as we passed. On the main paths, there were spirit lodges - great, flat-topped rocks on which we tossed sticks or branches while saying prayers. These could get quite high and looked like longhouses. Sometimes in abandoned village sites you would find these tciapi- for we know some spirits never go to the southwest.

"Stopping often for this or that, it took us a while to reach the fishing camp. The sun was close to the treetops when we reached the weirs below the falls on the Quaboag river. Rounding a bend I suddenly saw and heard a crowd of people below in the valley. How many there were I didn't know for I could not count beyond the numbers on the counting sticks we played with. In the middle of the wetus was a large clearing and the biggest longhouse I had ever seen. People were talking, working, fishing and the scent of smoking fish filled the air.

"My father said to me, 'Look well, Strong One. All of these people are your family. A child of the tribes is never alone.'

"My father then turned sad and said, 'Not many winters past

this whole valley would have been filled with our people. So many have died it looks as if many are on the paths and we are still waiting for them to arrive.'

"My heart was always pierced with an arrow of pain when my father spoke sadly, so I tried to get him to forget. I tugged on his hand and we hurried into the camp.

"Later, with a full belly and tired legs, I leaned against my father near the fire circle. The drums beat steadily and I felt my eyelids grow heavier and heavier as I watched the leather balls wrapped over the forked ends of the hickory handles move up and down, beating on the tightly stretched deerskin of the birch log drum head.

"Each beat brought more men closer to the circle. But when the chief medicine man entered, I drew back, shrinking against my father as the sachem's horned rabbitskin mask came into my face, bobbing up and down, his turtle shell rattle shaking in one hand, his clay pipe in the other, its turkey feathers dangling from long thongs like living creatures in the firelight. He sprinkled tobacco in the sacred fire and offered a prayer to creator, then offered tobacco to the four directions. Afterwards he lit his pipe and drew in deeply, blowing smoke to the winds then up to Kichtan.

"The shaman walked slowly around the circle, blowing smoke from the pipe into the faces of the dancers lined outside. They pulled the breath of the Great Spirit into their nostrils as the powwow's turkey fan smudged them with smoke.

"My father nudged me and said, 'Kujjooune?' (Sleep, you?)

"I murmured 'no' and then snuggled closer, pulling the bear skin tighter. I could hear chanting and saw the women enter the sacred circle, their pale doeskin mantles fluttering with shadows as they raised their high-pitched voices in a song of thanksgiving and then a song of fertility for the fields. They sang, 'My feet touch the earth, touch Mother Earth, my feet touch the giver of life...'

"I remember closing my eyes and hearing the old man who was my grandfather shake a long rattle as he spoke. Naddawahunt had a deep voice- strong and wise sounding.

"My grandfather told the people he had a dream many years ago and when he awoke he heard strange voices singing a strange, unknown language in the woods. They sang through their teeth, he said, and he tried to demonstrate, but his poor whistling was greeted with laughter. He said when he went with the great sachem Massasoit to the houses the English had built he heard the same song he had heard many years ago, long before their great floating island had carried them across Wechekum. He said it was an omen. An omen that the woods would someday be as full of the Englishman's songs as they were of sounds of the creatures of air and fields.

"Although I was fighting sleep, his story intrigued me and I opened one eye and looked across the fire to my grandfather. He had a firm profile with a high forehead. His nose was large and slightly downcurved and his mouth was large and straight. His hair was worn in two thick braids on either side of his head and a tall clump of eagle, hawk and turkey feathers sat on the crown of his head.

"Earlier I had sat next to him in his longhouse and had eaten fish soup served by my grandmother. I admired the animal carvings on the burlwood spoon and he told me when I was a little older he would teach me how to carve as well as he.

"The horns of the powwow now dipped down so close I thought they would sitck into me and I pulled back further. When I looked up again, across the circle I could see the maiden who would be my new mother. I stared at her face for a little while and then the drum took me into the land of dreams.

"The following morning was grey and foggy. Unlike the warm days we had known, it was cold and a few flakes of snow drifted through the smoke hole and fell on the tan dog sleeping next to me in my grandfather's four-fire longhouse.

"The men were talking amongst themselves. Would the fish run that night, now that the cold was back? Some offered bets and the gaming that we love so much began.

"The wetus and longhouses were filled with children and the elderly, who hugged the firecircles. Most of us had left behind our heaviest robes and furs for the snow had melted to mud a moon ago and the days had been warm.

"Some men went out to try their luck fishing but Grandfather Sun frowned, plunging the waters into darkness. Others joined the gaming circles and the sound of many stones being shaken in bowls filled the smokey interiors of the wetus. Voices raised and some grudgingly gave robes while others gleefully took them. Then they would squat again, ready to win or lose, tossing stones in the bowls.

"My father was sitting in Singing Water's wetu. They spoke in low tones and the maiden smiled often, her eyes focussed on the floor in front of her. She wore her hair over her eyes because she was a virgin. Her mothers and sisters sat inside, too, pretending to be busy with sewing and cooking as they listened and glanced over.

"All this sitting around made me restless. I wanted to go out and catch salmon with a pointed spear stick or catch alewives with my bow and arrows. I had watched the braves do this before at night-time. It was exciting to watch them hold birchbark torches over the water so they could see to the bottom where the salmon were swimming. They would close in, then quickly spear them with jasper or hornstone-headed spears. I wanted to watch this in the daylight, so, without saying a word, I slipped outside.

"The cold burned my feet but I ignored the pain and ran down towards the great black river. Through the fog it looked like a huge, twisting flat snake in the valley. One of the dogs was with me and we both stopped suddenly as we saw the river up close. Never before had I seen such a fast flowing river! The quinebaug near siog was deep but flowed slowly. It didn't rush and boil the way this one did.

"I put my spear into the water and the current fought me for it.

"All of a sudden a large grey and pink fish lept out of the water right under my nose and I jumped back, landing on a slippery rock.

"I felt myself being sucked into the cold, rushing water and carried downstream.

"I yelled to Muckquachuckquand (the children's god) over and over but no one heard me. I tried to swim but the river was too strong. The dog was running along the riverbank, barking at me. Then I felt myself being swallowed up by the snake-water.

"I felt my lungs tighten and there was a buzzing in my head. With a great push I broke above the water and saw a deer on the river's edge. It saw me then nimbly jumped away, back into the brush. I called out to the attuck (deer) spirit to save me but the churning blackness grew deeper and I could no longer see the village.

"I felt myself going limp and then saw a cloud above the water. It glowed as bright as the sun and in its middle was a squaw, all bright like embers. She wore a white mantle all glistening with metal beads. Her face was the most beautiful I had ever seen and somehow I knew she was my mother, Gentle Rain. Although her lips did not move, I heard her telling me to put my legs down instead of thrashing.

"Then, as suddenly as the vision appeared, it was gone, along with my last breath of air. I felt my legs go limp and was dimly aware of them scraping something. Something sharp caught my rawhide armband but I was unable to open my eyes to see what it is.

"I heard Dancing Moose yell, 'A papoose!' Another shouted, 'He's dead!'

"I was aware of being carried out of the v-shaped weir and being placed on the snow. Over me I could see sad faces. Then I was on my side, vomiting and coughing.

"'He's freezing!' Dancing Moose yelled, taking off his beaver robe and wrapping it around me. I was too exhausted to utter even a feeble thank you as he carried me back to the camp.

"The women began wailing when they saw me and I was aware of my father's voice in the distance gruffly calling my name as snowflakes melted on my lips. I couldn't open my eyes. Never had I been so tired in all my life. But when cold fingers stroked my cheeks, my lids fluttered and I saw the tear-streaked face of Singing Water. She took off her fox-lined mantle and wrapped it around me, then gently carried me inside her parent's wetu.

"I felt warm all over, like I had felt when I saw the vision, and then I felt pain as the squaws began to vigorously rub my feet, legs and the rest of my body. Two more squaws appeared, carrying hot fish broth and then the door flap flung open and my father rushed in, grabbing me tight to his chest. I could hear his strong heart beating hard against my face as he choked, 'I thought I lost you, Strong One. I was afraid you were dead!'

"Singing Water touched his arm and he released me, giving me back to the women who would nurse me to keep the evil spirits from devouring my lungs. The shaman came in and waved smoking sweet-grass around the wetu as he chanted and shook his rattle. I was happy to see him this time. He chanted and circled four times then blew smoke over me. I heard him tell my father that only time would tell if the spirits had claims on my soul.

"I turned to my father and whispered, 'I'm sorry I lost the spear you made me, father.'

"I thought I saw a tear fall down his cheek and then he said, 'Unlike Creator, we cannot make people from trees or stones, Strong One. Creator has given us many trees and stones to make our tools with, but he has given me only one son.'

"I tried to tell him about mother then, but I had no strength left and my voice disappeared upwards into the spiral.

"But I thought I heard Singing Water say, 'Don't worry about this one, Lone Hawk. He has two mothers to watch over him now.'

"With the return of the sun, the fish again swarmed through the waters to spawn.

"The next days were busy ones for the camp. The men were active from dawn to dusk spearing the salmon and eels and catching alewives in their weirs while the younger boys caught baskets of sun fish to take to the corn fields.

"The women split and smoked the fish on great racks of green sticks lashed together while the girls gathered pine boughs for the smokey fires and the little boys helped gather wood and water.

"The old women, those who had been able to make the journey, helped by watching the young children and by tending the pots of succotash and fish that bubbled in the circle.

"Old men had the important job of helping to clear the sacred circle for the dancing every evening and of firing the steam lodge for the men and young boys in preparation for initiation rites. They also helped the elders in the retelling of legends inside the longhouse.

"Singing Waters did not work beside her sisters at the smoking. She instead sat with me, holding me and rocking and singing to me by the warm fire. She made me drink a weak tea of skunk cabbage root and applied poultices of spiknard and sarsaparilla to my chest and feet to draw out the evil spirits causing my thick cough. She made me drink black alder tea for my fever but it wouldn't break and by the third day I was so red I looked like I had been painted with the red ochre they put on the dead in the graves. I had knives shooting through my head and moaned and tossed. Singing Water chewed bitter yarrow root then spat it on my forehead as she held me close, grabbing my legs and arms whenever they thrashed out.

"I called out to my mother over and over that day then fell into a deep sleep.

"Midday of the fourth day of my illness I began shaking without stop and the sweat poured out of me, soaking the small robe wrapped aound me and the larger one Singing Water held me in.

"After a while, I woke up feeling hungry and the powwow said the spirits had released me from their clutches.

"I guess you could say that was my first sweat lodge. And my first test by the spirits."

Chapter 7
(Firehawk's marrriage to Singing Water, 1624)

Firehawk again takes the talking stick. He had been very silent during Konkowasco's story. Memories could be like pouches of bloody meat carried over the heart. Once pierced, the flow wasn't easily stopped.

"A week went by while Konkowasco struggled with the spirits. Much fishing had been done that spring but now we turned our attention to readying ourselves for the adulthood and marriage ceremonies. Marriages were usually most popular in mid-summer, for babies of such marriages often were born in the spring - after the bitter cold - yet before the intense field work.

"In preparation for the adulthood ceremonies the braves who had survived the winter alone spent much time with the powwows telling them about their visions. Before any of us could enter the sacred circle we had to undergo purification through the sweat lodge.

"Sweats had been going on from the beginning of the camp but I had been too preoccupied with Strong One, Singing Waters and fishing for mesemanmock (alewives) to attend one.

"The shamans and elders had constructed a circle of stones in the reeds on the river's edge away from the fishing. The bottom of the reed house was wet and filled in with rocks. Nearby the young boys heated rocks and carried them on crossed sticks to the hut when the sweat began. We stripped and were smudged by the shaman as he chanted his magic words to the spirits. We offered tobacco to Grandfather Westwind as the drummers beat a healing song. Then we entered the thick reeds and sat on the logs placed there for us. The boys threw in the hot rocks and steam began to rise from the floor.

"With us that day was Elk Bones, a shaman from Squakeag. He tamped the knickinick into his white calumet (clay pipe), lit it and took a deep breath, drinking the smoke in deeply a few times before releasing it with a prayer upwards to Creator. He then offered the pipe to me as I was the one nearest to his left in the circle. I smoked silently for a while then passed it to the person on my left.

"I remember that sweat very well for it marked a transition in my life. Again I would be a married brave. It was also when Strong One's life path was first discussed with me.

"'Strong One has much medicine, netop,'" said Elk Bones, 'It would seem Creator has blessed him with the ability to withstand death by fire and death by water. I think he has the spirit of a powwow.'

"The thought had crossed my path before, but never had it passed over my lips.

"Elk Bones continued, 'When the time comes, I would like to train him. '

"I remember staring at the wizened old powwow. I wasn't sure if it were the heat of the dull red rocks at my feet or if it were his words but my heart began to beat as fast as a woodpecker's beak against a tree trunk. By now the heat was no longer just warm. It was pricking our skins and we oozed like roasting meat on a spit.

"I told Elk Bones I thought Strong One would make a fine hunter or warrior, maybe even a pniese someday but Elk Bones shook his head and said, 'He has the sight.' His voice then turned flat, drifting, because he had eaten plants that would send him into a trance. He said, 'Twice he has conquered Hobbomock's powers. Twice he has walked in-between. With eyes inside his head he sees what others do not see. He has manitoo, which, properly trained will make him as great as Passaconnaway. These things I know.'

"The sweat was dripping freely over my eyebrows and down my cheekbones and I could feel the poisons draining from me in a wet, almost unbearable slime. I told Elk Bones, 'His destiny is not ours to foresee. If it is Creator's will, he will be a powwow. I will not stand in my son's life path and direct his way.'

"Elk Bones' next words were to stay with me and return time and again throughout the rest of my life. His eyes looked like little flakes of black flint as he said, 'Lone Hawk, it is not you or I who control our children's destinies. There are others - the English, Dutch and French - who will have a strong bearing on his and all of our destinies. Our spirits are still strong inside us, but they appear to be sleeping. I am afraid if they sleep too long the white man's spirits will enter our dreams and steal them. We need powerful powwows to cast spells to break this spell of sleep.'

"With that we could stand the heat no longer and we rushed out of the lodge, jumping into the cold waters of the Quaboag.

"The next morning was the first day of aukeeteaumitch (the corn planting ceremony). I bundled Strong One in Naddawahunt's bear robes and carried him outside as the fires were extinguished in the camp. We all took seats around the circle and the chief powwow entered to light the new year's fire. This fire would be tended by the aged elders day and night and not allowed to go out. Such a disaster would surely have meant the end of our peoples. Embers from this fire would be carried to all our villages at the end of the gathering.

"As the shaman began his chant, two singers sitting on either end of a log began striking it with snapping turtle rattles. The braves responded to the call of the rattles and entered the circle, each wearing a single eagle feather in his headdress. The feather was so sewn into the hat that it swiveled as he walked.

"In the past I had been one of the dancers, but today I sat holding Strong One and I told him the meaning of the eagle feathers to our people.

"'The eagle is sacred to us, Strong One,' I said, 'because it flies closest to the sky spirit. It listens to men and takes their messages to Cauntatowwit. The eagle flies the highest of all birds, its nest is closest to the spirits of the winds so it carries our prayers to the grandfathers. It is a wise bird, strong, proud and able. It is a great honor to be named for the eagle or to wear its feathers, but you must never kill one without making a great sacrifice to Creator.'

"We watched as the bare-chested dancers raised their feet very high while holding their backs straight. They moved around the circle slowly, in single file, then they began jumping and twisting like prancing deer. The pace quickened and the heels, decorated with feathers and shells to make them clack, stamped louder and louder in rhythm to the turtle rattles. Then the women entered, their movements slower, graceful. Their soft mocassins caressed Mother Earth as they danced.

"I told Strong One that this great feather dance was a dance of peace amongst our tribes. But my eyes never left Singing Water as she danced. To me she was the prettiest, surest, most graceful dancer in the circle. Her noble blood showed in her tall carriage, her strength and steady gaze. Of course Naddawahunt and Mishalisk were the chief sachems of our area, but when they weren't residing in one's village, the sachems like Singing Water's father were in charge. Once married, in her father's village, I would be second sachem. The older braves would be our councillors or elders, as would be the aged women. The title of sachem was only a formality for dealing with other tribes. Actually, no decision was made by the sachem alone. We always went into council and if the others did not like what a sachem recommended, they would do as they pleased. And if someone disliked everything about a sachem, he was free to pick up his wetu mats and move away. Unlike the English men who were owned by their king, our people were always their own masters. Like crows, we lived together and hunted together but when we wanted to fly elsewhere, we were free to go.

"Next the children entered the circle and the old people stood at the ends of the log, moving their bodies back and forth as they joined in the singing,

"'My song is winging, winging...'

"For a while all danced wankewan (round and round) and then suddenly one of the singers struck the log twice with his rattle and they all stopped. During the previous ceremonies thanks had been given to the tree spirit and Mother Earth for creating the sap that flowed like blood through the trees' veins, but now the prayers were for planting.

"The shamans gathered together in the middle, and as keepers of Turtle Island, they slit their forearms and sacrificed their blood to Mother Earth so she would have the strength to feed our crops. The oldest woman from each village mixed the blood with a handful of earth, which each carefully wrapped in a small, soft hide. When they returned to their villages, they would bury the pouches beneath the first seeds planted in the mounds.

"Then the Keeper of the Stories told the following tale, 'There was a squaw named Morning Star many winters ago, in the time of the ancient grandfathers. One Corn Growing Moon it was so hot and dry that the people got sick. Morning Star forgot her sorrow over not being married and worked hard, carrying water to the wilting corn and nursing the sick.

"'Then her father, Thunder Cloud, received a sign from the sky spirit. As he headed back to the village, the sky grew dark and the rains came. When he arrived home he searched for Morning Star but she was not in the village or green corn fields. She had been taken up into the sky by the Great Spirit.

"And so every morning she looks down upon us at dawn to water us with her blessings.

"We do the corn dance in honor of Morning Star who worked without praise on earth but now shines bright in the dawn sky, blessing cornfields everywhere.'

"I remember Strong One looked up at me and said, 'I think mother is like Morning Star. She was so bright, almost like the sun.'

"As he spoke, Elk Bone's words came back to me and I knew they were true.

"The making of relatives ceremony was next. I entered the circle as the lead singer and his assistants struck deerhorn rattles on their palms. We moved in zigzags around the fire, the women behind the men. Singing Water and I stopped in front of Naddawahunt as he stood in the center of the circle near the fire and lit his ceremonial pipe, then offered smoke to the four directions, Mother Earth and Sky. He passed it to Singing Water's father, then to me and Singing Water. He then took my hand and joined it to Singing Water's. A few more couples were also married and the men stood on one side, their wives on the other.

"The sachem said to each of us , 'You entered the circle as two people. You leave now as one.'

"We turned around and the women, with their soft doeskin ceremonial shawls over their heads, began to step gently towards us. We danced slowly towards them around the circle until we met and we put our heads under their shawls. We then danced around the circle like that until we came to the entrance.

"The drums then began anew as more speeches were made giving thanks for last year's crops; for the maple sap; the berries; the trees for providing wood and fruit, nuts and bark for our wetus; to the bushes for providing mats for our homes and healing medicines and to the ponds and streams for providing fish and fresh water.

"Thanks were given to the corn and her sisters, the beans and squashes, to the wind for circulating the air, to the moon and stars for light when the sun journeys to its home in the west, to the sun for his light and warmth and his blessing on the crops and to the Great Spirit who takes care of all his children and is in everyone and everything.

"The powwow added a special thanks as he pointed his bone-decorated medicine stick at Strong One and thanked the spirit of the waters for delivering him into our weirs.

"Strong One shrunk back against me as the medicine man pointed the stick at him, dangling the bones under his nose. But I saw something in his eyes that day that said he would someday wear the shaman's paint and deer antler headdress and flap his feather cape like wings over his people."

Firehawk pauses, sips from the gourd offered to him, wipes his lips and then takes a deep breath as he begins again:

"Now I will tell you something very personal. I did not go into the wetu with Singing water right after we were married. We wanted to but Strong One's fever had returned and he was fretful so Singing Water held him all night, singing to him as she rocked him gently back and forth near the fire. I tossed and turned on the mats, my eyes craving her, but I did not interfere with the nursing. I watched her - her delicate features framed by the low firelight, her hair glowing as it hung softly around her face - but I did not touch her.

"The next day to get her out of my thoughts, I went duck hunting with Howling Wolf but after missing several shots, Wolf parted the bullrushes and whispered to me, 'You love is filling the wind, making your arrows fly crooked. A man can't hunt when his spirit is on the mats of his wetu.'

"This made me laugh, for he had been one of the braves trying to dissuade me from marrying Singing Waters the night before the ceremony. This was our custom. The women would get together and tell the bride all the bad things about her husband- even making up things - and the braves would do the same with the groom. This was to test our love and faith in the other person. Sometimes we would pretend to get angry about something but it was all in fun. I had been through it before so I knew when they said Singing Water was going to grow old and skinny and ugly as a toad they were just joking. To me she would always be beautiful. They were right about her growing skinny, though. Many of our webcowits died from starvation in the war with the English. But that is for another time. Now I tell about our happy time.

"As I laid back in the reeds, my eyes watched two hawks circling high over the flatlands. I felt like dancing and whooping and throwing my quiver high into the air instead of creeping through brush and stalking fowl. Beneath the blue sky I felt totally at peace, one with all my brothers and sisters of the earth and in the sky. I was so love crazy I pulled back when my elbow rested on a tender dock leaf because I didn't want to crush it.

"Like the hawks, our thoughts flew together, gliding on the wind, feeling the cool breath of it ruffle the soft feathers beneath our wings. There was such serenity in knowing I would no longer be flying alone.

"My hunting that day would not have impressed a wife, but that night I crept up behind her as she sat outside the dancing circle and crept away with her through the reeds, across a water-logged mossy field and up into the forest. When we reached the top of the hill we could see all the moonlit valley beneath. The quaboag river looked like one of the Englishman's silver chains as it lay beneath Grandmother moon.

"I said to her, 'Taubotne aunanamean.' (I thank you for your love).

"All the sounds of the night entered into us that night : the bullfrogs' croaking, the whippoorwill and owl calls, the small, scuttling noises of little creatures and the fluttering of bats' wings. All melted into one enveloping buzz as we lay on her pale rabbitskin shawl. When she looked up at me her face was a miniature moon. In the darkness, beneath the stars who had once lived on earth, on the blanket of the earth that was womb to all life, we became one. It was such a sacred act that even the plants beneath us curled onto our skin to join in the creation of new life. As the mating of animals creates young, we knew that our mating would bring forth a new member of the tribe. We knew we had mated for life on that hill."

"There were four more days of feasting and dancing, during which we sang many songs including crying out songs and bear spirit songs. Just before we broke camp and returned to our villages we sang our last song around the fire - the traveling song.

"As our feet walked the path back to Asquoach, I carried

Strong One on my back. I tried to get him to notice the plants or animals we saw along the way, but he was silent. When we neared our village, he finally spoke, telling me about a dream he had in his illness. He said he had seen a white bird and a crow fighting as a black wolf watched them from the bushes, licking his lips.

"I told him to forget it; that he thought too much. Then Singing Water tickled his feet and said, 'I will teach you to laugh, little one!'

Firehawk (Shatookquis) sighs deeply, his energy gone,

"That spring is my happiest memory of Quaboag. Later, when I feel stronger, I will tell you of how it was when the wars began. But now I just want to sit back and smoke and let my thoughts walk the sunny paths of long ago."

Chapter 8
(A re-telling of events from 1624-1631)

A day passed in the Oneida village. The snow stopped and the children went out to play and gather more wood and water. A buck had been shot in the woods and this night as they listened, their bellies full, the longhouse was filled with the delicious aroma of venison stew.

Again Firehawk takes the talking stick:

"When we arrived back at Asquoach, we were met on the path by a taggamut, who was en route to quobogud to try and catch up with Naddawahunt before he moved to his summer camp up north.

"'The great leader of the Wampanoags is dead!' taggamut shouted as his bare feet pounded the worn path. We pulled back to let him pass, all speechless at this news.

"I ran along with taggamut for a short distance and asked when he died. The runner said, 'By the time the sun rises tomorrow, he will have passed to the land of our ancestors. He lies now in his longhouse surrounded by his mourning subjects. He wishes to see Naddawahunt before he dies. Tuwuttin?' (Where lives he?) he asked.

"I told him he might find Naddawahunt in menemiset and then returned to the village. We called a hasty council and one elder said, 'This is bad news for us, my brothers. Our enemies the Mohegans and Narragansetts to the south might seize this time of our weakness to attack us like the snakes they are.' I said Massasoit (this was not his real name - just his title meaning big sachem) was not dead yet and I was going to go to sowams myself to see if it were true. I remembered how Squanto had sent false news about Massasoit's kidnapping the winter before. For this Massasoit had ordered the English to return him for execution. When the English refused, he sent his own knife with its carved handle and ordered Squanto's head and hands returned to him but again the English had refused.

Although Squanto had died in the fall (some say he was poisoned in his dreams by a Narragansett powwow), we knew there were many Massachusetts sachems near the new English village of wessagusset who wanted war with the English and might send false news to start one. I enlisted several braves to go with me but my spirit faltered when I saw the disappointment in Singing Water's eyes as she quickly packed some nohehick into a hollow leather waist pouch and dried fish into a hempen bag. She pressed a small thong-tied bag into my hand as I left and whispered, 'My medicine - to protect you from the yellow death.' (At the fishing camp, we had heard that the yellow death was again visiting Wampanoag villages near the coast).

"We ran along the path from asquoach past the little alum pond and pookapaug pond and quickly passed between the two breast-shaped hills next to the village in tantiesques near another pond. There we stopped for a drink of water. The taggamut had visited them and they, too, knew of Massasoit's condition for the women were weeping and carrying on. Many had painted their faces in mourning with dust from the black rocks close to the village of metewemesick nearby. We traveled hard through senexit, maanexit and keekamoochaug until we reached chabungagungamaug on the shores of the big pond. We were offered food and rest for the night but we rested only long enough to eat roasted fish and eel soup then continued on so we could be in sowams by kitompanisha (daybreak).

"We could hear the keening and wailing through the first light as we neared the hill overlooking the bay of Pawtucket.

"We were met at the bottom and escorted to the top of the mount, through the thick double-pallisade fort to Massasoit's ceremonial lodge. A great many people were crowded in the village and the wetu but we finally pressed through and saw him lying on his large bed. The sound of his people singing filled our ears as we looked at him, pale as a corpse. The powwow shrieked his spells as he placed small bowls of burning sweetgrass, tobacco and other plants on Massasoit's chest. Through the smoke we saw our great sachem's chest rising and falling. He was not dead but we were told he was blind.

"We joined in the singing and ate the food pressed on us, but our weariness was so great that after a while we crawled onto the mats offered and slept. The sun had not yet reached paweshaquaw (midpoint) overhead when I heard a strange commotion and, looking outside, saw the man Winslow with another Englishman. I thought, 'So, are they going to be the first to challenge the alliance?' I reached for the knife hanging by a thong around my neck and followed them into the lodge.

"I heard Massasoit speaking, very faintly. He said, 'Keen Winsnow... I you never see again.'

"Although he couldn't see, he reached out for him like an old friend and then began coughing, blood spurting from his nose and mouth. The powwow took a pile of moss my sister had brought in and the sachem spit into it.

"The Englishman Winslow asked for permission to look into the sachem's mouth and then to take a flat stick and scrape the thick coating of white fur off his tongue and back of his throat. Massasoit almost vomited during this, but he allowed them to go on. Winslow then reached into his bag and was upset to find a broken bottle that smelled like their drink, only sweeter. He poured what was left of it into a wooden bowl and mixed it with the jellied rosehips he had then added water and made him drink. At every step, he argued with the chief shaman, who inspected everything and did not want to give it to Massasoit. But the sachem ordered him to allow it and he drank of their strange medicine. Almost immediately there was a change. Massasoit began sweating and opened his eyes. The Englishmen had shot quequecummauog (ducks) on their way to the village and ordered the women to boil them up for the sachem, who sat up and ate so much he threw up. He bled again after that but it was just a little bit, not the pouring forth of blood like earlier.

"It was indeed magic. The transformation was so fast it seemed to us that the English had instantly, without chanting or smudging, driven away the spirit trying to take Massasoit's life. The knifemen gave thanks to their god for the cure but we said it was the powwow's magic and all the songs finally working and that is was a coincidence it happened when it did. In our hearts we wondered, though.

"After he awoke from a deep sleep, Massasoit called a council of all the sachems and sagamores who, like myself, had come to sowams.

"He looked at all of us and then told us he had not trusted the English after the affair with Squanto. He said many of the Massachusetts sachems, led by Caunbitant, told him the English were his enemy. The sachems near wessagusset were planning to knock them all on the head. They called the English men who lived there "cornstealers". The men did not work hard the way the men in Plymouth did. They looked for ways to steal from their neighbors and when they were starving, they debased themselves by living as slaves, carrying firewood and water like the women. They didn't carry weapons to protect themselves and were scorned by the people in the area.

"The sachems living in the area knew he was referring to Obtakiest and Wituwamet, who along with Pecksuot were trying to get the tribes to gather up and drive all the English away. They were at this time camped outside the village of wessaguset, waiting for others to join them.

"Massasoit told us that he now knew the English were not his enemies, but were his friends. He said Winslow had saved his life and for that he would always be a friend to the Englishman. As long as he lived, he said, he would expect all of his people, meaning those who were allied with his confederacy, to live in peace with the English.

"These words fell hard on our ears. There were many arguments, many speeches. Some said the birdship would soon come across wechakum with more men, cannon and thundersticks. They said Wituwament was right: the time to strike was now when they were starving and weak. But Massasoit would not hear such talk. In the end, all agreed to live peacefully with the English. Afterwards the ones who did not like the English said in private that Massasoit was still ill and would probably not last the winter. They could keep their agreement that long.

"Massasoit then sent all but Hobbomock out. We learned afterwards that he had told him to wait until the English were away from sowams and then warn them of Wituwamet's plot. He told him to tell the English to kill the ones leading the plot.

"We heard later that Standish and his warriors had gone to wessagusset and murdered Wituwament, Peksuot and Wituwament's young brother. But what we next heard made us wonder about Massasoit's peace treaty.

"The English had not only tricked and fallen upon the plotters, killing them with their own knives, but they had taken off Wituwament's head and it now sat on the top of a pole outside Plymouth.

"This did not seem like the actions of men desiring peace. To us, it seemed like a declaration of war. Chickataubet was so angry that he killed the three Englishmen living in his village when he heard this.

"But my father told me to keep silent, for we in the west would not see the white man again. He said that he had heard the Narragansetts were going to kill all the English and so they would trouble us no further. But I did not like this either, for living in Quansik, the Narragansett lands were close by. Any war with the English while Massasoit lived meant we would have to war with the Narragansetts.

"And so I returned to Quaboag with a heavy heart. I knew my days of peace with Singing Water would not last. For the first time I became afraid of the English, of all the white men. Though their warriors were few, they carried a powerful medicine bag from their god that, when opened, spread war amongst the peoples wherever they went."

Chapter 9
(Konkowasco's winter manhood ordeal, 1632)

Konkowasco next speaks:

"Almost two handfuls of winters passed. The English were busy building up their villages. They had a large village they called Salem in Winnepurkitt's territory at naumkeag and another nearby in his brother's territory at massebequash (Marblehead). The men at Wessagusset had left but they established a trading post in pentuckett in Mettacomen and Pissaconowet's territory where the pascataque river met the sea. There were other small trading villages at monhegan island, pemmiquid, and kennebec. Mostly we heard about them when Konkowasco and my aunt came to visit. He said they often traded paskiganash (guns) for furs and our braves often talked about how they were going to load their canoes with beaver pelts one day and take them upriver to Kongawasco's village to trade for muskets.

"To our south a band calling themselves Mohegans were growing bigger and warred with their Pequot relatives. The Pequots chief sachem Tatobem drove the Mohegan chief sachem out of Pequot and into Narragansett territory. The Narragansetts drove them north into our area.

"The Pequots invaded podunk and drove Wahginnicut out. My aunt and uncle felt sorry for him and invited him and his people to live in Agawam. The Pequots then invaded sequan and drove the chief sachem Sequassen into Narragansett. Wahginnicut went to Sagamore John with Jackstraw, who had lived in the English colony called Virginia. He accompanied them to the English to ask them to set up a fort at the great fishing falls on the quonicticut in podunk to drive away the Pequots and their Dutch friends. The Dutch were now trading wampampeag beads for goods. They measured them in "fathoms", with the purple beads worth more than the white. This was good for the Narragansetts for they had the seashores where the shells were found, but not so good for the inland tribes. All we had were pelts and there were times of the year when they were in short supply.

"To our south, Aquittimaug and his son brought corn to the English, who were starving again, to ask for their help in defending the Wabbaquasetts against the Pequots.

"My father tried to avoid the English for he said wherever they went they brought their box of plague with them - and English rats the size of our mushquashcutog (muskrats) came with them and got into the corn supplies wherever they went.

"Many winters before my manhood ordeal my father started teaching me the ways of a quankiash brave. He had taught me how to find the stones that made the best arrowheads. We liked best the clear, shiny rock that looked like ice for it would take a very sharp edge. When we found a stone full of this we chipped off big sections and carried them back to our village. There, in the winter, in the warmth of our wetu, we would chip many arrowheads. The black rock called flint, plus obsidian and chert were also good but my father showed me how to use the talon of a large bird or animal bones to make arrowheads if good rocks were not handy. Some stones were too soft and would crumble when struck with the larger rock, and others were too hard and would not chip at all. Even a good arrowhead could be ruined by a wrong blow, so I and the other boys spent many long days practicing chipping while growing up. Some of us even had the powwow make magic water in which we would soak our flints. We also tried soaking them in deer grease and packing them in containers with tobacco and sacred roots to charm them into breaking easily for us. Our ruined arrowheads and chips were scattered around the village and the women complained when they stepped on a sharp one. Sometimes we would trade face paints for a bag of unfinished arrowheads with a neighboring brave from the next village of metewemesick, which was between our village and tantiesques on the path towards manexit and chabungagungamung. We used bone or antler tips to finish off the edges of our spear and arrow blades. Brother moose left his antlers on the ground for us in the spring so we always had plenty of antlers in our village.

"My father taught me how to select the proper arrow shafts from hickory tree branches that were no thicker than one's little finger. These we tied in bundles so they would dry nice and straight.

For our bows and arrows we liked a wood that had some give to it, one that would not become brittle. He showed me how to cut a bow and how to shape it so when it was bent, it would not crack. He showed me how to string sinew from one end to the other and how to make it very tight. He told me a brave always carried extra thongs and sinews in his pouch to repair anything that broke. He showed me how water would damage our mocassins and bowstrings and how to rub nahmospummi (fish oil) into the mocassins to make them supple and waterproof after they got wet. A warrior always carried an extra pair of mocassins with him. He showed me how to split two turkey feathers and twist them into the shaft of the arrow so when it was shot it would fly true to its target.

"When he shot his arrows they usually hit their target but it took me many winters to even get close most of the time. We practised all the time and competed with each other, gambling away different things we made or killed. Besides the bows, we made spears and snow snakes. A brave would roll a hoop made from lashed ash strips down the snow and we would run along with it, trying to get our spear in its middle to make it stop or we would throw our snow snakes and try to see whose would slide farthest. By the winter of my ordeal, I could shoot and spear almost as well as my father.

"My father took me to the cauompsk (whetstone) places so we could gather the stones to sharpen our knives and tools with. There was one near asnuntuck brook and other south of mashapaug.

"We hunted often and I learned how to hunt with a party, making a deer run that got narrower at one end. This would confuse the deer and we could shoot them easily. We would take many deer this way in early fall.

"My father showed me how to make different traps for other animals. For some animals we dug holes in the ground that were as wide on the bottom as the animal hunted, but narrow and steep on top. It was important to remove all traces of earth from the hole so the animal wouldn't sense that something was different. Then we covered the pit with small branches or reeds and put a piece of bait on top. This was especially good for wild cats such as the ounces and mountain lions, who provided us with valuable pelts. When we killed them we ridded ourselves of dangerous beasts near our villages and their meat made a feast for our dogs.

"Another pit was for small animals and birds, especially

turkeys. For this one, we dug a hole and hid in it, covering the top with crossed sticks and grass. When something came for the bait, we would reach up from beneath, grab its legs, pull it down and crush it between our knees. If the animal was larger, we could spear it in its belly as it ate.

"Sometimes we used snares to strangle birds with but most of our snares were hung on bent saplings and caught larger game. The sapling would be bent over and held in place by a piece of branch tucked into the notch of a tree. When the animal took the bait, it had to put its head through the snare, which would knock the branch out of the tree and spring back the bent sapling. We could also throw strong hempen rope over the top of a tree with a noose handing down along an animal path, then stick branches on either side so the animal would walk into it. This required a lot of strength, for we had to pull it tight while the animal struggled.

"We had other traps that used baited snares for gnawing animals. As they chewed the bait, they actually chewed away the snare spring pole, which then released, killing the animal. My father taught me that to hunt an animal you have to spend many many hours observing what it likes to eat, where it eats and when it feeds. Then you copy nature and set up your own feeding station. As you know, we braves prefer to take our flintlocks out to the woods and shoot game, for there is thrill in the hunt and chase, but many nights our bellies have been filled because of our trapping skills.

"For bears and the largest game we set sunnuckheag (wolf-catcher or deadfall) traps. We would prop up heavy logs on top of a small rock on a thin branch attached by a rope to the bait, which sat on small rocks. Around this we placed branches so the animal had to stick its neck under the logs to get to the bait. The logs would then fall and break its neck.

"For fishing, we made our weirs, which were something like the deer funnels. We placed rows of rocks in the river, angling them inwards like the sides of arrowheads until they got so close we could stick a row of branches in the river across them. The water and small fish could pass through, but the salmon and alewives would get caught and we could spear them at that point. After our spring fishing camps, we would remove the sticks so leaves and branches wouldn't get caught and dam up the river. We also had nets we could use from our canoes plus trawl lines and bait.

"We hunted game often from our canoes. Some of us practically lived in our birchbark canoes when we were young. Several of us would take off on hunting trips up and down the rivers and stay away moons at a time. We could eat the smaller game but any large animal killed in the water belonged to the sachem who controlled the river and had to be brought to his or her village.

"Every village had an elder who would teach the boys how to make canoes if they offered him tobacco and asked to be taught. Ours told us that canoemaking is a long process and must be done at the driest time of the year. We waited until the time was right and then went go out with him to the forest to find a cedar, hickory and our birch bark tree. For the bark tree, he choose a tall, straight one with a firm, tough bark free of knots. Then we packed mud around the bases of the trees and began charring them, for before the English axe, this is how we felled our trees.

"The burning took a long time. We camped nearby, building our canoe frame as soon as the young cedar and hickory saplings were felled.

"The frame was made of cedar split into ribs running along the grain. The ribs were as thick as two fingers and about twice as wide. The surface that was outside on the tree would be outside on the canoe, for it was seasoned and would not soak with water. The heartside, or inner surface, was the inner surface of the canoe. To bend the ribs we dug a bed in the clay near the river, filled it with heated stones and then steamed the wood, tying pairs together for bending. These were matched according to shape and tied together in pairs. The gunwales were difficult to bend, but since they gave the canoe its shape from end to end, we kept at it until they had just the right upward curves on the ends. To get the proper shape, we took an old canoe and stuck pointed framing stakes in the ground all around it. The ground beneath was cleaned smooth so the bark wouldn't get bruised. We cut the crossbars from a hickory tree and cut the interior sheathing mats from the cedar tree.

"When the birchbark tree was ready to fall we propped it with logs and gently pushed so the bark wouldn't be bruised in the fall. Then we placed logs beneath it so we could cut the bark . The canoe maker had the tallest brave lie down towards the end of the log and he marked on the ground where his feet and head were. Then he laid down with his feet on his head mark, over and over, four to five times in all. The trunk was circled at the topmost and bottommost marks and then he cut the bark lengthwise. The next step was the trickiest. We had to peel the bark off in one piece with wedges without buckling, bruising or tearing it. Once we had it free of the trunk, we made torches with dry, outer bark scraps and ran them over the inside of the bark. This flattened it like a blanket. We then turned it over and very carefully rolled it into a bundle to carry it to our frame.

"The bark was very gently placed inside the stakes and then the gunwales worked in. We put temporary spreaders in to hold the shape as we worked, adding the bow and stern shapers then the ribs-the widest first- followed by the rear and bow boards and hickory spreaders. We were careful to gently mold the wood and bark together to prevent tearing. We then lined the inside with long basket splints that set over the ribs and protected the bark from our feet. This is where the skill of the canoe maker was so important. We struggled with these splints to make them lie smoothly without breaking at the ends, but he knew how to coax them in and fastened them at the bow and stern where they were the most difficult. He told us that we could sew the wood and bark together with the inner bark of the elm or butternut trees but we just used pitch sap to seal it.

"After our canoe dried completely, we tipped it upside down and heated tallow (hard, white animal fat) with resin until it was like paste. This was spread over all the seams and areas where water might leak in. We added soot to some of it to make black pitch, which we used to paint a design on either end of our canoe. This design would identify us when we were on the river. After a dream, I chose the design of two lines joined so as to look like a bird's leg.

"This was our first canoe. To us the canoe was a living, breathing thing. It had ribs and skin and we respected it and appreciated the tree lives sacrificed for it. Canoemaker told us if we treated it right it would serve us well on the rivers but if we were rough with it or did not inspect it for wear, its spirit would be sad and it would no longer go fast. As I grew older, I built other canoes, but this is the one I remember the most.

"My father taught me which plants to look for when hungry: the tall yellow flowers and stalks in sunny places that had groundnuts beneath; the small groundnut plant that had a vine with many little nuts beneath; wild raspberry and milkweed sprouts; cattail shoots, buds and leaves of the sassafrass, linden and hemlock trees. Our whole area, all of quansik, was full of tall chestnut trees and their nuts and acorns were a staple in our diet for breads and soup thickening. But if starving, one could peel the inner bark of basswood, slippery elm, birch, striped maple, white oak or sassafrass tree and boil it into a stringy soup. To keep from starving, one could burn the fuzz off cattail seeds, grind them and boil them into sampum. There were others such as pond lily roots and jack-in-the-pulpit root (which bit the tongue unless it was dried, sliced and roasted then ground into flour and again heated and dried). We could gather the leaves of wild mustard, clover, young unfuzzy ferns, trilliums and wild onions. Even mushrooms could keep us from starving, but we preferred them cooked with grease.

"We spent many days hunting deer. He told me the deer made trails alongside areas of brush. He showed me how to recognize the marks made on the tree trunks from where they rubbed their antlers when shedding. We spent many days observing them from tree crotches. The whitetail were hard to kill from the ground, but didn't look up, so a tree overlooking a pond or trail near their bedding areas was best. My father told me they always made a circle going to the pond or returning to the meadows where they slept. They were most active at dusk and a little after sunrise. Creator gave them extremely keen ears so a hunter had to stand or sit perfectly still. My father said he had often been outwaited by a deer, who could stand so still its antlers looked like the branches it of the trees it was hiding amongst. One time, a deer sprung up right in front of us from its hiding spot.

"He taught me to aim for the neck area, for a gut-shot deer could travel far and the meat would taste bad. He showed me how to track a wounded deer, to look for brittle hairs and blood spots. He said it was best to let it be for it would go and lie down, but if I tried to follow it, it would go on and on. But it wouldn't go uphill, he said.

"Then he taught me how to hang and gut a deer. First he cut around the genitals then removed the furry glands on either side of the thighs so their scent wouldn't ruin the meat. He tied off the anus with a piece of thong then cut from the abdomen to the ribs, his fingers feeling underneath so he could cut the muscle free. After it was split up the middle, he made a crosswise split then cut the diaphragm, lungs and intestines out, rolling them free onto the ground. Then he used a long branch and hempen rope over a tree limb so he could pull the deer up, head first. This allowed the blood to drain. This had to be done immediately, he said, for the meat would spoil otherwise. He showed me how to cut out its tongue, left hind foot and sinew and the prayer to say when offering it to Mother Earth and the deer spirit.

"Since the deer would hang for a while until one's webcowit got it, its insides were separated with a sharp stick and stuffed with boughs to keep birds and flies away.

"Although it was women's work, he showed me how to scrape the clots and some hair off then how to soak the deer hide in a stream so the rest of the hair would rot off, then how to take its brains and rub them into it to tan it and prevent it from spoiling. If I were hunting alone I could do this or I could drag the carcass over the snow and rehang it near the village so my webcowit could butcher it.

"For winter, he showed me how to make snowshoes and my mother made me an extra pair of fur-lined mocassins to take while on my manhood ordeal.

"These were all things I knew how to do before I spent a winter alone in the woods away from my village.

"I knew when I emerged from the winter of solitude I would be accepted into my tribe as a man. The visions and experiences I had during this time would determine which path my mocassins would walk. I knew that the way of a brave was to provide for his wife, or wives, and to be honest with other braves, never representing himself as anything other than he was or to lie about his coups in battle."

Konkowasco pauses, taking a drink of tobacco from his pipe,

"The brave never forgets his winter ordeal.

"The summer and fall before had been dry and much of our corn had withered on its stalks. Our women had just barely finished storing the corn in caves and underground pits when the wind turned cold and the snows came. The elders decided to wait a moon before sending us out and during that time I wandered around the village, remembering trees, streams, ponds and hills so when I was blindfolded and led out, I would remember where I was. I found a small cave near a beaver pond in the territory just bordering Wabbaquasett and this I planned to use as my winter home - if I could find it again.

"The day before we were to leave, we took a sweat together. My closest friend, Thundering Frog, and I sat in the steam lodge next to the partially frozen river and talked of our fears. Frog said,

'Tonight will be our last night in the wetus until sequan. Are you feeling afraid, netop?'"

"Strangely, I wasn't afraid of being alone in the forest, but I didn't know how to explain to him that the animals spoke to me and I felt a communion with my ancestors when I was alone. I said, 'A little, netop, but I am eager to become a brave. I have been a boy long enough.'

"As the sweat worms began biting into my flesh, I thought about my tomahawk. My father had started it for me when I was a nipamoose. We had gone out together in the woods, found a forked hickory sapling, placed the tomahawk stone blade into it, tied the tops together, and let it grow. It took ten winters to grow big enough for me and that morning I had gone with my father to the spot and cut the sapling. Using my father's tomahawk, I chopped above the blade and below it for a handle. My father told me I was like the tomahawk. I had been growing as part of him and now it was time I separated and became my own person. He said the tomahawk and I were brothers. I would have the long winter nights to finish it in, chipping designs into it and dying it the way my uncle Konkowasco had shown me.

"My uncle carried a war club made from a large tree root. The root ball was the top of the club and the handle the long, thin trunk. The root had been cut so it looked like a head with two horns on either side. In the middle my uncle carved a face with its mouth wide open, showing carved teeth. It looked like a warrior yelling his war cry. The whole club was died blood red from sumac berries. On the handle, my uncle chipped out leaves and arrows. It was the club he used when fighting the Mohawks, he said, and every arrow represented a coup. The bottom was wrapped in leather that ended in a thong for carrying on his back.

"My grandfather, Naddawahunt, told me about the war club Massasoit owned. He said it had a dark root ball in a lighter handle. It was inlaid with wampum triangles and was so shiny you could see your face in it. Naddawahunt said Massasoit's son Mooanum, who was about my age, had said his own would be stained red with English blood and his father had been very cross with him for saying such a thing.

"My father said the English could take one's soul if they knew his name so we were always careful never to tell them our real names. Even the names you children have heard are not our real names. We tell you the names we gave to the English - titles, mostly, like big sachem (Massamet and Massasoit) or sachem from the canoe-place (Naddawahunt). Sometimes we even said 'I cannot tell' (Tahattawant) and they called us by that. Squaw sachem said her children would be safe from the plague if they received English names. This would fool the English god, she said. My father told her that the English had powerful medicine and could find out one's name. But to be on the safe side, Naddawahunt named one of my uncles David.

"The morning of our ordeal, our fathers woke us up at dawn. We dressed and gathered our supplies for the winter. We were given one last meal by our mothers and then led out of the village. That moment before I was blindfolded was the most precious to me so far in my life. My eyes couldn't get enough - I stared at the pale sunlight rising through the smokey haze over the ravine where our wetus sat nestled in long purple and blue shadows. One of my brothers was feeding scraps to the dogs outside the wetu, my mother and younger brothers and sisters were in the door flap, watching us leave. Singing Water held her plump hand up softly in a sad farewell. I was leaving as her son but if I returned, it would be as a man.

"In front of me I could see the back of my father's head as he led the way. The brittle cold shone on the two hawk feathers over his thick braid. Like him, I was heavily greased and wore leggings and a tunic.

"He stopped outside the village and pulled a soft doeskin out of his belt. As he covered my eyes, he said, 'I took forward to sharing the pipe with you in three moons. Bring honor on your family.'

"I was led, blindfolded, into the woods. I tried to remember the streams we crossed, the slope of the land, but when he sat me down in the snow and said goodbye, I was disoriented. I spent most of the day climbing up the waddaquadducks to the high rock that overlooked the valley, for once I looked from there, I could descend and go south to my cave.

"Although I had checked the cave out a moon before to make sure no other animal had claimed it as a winter home, I approached the pond slowly, circling, my mocassins silently slipping toe first into the snow. There were no tracks near the cave, so I slipped into its long, low belly. It had a musty odor and I could see old animal bones and dead leaves at its end. I rested for a while then went out and found a cedar tree. With the steel-bladed knife I had obtained in trade with the Agawams near Chicopee, I cut off boughs and staked them down on the floor of the cave for a bed, covering them with a hide.

"By now the sun was dipping low to the west, so I took my deer bladder, broke a hole in the ice and filled it with water from the pond, gathered some dry wood, made a small circle with rocks and lit a fire at the entrance to the cave.

"During that day I had been so busy looking for my cave, I had not caught any food. Since this was a test of our survival skills, the mothers did not provide us with even a handful of nohike. As I lit the fire and drank the cold water, my stomach began to ache. Tomorrow I would have to hunt.

"I laid down on the bed, the fur side of my deer mantle warm against my skin, and looked up at the blinking white stars in the black sky. I heard brother owl hooting in the distance and something rustled nearby in the trees. My hole in the ice had attracted something for I heard paws scuffing near the shore. These sounds frightened me a little for this was the first time I had slept completely alone on Mother Earth. I softly began to sing a song of courage to myself, a song telling the creatures I was their brother and came in peace. I must have sung myself into a trance for the next thing I knew, I was looking out of the cave entrance at a black haze that stunk like burning hair.

"I knew this was not a cheepi. The fear I had that made the hairs on my arms stand up could only have come from Hobbomock. I had heard it said that he could tear a brave apart from limb to limb and he could make braves lose their way in misty swamps. His tortures were terrible, for their calls would be heard for many winters afterwards. His medicine is what braves feared in the shadows of the night.

"My fingers trembled as I touched my medicine bag. My heart was beating rapidly beneath my fingers and I was aware of cold air hitting the sweat on my brow.

"He was calling me in a voice without sound. As I crept outside and stood in the brittle, black night, I was aware of an even colder blackness moving around me like a huge, invisible bear.

"I raised my tomahawk and shouted, 'Hobbomock! If you come to fight, then appear in the flesh of a brave!'

"Suddenly I felt a powerful blow across my upper back. It

knocked me face forward into the crusty snow, cutting my lip.

"I sprang up like a cat and, crouching, turned to face the tallest, most muscular brave I had ever seen! His hair bristled with a tall black and red roach and his face was all black except for a white zigzag running from his forehead to his jaw. His eyes glowed red and his body was painted black. He wore only a small black loincloth. 'This is a beast in man's shape' I thought. He opened his mouth, curling back the lips to bare huge white fangs. His hands were huge, black claws.

"I knew no man could fight this beast and win so I decided to try to reason with it. I said, 'Hobbomock, you do not fight fairly. Are you afraid to fight me as a man?' He let out a terrible roar but I continued, 'At least give me the weapons of an eagle also.'

"There was a confused swirl and I felt myself being lifted from the snow. My arms were now huge black wings. I dodged his talons as we flew above the black stream-snake in the snow below. I had never seen such a sight as this even from the tall rock place near the old fort: all of the lands lay beneath me, the mountaintops, the rivers and ponds. The air was so cold it hurt to breathe. My arms hurt so much I thought they would fall off, but everytime Hobbomock flew at me, I found energy to avoid him. He was now above me, shrieking as he dove straight down at me, the talons like handfuls of knives. I dodged him and down he fell, rolling over and over. Then he righted himself and flew at me again, spitting forth a stream of stars.

"I grabbed them with my claws and flung them back at him like a full quiver then the air was filled with a frightening, otherworld roar and I felt myself falling, my feathers gone.

"I awoke later in my cave. I was on the boughs but the fire was now only pale embers. I wondered if it had been a dream or if it had been real. I crept to the mouth of the cave and looked out. There were two sets of footsteps outside in the snow. And one set was much bigger than the other.

"I ran back in and got under the mantle, my eyes never leaving the entrance to the cave until my eyelids became so heavy I couldn't hold them up. I slept that way until Grandmother Dawn slid her fingers across the churned snow and feebly touched my face.

"During my long winter's ordeal, I was visited by other spirits. Perhaps it was the scanty food supply or the cold and loneliness but I was closely in tune with the other world that winter.

"One time when the skins of night fell off my eyes, I stretched, walking out of the cave. Where the pond should have been was the valley of quaboag with its rivers. A spirit touched my chest with heat. As I touched my medicine bag and recited a prayer to the Great Spirt to endure the ordeal for my people I became aware of this spirit on my left.

"Unlike the first, who had been all in black, this one was all in white. He looked like he was made of smoke. He said, 'Brother and seeker of wisdom, our Father has sent me to be your spirit guide.' He held out his hand and all along his sleeve hung long white feathers.

"When I took his hand I was amazed at how solid and calloused it felt. We were suddenly engulfed in what appeared to be a snowstorm without cold or wet. There was a loud buzzing in my head and many flakes of brilliant white flew around me.

"Then they were gone and I was on top of the steerage rock overlooking my valley. But everything was different. The hills were brown and red, as if painted with ochre. The trees had been felled and they lay chained together along the ground. Everything was burned. I walked across the dry, scorched earth, my bare feet burning with pain from the needle-like stubble covering our corn fields. This was not the normal burning we practiced. The time of the year was wrong and the extent - never did we burn our mother's flesh so bare. Never did we parch the faces of our hills to bare skulls.

"I stopped at the base of a nude, wrinkled red hill. A white rock broke loose and rolled down towards me, stopping against my foot. I gasped as I saw it was a human skull. I looked at the mountain and saw it was made from human skeletons.

"There was a pungent, acrid odor in the air, the odor of burned bodies. A keening, a wail of mourning, filled the wind, growing louder and then stopping. The silence held a terrible emptiness.

"The skulls then began to tumble down towards me and I ran back up the hill where my spirit guide stood. I watched as Mother Earth opened up and swallowed the mountain of bones, the blackened earth, the rivers that were dry and crusty. All that remained was a ridge of red craters which pulsed as if over a huge heart.

"'What does this mean?' I asked and he replied, 'Where is your heart, Strong One? In here or down there? Find your heart and you shall find your answer.'

"I awoke from this trip with a sharp stab of pain in my chest, so sharp it made me clutch my left shoulder. Had he plunged a magic spear into my heart?

"My thoughts were suddenly interrupted when a deer came crashing through the dry branches outside my cave. I grabbed for my bow as the buck sniffed the air and warily walked to the inlet of the pond. I held my fire for an instant as I watched him drink from the frigid black vein lacing the frozen swamp. As I pulled the bowstring back and squinted, I saw the rose-colored aura of dawn surround the buck and he seemed to disappear into a mist. The red mist and horrors of my vision returned to me and I lowered my bow, confused.

"I studied the buck in silence. Like me, he was alone, testing his abilities to survive the rigors of winter. But whereas he was fighting other bucks to win his place in the woods, I was fighting strange creatures of the sky and earth, spirits who had roamed the land with the buck's grandfathers.

"The last vision had left me terribly confused. I had never seen Mother Earth, the nurturer, so violent, so hungry as she devoured her barren hills and flesh. She had shown a side of herself that I had only been vaguely aware of: Mother Earth the destroyer.

"I did not kill the buck but I did kill other creatures to survive. I could feel the outlines of my ribs and when I looked at my face in the pond, there was a sharp edge to my jaw. I missed the warmth of the wetu. I missed the smell of soup cooking and my friends and family.

"My only companions that winter had been spirit ones who visited me in the night. And the shape shifters. These I liked the least for they appeared suddenly like snakes out of trees or rocks. I talked to them like naughty children and told them to go away but they made me doubt my sanity. I knew that this winter I was in touch with the spirit world in a way I had never been before. This sometimes frightened me and at others times it made me feel special, chosen.

"My last and strongest vision came towards the end of my ordeal. The sequan moon was almost full as it rose over the deep blue snow, awakening me with its light.

"I pulled my mantle closer and crouched in the opening, watching a dark shape slither across the snow.

"I had seen large water and black snakes before and had even caught an eel taller than my father, but this snake was enormous and as thick around as a canoe.

"Its head was shaped differently from other snakes and it had long, stiff antennae like those on a catfish sticking out from its chin and the top of its head. It had teeth like pike, long and thin, and its snake eyes glowed like coals.

"A long, forked tongue flicked out of its mouth and it opened its jaws to roar. This roar was so terrible it sent ice tingles down my back.

"I knew I was in great danger. This creature was death. This creature came for my blood.

"I grabbed my spear and hoisted myself up into a pine tree as the snake turned in the direction of the cave. It hissed, 'Don't be afraid, Strong One. I have not come to hurt you.'

"I did not answer but instead climbed further up. My eyes widened as I saw it dart its head into the cave and pull it out with bits of my bedding in its jaw. There was blood lust glinting in its eyes. It turned slowly, its black coils gleaming in the moonlight.

"It hissed again almost singing, 'Strong One - I bring you knowledge.'

"I crouched down on the tree branch, blending with it. I knew I had one stab only with my spear. Any hesitation, any error, would mean death. Its tongue sought me out and it moved towards the tree. I held my breath as its head came closer and closer. My eyes were narrow, concentrating on its hideous head so when it sprang to strike me I was ready and the spear jabbed hard into its jaws. The strength of the throw took me with it and I felt myself falling from the tree. I landed on the creature, on its cold scaly back. Its body coiled around me as it thrashed in death and I felt myself being choked as I tried to push myself out of it.

"The stars above in the black sky slipped and I felt myself sinking into its cold body, choking, my chest bursting. When I awoke the next day I was lying on the snow outside my cave. My lungs burned and by the time I made it back to my village, my whole body burned and I struggled with every breath.

"From that day on, my lungs have not been well. This was the price I paid to be able to call upon Hobbomock when healing others.

"Every gift we receive requires sacrifice. If it is a great gift, the sacrifice must also be great. Remember this, my children, when you want things."

Chapter 10
(A re-telling of the war with the Pequots, 1632-3)

Shattookquis (Firehawk) now takes the talking stick. The effort of remembering has wearied him greatly, but he knows how important it is to tell his people about their past. He knows how the white man changed the stories to make them look good and his people look bad.

"The winter Strong One went away taggamut brought news that the Narragansetts were laying seige to the trading fort Massasoit had allowed the English to build in the great bay the Pokonokets shared with the Narragansetts. Massasoit, his best warriors and the English traders were trapped inside the fort, the taggamut said.

"Massasoit had held a war dance and changed his name to Ousemequin (yellow feather) and was asking for warriors from our area to join the Pokanokets, Wampanoags and Sakonnets who had already joined him.

"This war with the Narragansetts was no surprise, for even before the English arrived, they had warred with Massasoit over the great bay. They conquered as far into our territory as the long pond on the quanabaug river and collected tribute from our bands through the three Mohegan sachems Konkowasco told you about. The area in between the two federations was held by Punham in Cowesit to the north, the Pequots and Mohegans to the south and the Niantics on the coast. It was a hot coal between the Wampanoag federation and Narragansetts and we avoided it when traveling. After the English arrived, Canonicus wanted no part of them and made Massasoit agree that the western side of the bay would not have English in it. This fort was too close to that side, they thought.

"Taggamut arrived at Quaboag old fort at night and we invited him to sleep with us in the longhouse. A fire always burned in the middle of the longhouse but that night it became a war dance fire. The old men chanted as the drum was beat to call the braves to join in the battle.

"Massasoit had sent his red pipe with the runner. The leader of the war dance lit it, chanting,

"'Look now on this pipe!
It is a man!
I have placed my body in it
If you place yours in it, you shall not die!

'Look now on its neck!
It holds my neck
Put yours in it too
If you do, you shall not die!

'Look now on its mouth!
I have placed my mouth in it
Put yours in it too
And you shall not die!

'Look now on this side!
I have placed my side in it
Place you your side in it
And you shall not die!

'Look now at the spine!
I have placed my spine in it
Place you yours in it
And you shall not die!

'Look now at the other side!
I have placed my side into it
Place you yours into it
And you shall not die!

'Look now at the bowl!
I have placed my hollow parts in it
Place you yours in it
And you shall not die!

'Look now at the thong that fastens the bowl and stem!
I have placed my breathing tube within it
Place in it yours
And you shall not die!

'When you go forward from the dawn place
To the land of the setting sun
To fight your enemies
Take this pipe with you
And Creator shall answer your prayers!

'Drink you from this pipe
Become one with it
Carry its power with you
And you shall not die!'

"I was not eager to join in for part of me agreed with Canonicus. In quansik, we thought Massasoit was too friendly to the English and allowed them privileges they had not earned. Another reason was that Singing Water was to be delivered of child soon. The memory of how I had left Gentle Rain at such a time and returned to find her dead warned me to stay with my family.

"As I looked across the circle at Singing Water, these doubts in my head, I felt a breeze ruffle the two hawk feathers at the back of my head and I knew Singing Water had sent it to tell me to follow my heart.

"I felt my legs move and I rose, drawn to the circle by the drums, like a moth to flame. I crouched then jumped, shaking the ceremonial turkey bustle at the base of my spine. My wampum beads rattled as I continued dancing around the circle, my soft, quill-trimmed mocassins slapping the ground toe, heel, toe, heel. I whooped a war yelp and thrust my root ball club high as I sang of how I would coup many Narragansetts before the battle was over.

"The rawhide thongs on the sides of my leggings dragged, then shook as I lept and turned in a frenzied way. The light flickered over the black band I had painted across my eyes and cheeks as I plunged the stick of war into the fire and screamed to fight for my people and avenge our enemies. But as I yelled that vow, I did not visualize a Narragansett warrior's face. I saw a white face covered with blood from its m'hogektn (ripped scalp). My eyes were now blind to Singing Water's soft brown ones. They were wild with revenge. The war dance had worked its magic and the men of ashquoach were now warriors.

"We were joined by warriors from the villages along the way so by the time we arrived at sowams, we had a good army from quansik. There were Pocumtucks, Nonotucks, Squakeags, Nashaways, Naticks, Nashobas, Wamesits and even Massachusetts warriors there to fight the Narragansett. We all had scores to settle with them. But the people of Agawam and the leaders of the W abbaquaset and Warranoakes were not there.

"You can imagine our surprise when we arrived to find Ousemequin in his longhouse, surrounded by a great crowd of men. There were many Englishmen sitting on one side of him, including Standish and Williams, who had been kicked out of Plymouth and had been given refuge in Narragansett. Ousemequin's councillors sat on the other side of them, in front, followed by lesser sachems and sagamores behind. Canonicus was absent, which in itself could have been interpreted as an insult.

"We were told to leave our weapons outside and, reluctantly, after much discussion, we added them to the pile of knives, bows and spears outside the longhouse. They were guarded by a Wampanoag and the thundersticks were guarded by a white man.

"The whole thing stank of ambush and I did not want to enter, but the women bade us in and offered hot steaming bowls of sea fish. They asked, 'Ascumetesimmis?' (Have you eaten?)

"I heard Ousemequin say to the Narragansett sagamores, ' So: you come to me, asking for help from my people when just a sleep ago, you were attacking us? It appears you are like the fox my friend - you were trying to dig us out of our homes and while your face was in the burrow, your hind end got attacked. Now you enter our homes and cry and ask us to help you?'

"We all smiled and yelled 'Ho! Ho!' in approval, but we did not know who had attacked the Narragansetts' hind end. The Narragansetts glared fiercely and threatened to leave when they heard Ousemequin's words but the man called Roger Williams, who spoke our tongue well, intervened and argued with them. He then took the talking stick and addressed the councillors saying in the Narragansett tongue, 'Your two great nations are at war because the two great nations of England and the Netherlands are enemies. The Dutch have given Wopigwooit's Pequots the idea that he should control Punham's territory in Wekapaug because it would give them a trading post on the great bay. Wapigwooit got the Agawams and the Cowesit sachem at Egunk on his side and with them attacked the Narragansetts. He told them they and the Dutch would control the trade all the way up the Connecticut to the great bay in the north. He said they would drive the Narragansett and English out.'

"This I knew was true for Wequagan had called my father and me to a council earlier that winter in Agawam. Besides my father, his sisters and their children, Aquittamaug and his son John Aquittimaug of Wabbequasset, all the leaders of Agawam and Nontuck were there: the very aged Commucke, Wahginnicut, Coa from the Coos tribe to the north, Wenaswis, Cuttonas, Menus Kenix, Ussessas, Winepawin, Macheetuhood, Keckusnek and Makassack were there along with my mother and Niarum. As tamashams (wives) of the sachems and the royal line carriers, they had voices in council.

"They said the Pequots wanted to drive the English away and that the Dutch, who were on montauk (Long Island) and at the mouth of the quonicticut, would help them do this. They said they would give the leader of each warrior band of a hundred men a thunderstick if they would help. They said after they had won, they would set up trading posts and give our people many fine things, including muskets, in trade for beaver skins, sassafrass, sarsparilla and the tall silky grass that grew near swamps. If we had the most muskets, they said, we would be able to drive the Mohawks away forever.

"The thought of being stronger than the Mohawks is what brought most of us to the council, but none of us trusted the Pequots. My people spat in disgust at the offer and left, thinking the others would also turn Wapigwooit's messenger away. Commucke was also against the plan but he was old and Wrutherna was really in charge. We left the council and, since we heard no more of the matter, we thought the others had also voted against the plan.

"Sitting in Ousemequin's longhouse, I realized the matter had not ended. As long as the people wanted the iron and copper (mishquockuck) cooking pots, koppocki (thick cloth), clothes and coats, blankets, glass beads, knives and hatchets it would never end. Like a bear raiding a hive they were willing to endure the stings to get their prize. Especially the prize the English called strong spirits.

"In low voices the powwows sitting in council asked Ousemequin to let them hold another spirit dance near the Dutch. They said the first one had killed half the white men, perhaps another would kill them all. Williams could now speak our tongue and he argued back that their thundersticks had powerful medicine and that it was the Pequots and their allies the French and Dutch who were our enemies, not the English or Narragansetts. He said if we did not help the Narragansetts, the Mahicans would and then they would have control of the rivers and coast. They would be the ones who got the trade goods.

"As I looked around the longhouse I saw many sachems wearing English coats and shirts. Some had large silver pins or beads hanging from their ears. Williams had seen this too, and had said the right words.

"When Naddawahunt argued against helping the Narragansetts, Ousemequin told him, 'If you do not join us, you will be in great danger. The Pequots will sweep north and make you join them. But if we all unite, we can push the Pequots back across the rivers, maybe into Mohawk teritory, where they will be killed.'

"The words of the great sachem were indeed true and our tribes threw in our war sticks with Ousemequan and the Narragansetts.

"Later my father came into the wetu where I was staying and talked to me about the matter. I told him I didn't want to fight side-by-side with the English but he put his gnarled hand on my chest and said, 'Nommoshot, it is better to fight with them than against them. Today we will use their muskets and let English blood be spilled for Pequots. Every English warrior who dies will be one less to bother our people afterwards.'

"I said, 'Yes, father, but who is to say that these English who are our friends today will not turn and join with the Mohawks and be our enemies another day?'

"So I found myself in a war camp that sequan. We had some small skirmishes and as the days grew warmer, band after band left for home. The Nashaways seemed to be enjoying the life of warriors. While the rest of us sat missing our families, they told tales of their fights with the Mohawks as they sharpened their weapons. Their war chief was a cousin of mine through his mother, Mishalisk, and he persuaded me to stay on and help when Caunbitant's war chief spotted a party of Pequots outside our camp.

"We ran through the snow to the thicket where we were told to wait in ambush. Dusk gave way to moonlight and I felt the cold piercing my back while I waited. Soon I heard a muffled shuffle noise on the other side of the dense thicket and heard the owl hoot signaling attack. As I rushed out, I didn't hear or see my fellow warriors. I had no way of knowing if they were alive or dead, their heads crushed by blows from Pequot clubs, but I then heard a single hoot followed by their murderous screams as we fought Pequots hand-to-hand with knives and tomahawks.

"The one I was fighting with kept trying to bring his root ball club down on my head. I was holding his arm with the club away but the sharp fingernails on his other hand clawed at my face then at my arm as I brought my knife closer to his chest. Our breaths were as thick as fog in the night air. He kicked my leg and as I fell, I lunged forward and thrust my knife home. It sank in softly, like a stick in sand, not hitting bone.

"While we celebrated the victory later, my cousin, the leader of the Nashaways, whose battle-name was now Monoco, lay in pain in Canonicus' longhouse. One of his eyes was covered with a mash of mallow and tobacco as the powwows tried to stop the bleeding in the socket where once an eye had once been.

"I stayed on a few sleeps then returned to quansik with a third feather in my hair."

Chapter 11

(Squash Blossom tells of her herbal training and of events in 1633)

An old woman stands up. Once beautiful, her features now are shrivelled, as if her face were sinking in on itself. The copious hanging skin of her underarm flaps as she raises her arm to take the talking stick.

For this remembering, there are no men or boys.

"I was called Asquopeshauau (Squash Blossom) when I was young. I lived in quansik, in the village where Konkowasco grew up. Unlike his family, mine was not royal. Through my father I was of the pequan clan of the chabungagungamug area, so I was related distantly to Naddawahunt's family and the Massachusetts.

"While our men were fighting Pequots, we women spent long days in our smokey wetus cooking, our dried venison stews often salted with tears. Our children wrestled and squabbled, playing on the fur-covered sleeping platforms. We sang medicine songs for our men and boys in the woods while we sewed clothing, wove baskets and bags and bit birch bark patterns into the tops of the birch bark containers we sewed together with basswood strips or wadchabuk (spruce roots).

"We also did fine quill work. For this we would soak the quills in our mouths to soften them, then push them into the baskets, bags or skins, pointed edge first. Then it would go through again and we would fold it under. The brown and white markings on the quills could be arranged in such a way as to create patterns. If the article was to be worn, we would then sew soft buckskin on the inside. It was hard to talk when we did this for we knew swallowing a quill by accident would cause us to die a long, painful death. But we would be able to chew and listen to the women who came to visit.

"There was much talk that winter about who might marry

whom when the boys returned from their ordeals. We recited clan lines as the girls asked us about this one or that one. A couple of the boys returned before the end of winter, sneaking back into camp like dogs with their tails between their legs. While we pretended to be angry with them, we secretly were glad to have some able-bodied males in the village. They would have another chance next winter to become men.

"The winter before the men went away, Singing Water had come to me, for I was known as the village's plant medicine woman. She had come to me before for herbs to help her with her monthly bleeding. Since she was older, I had given her mugwort. You see, the plants we give our young girls with pain or bleeding problems are different from what we give to older women. A maiden with her problem would have been given tansy or snakeroot. I often gave maidens and young wives thistle and balsam poplar roots for cramps or poplar root to prevent premature births. After birth, I would give them poke root or collinsonia for swollen breasts.

"Singing Water came to me the winter before the men went away because she wanted the herbs that would keep her from having children. In the past I would have been able to give her stones from the heads of codfish but I hadn't been to the ocean in many winters. So I gave her moss that had been soaked with helllibore to put up inside. But it did not work and a moon later she came back for herbs that would keep her from having the child that had begun growing in her womb. Her youngest was through nursing and she was tired of bearing children. This happened to our women as they got older and they used herbs whenever they got pregnant. Some of them would even get their husbands to marry younger squaws to make children with.

"I told her to wait until the full moon and then go and spend a few sleeps inside the women's hut (moon lodge). This sometimes brought the bleeding, but it didn't work and so I gave her powdered hellibore root and skunk cabbage root and told her to cook them together with raccoon grease. She was to rub it on her stomach when the moon was waning and at the same time bury a cornhusk doll in the woods to the west.

"She didn't do this, though. After thinking about it, she decided to have the baby but later she returned to me because she had pains that made her stop in her tracks. I gave her more mugwort and some of my precious store of grated codfish scales and told her to drink lots of raspberry leaf and gooseberry tea.

"I think I knew the child wasn't right, but when a woman gets the contented pregnant look, it's hard to tell her such a thing.

"Our women bore children easily. Like the animals living in the woods around us, we knew when it was time and would go out to the women's moonblood wetu. The young squaws often needed help their first time but after that their birthpains brought a nippamoose quickly.

"Singing Water had so much pain during the end of her pregnancy she could barely climb the ravine. When the day came, she did not have the warning pains. She began bleeding inside her wetu and was in so much pain that the other women and I decided it would be best to leave her in the house even though it meant bringing woman's blood into the village. We gathered by her side, burned sweetgrass and sang songs to drive the evil spirits in her birth blood away. The powwow wouldn't come near to help. Like the other men he felt the blood would take his powers away. Women's blood was so powerful it could only be spilled on Mother Earth in the women's hut.

"Shadows on the Moon took Singing Water's male children into her wetu so they wouldn't see the birth and I went to the powwow to get dried snake flesh. This I made into a powder and boiled, then gave the liquid to Singing Water to drink.

"I told her, 'It's not as good as fresh snake blood, but the shaman said it will work.' I preferred to use dried cod powder mixed with sarsparilla root, but these things were not easily obtained in quansik now. When her pains did not stop and the baby did not come, I went back to my wetu, found the bag with alder root in it, took and scraped some of it into a bowl then opened the little box I had trapped live bumble bees in the past summer and took four out, putting them in the bowl. I returned to Singing Water, and sat next to her, singing as I pounding my medicine together in the bowl, then I added hot water and gave her a gourd of it to drink.

"This was the most powerful medicine I knew. It was to be used only in the most severe cases of stomach and eye pains. A medicine man had told me about this medicine the winter before but I had never used it so I wasn't sure it would work. He said he had learned it from a midiwiwin Iroquois medicine man.

"I also steeped more mugwort for her because I knew there

would be too much bleeding after the baby came.

"This troubled birth was a bad omen for our people.

"After she drank, Singing Water cried out that a bear was ripping her insides and then she fell back, her eyes shut. We listened for her heart beat and after a while she woke, then screamed like a warrior. She was shaking so much we had a hard time getting her upright so she could push.

"I caught the baby, but when I pulled it out from under her, we all gasped. This baby was a terrible omen. It was not shaped right and it was missing one eye.

"Singing Water was weeping in exhaustion and so we did not let her see the baby. I wrapped it quickly so it could not cry out and took it outside the wetu. I carried it outside the village to a tall rock. I prayed all the way for the strength to do this thing that had to be done, but when I unwrapped him and he began to scream, I had a very hard time grabbing his slippery feet. Even though he was tiny, he struggled and twisted as I held him upside down. I swung hard for I wanted to kill him swiftly, but the sound of his skull smashing against the rock made me sick to my stomach. Afterwards, I buried his little body into the water of a nearby swamp.

" This I did for my friend Singing Water while her husband was fighting the Pequot."

Chapter 12

(Konkowasco's early shaman training and the first white men visit Quaboag, 1633-1634)

Once again the longhouse is full of boys and girls, all listening to Konkowasco.

"At the ceremony for those who survived the winter, after the shaman listened to my visions, I was given the name Konkowasco - dove or bird of peace. When I came back from my manhood ordeal I spent many moons trying to make my lungs well. Besides tukahoe (Jack in the Pulpit), I was given honeysuckle and goldenrod tea but a tea of the yellow stalk and roots of bears' ears (cowslip) helped me the most for it loosened my chest and made me sweat out the poison that Hobbomock's cold coils had filled my chest with.

"As my lungs were healing, the Pequots were busy making more problems to our south.

"Wopigwowit had driven Sequassen into Narragansett and then allowed the Dutch to build a trading post overlooking the quonicticut river at Podunk. The Dutch said they were enemies of no one and made the Pequots agree to let Sequassen come back and live in peace on his lands. But the Pequots' words were not true and as soon as the two cannon were placed on top of the fort the Pequots killed two of Sequassen's braves who had come to trade. The Dutch then did a strange thing. They lured Wopigwowit onto one of their boats at the mouth of the poquetanuck (Thames) river and killed him. This caused the sachems of Pequot and Mohegan to vie for the title of chief sachem. Tatobem was chief sachem but he was very old and no longer spoke for the people. He had three sons - Sassacus, Sacowausin and Puppompogs, plus a daughter who lived at soudahque on the shetucket river with her five sons. Uncas, son of

Oweneco, claimed the right to rule because he was married to Wapigwoowit's sister Meekumump.

"When Sasascus was given the title, Uncas split away and Tatobem drove his people north, into Wabbaquasett, and east, into Narragansett, and the Mohegan sachem Wequash was driven into Niantic.

"Getting the brunt of the invasion were Wequagen and his son Allumps on the quonicticut river , Mesea in W abbaquaset, Massashowett on the quanabuag and his brother Haguntus (Aguntus or Hyems), further south of Cowesit in his fort on the quanabaug at egunk. Through their mother, these sachems were related to Uncas and Hyems and shared the name Pumquanon with him. To consolidate his position in quansik, Hyems, who was the oldest of the three brothers, married his daughter Ahawayetsquane to George, the son of Nanepashement and Mishalisk. Uncas, now in Narragansett, married the sister of the Narragansett chief sachem Miantonomah, who ruled with his uncle Canonicus. They would later have Oneko, Abimileck, Wanutto and Chimough. Oneko's son was Sunseeto. Uncas' brother Nowequa was also in Narragansett at the time.

"During this time, we hoped to push the Pequots forever out of our area. These Pequots had visciously terrorized us long enough. They still controlled the river in Podunk so Wahginnicut remained near Agawam. But soon after the Dutch built their trading post, the English came in and built another upriver on the other side in territory still controlled by Wahginnicut. Many of the people thought this was a good thing, but to me, it seemed that, to get our river back, our people gave it away. The people who liked the fort thought the English were only there for a while, that one day they would pack up and sail back across the sea like they had done in some of their other settlements on turtle island. The others thought they would never leave our lands unless we killed them all.

"In quansik we mostly thought the first way. While they were here we would take the goods they traded and the protection they offered against the Mohawks but once we had more muskets than the Mohawks, we thought we could ask them to go away and they would. These things were discussed much by Naddawahunt, my cousin Wetolechen and my brother Nassowanno, but I was not interested in political matters. Mine was a spiritual path.

"I often climbed the path to the rocks at nahoosic, the top of the highest of the waddaquadducks. From there I could see all of quansik to the river and to the blue mountains in the distance. I could feel the vibrations of my people up there; I could almost hear their prayers and sense their needs.

"The climb was hard on me for my lungs were still weak, but when Grandfather Sun's warmth soaked into me atop the mountain I felt a healing in my chest.

"I was on the rock the day the white man first came to quansik.

"It was the autumn after my manhood ceremony. Creator was painting the forests with bright yellows, oranges and reds as the women gathered the last of the corn and placed it on reed mats to dry. The rivers in our long valley murmured a song of plenty and all the land seemed caught up in a slow-moving trance, like a snake basking in the mellow warmth. From my vantage point the fragrance of the harvest filled the air. I closed my eyes and drank it in. A gentle breeze played with the crow feather I now wore at the back of my head. I had taken clamshells and pulled out all the hair except a swath from forehead to the nape of my neck. At the top of my head, I had gathered my long hair into a tail with the thongs that held my feather. My muscles were solid and strong and the bones running under my oiled face gave it a sharpness. Around my neck I wore a strand of wampumpeag - a gift from the sachem in Shenipsit when I called the spirits to help his ill daughter at the strawberry gathering near the place of the medicine water. I wore a medicine bag around my neck containing a bird stone for use in calling upon the thunder beings, four small deer hair pipe bones used to suck evil out from ill people or to blow sweetgrass into them, and a magic white stone that had chosen me one day as I walked along a path.

"A few moons after my return I began training with Elk Bones. He told me to fast for several days and then, after a sweat lodge, he led me to the place of the great rocks.

"At the rocks he said I was to undergo The Night of Fear. This was when one confronted his deepest fears.

"He brought me to the place most sacred to my people- womb rock. There, he chanted and smudged, then gave me a some jimson weed leaves to chew. They were bitter and I vomited. He said they were used for this ceremony because they were the flowers of the night. They were attuned to the night spirits for their white flowers opened only at night.

"As the light began to leave the woods, I put my toes into the groove steps and climbed into the womb-shaped opening in the side of the huge boulder. I fit perfectly inside, like a baby in its womb. The cave was open on my right side. There, I was totally exposed, my skin outside the rock. I was told I would spend the night there, naked and unprotected.

"Elk Bones said he would come back for me in the morning and I tried to get comfortable. I was cold. The rock was hard. My first test was my fear of the cold. Later the moon came up and I heard night birds and saw shadows cross the sky. I felt very vulnerable. There was no place to hide and I could not protect myself in my fetal position. There was no room to move around in. All around me I heard branches crackle and screeches.

"I felt as if I were suffocating and wanted to climb out but I knew this was a test and I must pass.

"The leaves I chewed made me sleepy and I began to dream. I dreamt I climbed out of the rock and was walking in the woods. I walked aways and stood in the middle of a large circle of huge boulders. There, the stones changed into spirits and I danced and sang with them, moving slowly round and round in a circle under the full moon. The songs were sweet, sung to rattles, drums and flutes. For a long time I danced with my ancestors this way.

"Many handed me presents - a feather, a shell, a stone - they said if I used them they would help me to treat the sick people. They said their spirits would come so I could help our people.

"Then I was back in womb rock. I was cold and shivered often. I closed my eyes but then felt something that added bumps to the coldbumps already on my flesh.

"It was a warm breath with whiskers. It tickled my exposed side, slowly moving down my arm, my neck, my leg. I slowly opened my eyes a slit and what I saw almost made me die of fright!

"A black panther was standing on its hind legs, its forepaws resting on the bottom of the womb-opening.

"Its large yellow eyes were watching me, waiting for me to move.

"I kept perfectly still, holding my breath as its whiskers explored. Even though my eyes were almost closed, I could feel its two yellow moons boring into my lids, waiting to catch my eyes.

"This went on for a very long time and then I fell asleep.

"I felt warm and in my dream the panther was in the womb with me, sleeping over me, its huge claws digging into my flesh, kneading as it purred. When I awoke in the morning, I told Elk Bones about it and he said it was a spirit panther. He said the greatest powwows never died, but lived forever as spirit creatures. He said I could call upon the power of all the creatures I had dreamt of that night. Especially the panther: it was my special spirit helper.

"Afterwards, I collected the items the ancestors had "given" to me and traded some of my beaver furs for a black panther fur. When I went into my healing trance, I would feel the panther by my side, its tongue licking the evil spirits off the sick bodies.

"The bird spirit I had encountered during my winter ordeal was represented by a birdstone in my bag. The bird spirit would sit on my shoulder and pick out the najiniweska (bad spirit things) in my patients.

"I learned quickly. But early in my training I had forgotten to smudge a circle around the patient and myself. This was done before going into a trance and painting the symbols I saw on both us as we waited for the spirits to help. This time, unwanted spirits entered the circle and nearly took the patient away."

Konkowasco takes a drink of water from the gourd dipper and then says a magic chant four times before resuming:

"I return now to the afternoon the white man came to quansik. On my arm as a symbol of my royal status and my position of powwow I wore the panther skin. I pulled it closer to me and climbed a short way down the mountaintop to the natural stone half-circle seat where I would often sit to observe the stars. As part of my training, I had gone with Elk Bones and our local powwows to similar seats around quansik. Near the place where I was born in quoquanset there was a bowl valley at the bottom of the hills with a small cavern in the bottom that we used as a watching place. There were notches and piles of stones along the rim of the bowl and I learned how to watch for where the sun, moon and certain stars set and rose in relation to them. Off the path from quoquanset to asquoach there was a very ancient sacred site near the stream. Overlooking a crudely-shaped Mother Stone there were several circles made from stones, each large enough for a brave to sit in. The area was full of quartz rock and I was told it was where a man could talk directly to Mother Earth. The nukkonogs (ancient ones) used to sacrifice infants to the Mother Stone, they said, in times of great starvation. We no longer did that but we did rub red burial powder over it.

"That afternoon as the valley below turned purple and gold and then a mutta (dark) purple-black on top of the mountain in the direction of wutchecksayea (west), I noticed a signal fire from the rocks above where siog pond was. A reply from asquoach signalled back and the drums began beating. I wondered what our braves in the semicircle-shaped observation posts could be warning of. But my eyes were heavy from the plants I had taken. I couldn't move. I felt myself melting into the great river of stardust, one with the three wattawessunash (stars) that made up the great sky arrow's shaft.

"At wampog (dawn) I returned to asquoach and learned the fires and drums told my people two Englishmen had traveled from Boston on foot along their paths en route to the quonicticut river. My father and I collected some pelts and then went to see them, along with Waban, a Nashaway trader who regularly stayed in our village. He could speak their tongue.

"The village of tantiesques appeared through a haze of corndust as we approached on the path along the ponds and hills that led through alum, the dog pond, and the place of the black earth, metewemesick.

"The ears in the baskets were smaller than normal, reaching only the length of a woman's forearm as opposed to that of a brave's. They were thinner and paler and the kernels were not plump and juicy for thunderbird had not visited his people much during the growing moons. But once dried on the mats, this corn would made fine bread meal after powdered in the hollow log sampum mills.

"We followed the small stream, skirting it where it joined the quanabaug. This river could be powerful and fast-flowing, but after our dry summer, rocks and banks showed everywhere. It would not be a good canoe route again until next sequan.

"Wetolechen was living in Tantiesques, in the village at the pond's outlet. We saw the white men sitting in front of his wetu with wampumpeag strings, colored beads, cloth and magic wands on blankets in front of them. With them was a Pequot. My father went for his chest knife but Wetolechen stopped him, whispering that he was not a Pequot but was a Mohegan named Cassasinnamon. He was the guide for the two men who called themselves John Oldham and Stephen Day.

"A squaw picked up a wand stick and screamed, 'It stole my face!' The white men explained through Cassasinnamon that it was a looking glass and the English looked at their faces in it to see if they were clean. We thought this was very funny for to us their beards made their faces dirty. But we each looked at ourselves in it and said how it would help when painting designs on our faces. We called it pebenauchitchunkgnonk "that me thing separated from me".

"We handled the beads and commented that they were very nice. They were not just white and purple like wampumpeag, they were all colors and sizes. The woolen and linen cloth was nice and we liked how light and warm the wool felt between our fingers. There were also silver earrings, pins and pewter spoons but what we all wanted was their steel knives.

"Oldham said they were on their way to visit Wahginnicut and asked us many questions about our lands. He wanted to know how many people lived in quansik, which he called nipmuc, how much corn we grew, how many animals we caught and which kinds. He told us if we returned the next day with beaver pelts they would trade them for the goods on the blanket.

"That night there was a big fire circle and we sang and danced for the awnoots (strangers). Oldham kept staring at the black rock hanging from the thong around Wetolechen's neck. In the firelight it shone like the metal the English called silver.

"The next day Oldham noticed two young braves looking into the hand glass as they painted their faces with shiny grey-black paint made from the same rock. He asked them how they got the paint and they showed him the black rocks they crushed for the powder. This excited Oldham very much and he asked to see more of these rocks and asked where they came from. He followed the braves to the black rocks and spent a night in siog village before continuing on the path that led through Wabbaquasett to Wahginnicut's lands. The sachem from siog later visited our village and laughed as he said Oldham had traded a knife for some of the worthless black rocks. His people had traded fine woven mats for other goods but the only one in our village who got anything from the white man was my father. Since he was a sachem, the white man had given him a pearl and silver earring.

"They also gave us drinks of bottled spirits. Just smelling the stuff made my eyes smart and I asked them how their powwows kept spirits inside the wooden cask. They laughed and said these were corn (grain) spirits and had much medicine.

"This was true, for when we drank we felt the spirits burn our throats and insides and when inside us the spirits made us feel very brave and very loud and happy.

"Before they left they poured some into bladders and gave them to each sachem. This was because the sachems now wanted these spirits inside them.

"Later I had a vision and I told my people not to take their spirits for it was a trick. It was how the whiteman was stealing our souls. My vision showed me that, as we drank, instead of taking in other spirits, we lost our spirits as they entered the casks and were bottled up. This was bad medicine for our people, but powerful medicine for a powwow to use against an enemy.

"I told myself one day I would learn the incantations they used when mixing this magic fire water. But first I had to learn the secret way to call their god.

"While I was away on my manhood ordeal, a trader from Piscataway visited our area. He called my grandfather to council in Pigwacket because Manatahqua, whom the English called Black William, was hanged by English pirates at the mouth of the saco river. The English said he had killed a dishonest English trader by the name of Walter Bagnall but the people in Saco were very angry with this for everyone knew it was the sachem Squidrayset who had killed Bagnall. Any talk of vengeance included Naddawahunt because he had married the dark skinned daughter of Old Tuspaquan, who was brother to Black William and Montowompe, all coastal sachems. It was said that their mother, mother of the chief sachem of Nanepashement, had claimed the right to ransom a black slave who jumped off a ship as it anchored in the harbor off naumkeag. She took him as a husband and their children were all darker than the rest of our people. The dark skin also showed up in a cousin, who was called Black James. We thought this color had much manitoo (power).

"The trader had also told my village of a strange new plague killing the peoples - a plague that made big, red sores on their bodies. When I told my dream to the shaman, he said I had seen the sickness and that mother earth was telling me she suffered with her people. For six moons I hadn't thought much more about it but a few moons after the white men left our village a brave from asquoach called Laughing Bird went to the trading posts on the river. When he returned, he said the plague called smallpox was killing all the people. He said Dutch traders who were staying in a village near the river in order to get the first furs got sick with sores that left deep craters all over their bodies. They recovered, but everyone else was dying. This plague was worse than the yellow death. By the time the winter was over, it had killed people all over: Pequots, Mohegans, Narragansetts, Konkowasco's people in Piscataway, and most of all, the Massachusetts. I lost two cousins that winter as Squaw Sachem's sons James and Wonohaqwuam (John) died from it. The sachem Chickataubet, who like John was a friend to the Narragansetts, died. Awonsk was so afraid of this English plague that she sent her younger children to live with the English. She said their god would protect them. Other sachems living near the English also did this, they were so afraid of the plague.

"I went with our powwow to Wabbaquasett to treat some who had fallen sick. The people were gathered in the wetu of an elder called Wise One. We heard the sound of their crying while we were still on the path from the black cat rocks. Elk Bones made everyone leave the wetu and he burned sweetgrass , smudging all around the wetu four times while invoking his spirit helpers.

"I was seated near the fire and Elk Bones smudged me with his turkey feather fan as he placed his pipe bones in a gourd of hot water and sassafrass root. His chanting sent me into a deep trance. I cannot begin to tell you of all the creatures we called upon inside the wetu. The walls were darkened with their shadows as they flew, crouched, lept and crawled. I remember a high-pitched sound coming from somewhere deep in my chest as I flew with Eagle and took one of his feathers to dust magic white earth powder on Wise One.

"Day turned to night and then back to day outside as we called upon all our spirit helpers to cure Wise One. In our trances we blew smoke and ashes onto the sores from our pipe bones, but in the end our spirit helpers turned their backs on us and left. Wise One died and, remembering my vision, I told his wife to burn his body and their wetu. We were then called back to Asquoach where Laughing Bird was now possessed of the English plague demon. He had run out onto the pond and was lying face down on the muckuppet (ice) when we arrived, his body on fire with fever.

"The sickness took Elk Bones and many of the people in quansik that aketaquatsha (winter). Our faces were black in mourning, our bodies ripped and bleeding in our grief.

"When the thawing moon (March) came, there weren't many grown men left to harvest the sap in the trees.

"Normally this was a time of celebration for our people for it signalled the end to winter. In preparation for this the men burned out logs during the winter and cut sumac branches as big around as their thumbs, scooping out the heartwood to make them hollow. When the time was right, they made gashes in the maple trees and put the bevelled sumac spiles in the trees. A hempen rope ran from the spout to the logs, where the sap collected.

"The boys and girls would scoop out the logs with birchbark pails, bringing the sap to the large fire beneath the tripod where clay pots hung. There, the women cooked the sap, boiling it into a hard mass which they packed into balls and put in cone-shaped bark containers. They also packed some in little cones to hang over the cradleboards. By the time the sugaring was over everything in our village smelled like sweet smoke.

"But this sugaring moon time, our village smelled of smoke from burning wetus. This time the smoke smelled like human flesh. It was too much for my father and he moved away, taking Singing Water and my younger brothers and sisters to his mother's village in the big fort on the hill overlooking the quonicticut river."

Chapter 13

(A re-telling 1632-1637, of the smallpox and Narragansett-Pequot wars)

Another man rises. His headdress is a circle of broad leaves sewn together. He is shorter than the others and his voice is reedy, high-pitched.

"I am Tom Pequan of the Peqout Quans. You have noticed that many of our personal and place names end in quan. What precedes it tells you where exactly we are from. Quequan means middle quansik and Pequan means of the area of quansik controlled by the Pequots. We, Wa, Wu or Wo, Nassa, Massa, Nadda, Natta, etc., means chief of what follows. This is how we knew where people where from when they came through our villages or we met at the gatherings. My private name is neither Tom nor Pequan. When traveling or dealing with the white man, most of us merely called ourselves ono "brave of" and our village or territory. To identify me personally, I added the name Tom. Now that so few are left, my brother, who lives with the English, calls himself Ono, Elizer or Razer Pequan. I am related to Tuspaquan of cummassakumkamit in wampanoag territory.

"I will tell you how it was that the numbers of my people became so few.

"When Sassacus kicked Wonkus (Uncas -the fox or circler) and the Mohegans out of his lands, he realized he had given his enemies the Narragansetts new warriors, so he sent word to Uncas that he forgave him and his people could return. Uncas Poquiam and some of his Mohegans then built a village on the Mohegan river but many joined the Narragansett war parties raiding his outer villages.

"Sequassen had returned to his lands and had invited John Oldham and his friends to build an English village at pyquog (Wethersfield). They would protect him from the Pequots, he thought.

"About this time, in auketaquatshaukeaswush (the Freezing

Moon - January) an English captain named Stone lured two Pequots on board his vessel at the mouth of the quonicticut river to make them guide him upriver to trade. They escaped and went to Sassacus. In retaliation, Pequot warriors slipped on board Stone's ship and killed him.

"It was while the Pequots were gathering an army that the smallpox that Konkowasco told you about struck their nation. Sassacus, whose village was at weinshahuks, a short distance from owauke (owl's nest) and his brother Monotto, sachem at mystick, learned that the Captain Stone was not liked by the English for crimes he had committed earlier at the Dutch trading post at pashebesauke (Saybrook). Sassacus sent a brave with a peace offering to the English at shawamut (Boston) but they sent him back saying they would only treat with a chief sachem.

"So at this time Sassacus was the enemy of the Dutch because of Wopigwowit, the English because of Stone, and the Mohegans and the Narragansetts over wekapaug.

"That year we again had little rain. Many of our adults had died in the plague so the fields were not as large as in the past. The Narragansetts had been spared the yellow death plague in the past but this time the plague spread like fire throughout their villages. Canonicus blamed the Englishman Williams for bringing the smallpox into his lands but when he heard it was everywhere he agreed to let Williams stay in Narragansett. Some of the Narragansett sachems closest to pyquog had promised Oldham many baskets of corn but because of the plague and drought they could not give him the amount he expected after harvest. He was very abusive to their sachems, calling them liars and cheats. Then he tried to get our people to part with their precious stores of corn. He came to Pequot looking for corn and traded for it the news that the Narragansetts were planning a large ambush at neponsit.

"After Stone's death, Sassacus asked Oldham to go immediately to the English with two bushels of wampum to pay for Stone and two bundles, one of 30 sticks to represent the amount of otter skins, and the other with 40 sticks to represent the number of beaver skins his people would pay if the English and Narragansetts would smoke the peace pipe with his people.

"The English said they would accept if the Pequots would turn over the men responsible for Stone's death. This they could not do for two had died of smallpox and the third had been killed by the Dutch. So the English said they would agree to peace if they gave them land rights so they could build villages in Pequot. Sassacus and his brothers Ppompoges and Tassaquannott thought this would keep the Dutch away, so they agreed. Then Oldham tried to get the Narragansetts to agree to peace. At first Canonicus and his co-chief sachem, his sister's son Miantonamah, gave him a hard time because of the way he had treated their people over the corn. To please Ousemequin their mouths said the words of peace but their hearts did not.

"The English sent Sassacus a mooseskin coat to show that a peace was agreed on and the war drums fell silent for a while in Pequot.

"In the spring the Mohawks came down the quonicticut and forced the Agawams to give them furs as tribute. Ahaughton, sachem of Natick, guided John Pynchon and two other Englishman through quansik to the quonicticut river that spring, and when they got there the sachems begged Pynchon to build a fort and bring his English cannon there to protect them from further Mohawk attacks. Pynchon and his friends spent many months in the area and built a house and grist mill on the pewonganuck (Mill) river before returning to Boston.

"In the fall, another group of English from menchoiset (Dorcester) took over the fort at podunk (Windsor). Winter came early and hard that year. Pynchon left but a group of English from shawmut (Dorchester area) settled near the podunk fort and then took it over. When the cold came unexpectedly their supply ship became frozen in ice at the mouth of the river where a fort was being built by John Winthrop and new English immigrants.

"Their cattle got thin and died of starvation before the ship got through. The settlers would have died also if it hadn't been for Sequassen's people who showed them how to eat acorns and ground nuts.

"That year the English told Massasoit they would send warriors with muskets to help him if he claimed the lands of seekonk and aquidneck he and Punham had been skirmishing over. Later, when Punham and Wamsutta claimed the land, they gave Williams a deed to settle there. But the English told Williams they owned any lands Massasoit deeded through their king's grant so they kicked him out of aquidneck the way they had kicked him out of their villages along the coast. He fled south and stayed with Canonicus in Naragansett then.

How the English believed regarding their god was not important to Massasoit in this matter. What he wanted was the important trading route: the wunnashawtuckqut (Blackstone) river pathway from the seacoast into quansik. Before the Pequots had forced the Narragansetts into Cowesit, his people had controlled that area.

"To the north in quansik, Squaw Sachem married again- to a powwow who had been her deceased husband's best friend and advisor. She had called on him to help when her children were attacked by the smallpox spirit. Like her brother, she was getting older. This marriage was not to produce royal children. Now, in her grief, she sought a warm body in her bed and a friend to talk to in the long, dark days of winter.

"In Massachusetts, Kutshamakin, sachem of menchoiset (Dorchester) sold uncataquisit (Milton) to the English. Because he didn't want to lose the tribute his bands paid him, he had resisted English settlement, but after seeing many of his people die from smallpox, he asked to follow their god so he would not die from the boiling flesh disease.

"When sequan arrived in Pequot it brought more English settlers to the village growing at the mouth of the quonicticut. Besides the new settlers there a large group under Thomas Hooker came to live at sequasen (Hartford). These things made Sassacus and the Pequot sachems very angry. To make peace they had given the English settlement rights, but they hadn't expected so many so soon.

"The Narragansetts were also angry with the white man because they hated Oldham and hated being forced by the English to make peace with the Pequots. During the winter and spring, many of their sachems had met in council to plan a way to drive the English and Dutch out.

"In the time of nahmoskeeswush (the Fishing Moon - May) John Oldham returned in a pinnace to trade with the Pequots. He had his two sons and two Narragansetts on board as crew when he stopped off the shores of manisses (Block Island) to see if the people wanted to trade. The Narragansetts with him had already thrown their war sticks into the flame and they tricked Oldham to put anchor down and stay while they planned an ambush with the islanders. The sachems on the island were related to Wopigwowit, so they eagerly agreed to the plan in order to avenge their chief sachem's murder.

"As the storm blew, the English went below deck and the

Narragansetts sent the signal to attack. Canoe after canoe came alongside and the warriors silently climbed the rope ladder to the deck. Oldham was surprised in his cabin by blood relatives of Wopigwowit. They pulled him out onto the deck, knocked him on the back of his head and then they chopped it off. This head they planned to put on a pole outside their village, like the English did at Plymouth with Wittiwwuit's. Oldham's sons were taken ashore. They would either be ransomed or killed.

"The storm threw high waves up while a large war canoe below was loaded high with trade goods. As the waves and wind started to blow the ship away from the island and towards the Narragansett shore, some of the Manisses were hacking Oldham's arms and legs off and others tried to work the rigging and keep the ship from drifting. They tried to set fire to the ship but the driving rains kept putting it out.

"Just then another English ship came into view. The Manisses on the war canoe quickly began paddling towards shore with the trade goods as the other captain tried hailing Oldham. He sailed his ship closer and fired a musket, sending a rain of little lead pellets over the deck. The Manisses still on board hid under whatever they could find on deck and then the other ship slammed into Oldhan's pinnace, almost capsizing it. This frightened some of the warriors so much they jumped overboard and drowned in the high waves. The second time he did this the two ships stuck together. He sent more lead rain on board and began throwing his grappling hooks overboard and more jumped over and were drowned. When the other captain and his crew came on board, two warriors were captured and tied up. One was thrown into the hold and the other into the sea where he drowned. Two others barricaded themselves below deck.

"The English crew found Oldham's body, wrapped it in a sheet, said some words to their god then threw it overboard. Then they lashed the two ships together and set course for Saybrook. As the sun went down the winds grew so strong that Oldham's ship was cut away and it drifted towards the Narragansett shore with the two Manisses still huddled below deck.

"The two Naragansetts knew their plans were spoiled when they saw the other English ship. They jumped into a dugout and began paddling for Narragansett. They were with Canonicus the next day when Oldham's ship drifted ashore. When Canonicus saw it was an English ship, he quickly got Roger Williams to write a letter to the English in Boston, telling them that Canonicus' people had nothing to do with the attack and that he had sent his nephew Miantonomo and a war party to Manisse to punish those responsible. He immediately sent this letter along with one of the Manisses and the two Narragansett crewmembers to Boston. There, the Manisse told Winthrop about the plot and how the two bringing him as prisoner had been involved. He also told them the two Narragansett sachems Canonicus and Mianatonomah had not thrown their war sticks in with the others.

"The English returned the Narragansetts because they had traveled as messengers. With them they sent a letter to Canonicus and another to Williams. They told Canonicus he was right in sending warriors to Manisses. They said the Manisses were subjects of the Narragansetts and so he was responsible for their actions. They demanded the other prisoner and said if they sent for the two Narragansett crewmembers, he was to send them.

"Mianatonomah forced the Manisses to release Oldham's sons and sent them and all the trade goods they had stolen to Boston. The Manisse prisoner had escaped to Pequot so they could not return him.

"The English then sent Cutchamakin and two soldiers to Canonicus. After many hours of talk, Cutchamakin told them the chief Narragansett spoke the truth. He and his nephew were in no way involved in the incident.

"We thought the crisis with the English was over then. We turned our attentions towards our crops and fishing.

"But the English were not finished with us yet. Three moons after Oldham's murder, while Sassacus and Monotto were in council on Montauk, three English ships set anchor off Manisse. From them, many soldiers with muskets came onto Manisse land. Knowing their few bows and arrows were no match against such an army, the Manisse waited until dark and then loaded their people into canoes and paddled for Pequot.

"The next morning, the English searched the villages. They set fire to everything they found - canoes, wetus and cornfields - then warred on a small band of Manisse that had stayed behind.

"When the Manisse arrived in Pequot, Sassacus and Monotto immediately set out for Montauk to persuade their warriors to join them in driving out all white men.

"The English ships then went to the fort at Saybrook. As grandfather Wind blew the war wind across the waters of the sound, the English remained there at their fort and the Pequot leaders at Montauk.

"After four sleeps, the English, now joined by two more ships from the fort, sailed along the coast of Niantic to the mouth of the puccatannock (Thames) river. The Niantics were full of panic as the ships sat off shore. They kept calling to the English to ask if they came to trade or to make war but the English didn't answer.

"At dawn Ninigret, chief sachem of the Niantics, paddled out to the English ships. He asked why the English were there.

"Through Cutshamakin's tongue, they told him that they were looking for the Pequots responsible for killing Oldham. They said they came to take them by force since Sassacus had said he would surrender them but had not. They said they were there to collect twenty fathoms of wampum as a fine for this. They also demanded twenty Pequot children as hostages until the murderers were surrendered.

"The sachem told them how Stone had murdered their chief sachem and said through the law of vengeance Wopigwowit's relatives had a right to kill in return. The English told him Stone was Dutch and Oldham was English. Ninigret said his people did not know the difference between white tribes, to them all white men were foreigners.

"The English soldier called John Endicott got angry at this and shouted at Ninigret, 'You know well enough the difference for you have had many dealings with both. Since you have slain subjects of the English king we demand an account of their blood!'

"Again Ninigret pleaded innocence and the English dismissed him, telling him that his people could either bring the heads of those responsible for Oldham's murder or they would go ashore and fight for them.

"They then unloaded their soldiers and Ninigret told them for their safety to stay on their side of the hill for there was an army of Pequot warriors on the other side. He said no action could be started without word from Sassacus and Monotto, who were still in Montauk. The English ignored him and went to the top of the hill where they were quickly surrounded by Pequots. Many were used to trading with the English and they began to ask them questions. There were many without bows and arrows for no war had been declared.

"While Ninigret and the councillors waited for Sassacus and Monotto to return, they had the Manisse from Oldham's ship brought to them and began debating whether they would execute him or turn him over to the English for execution. To do either would mean disrespecting their laws of blood vengeance in favor of English laws.

"As the sun started to set in the west, the English said they were tired of waiting and sent the messengers back to Ninigret. They then marched downhill towards the Ninatic Pequots, firing their muskets as our warriors got behind trees and shot bows and arrows back. Before night fell, their muskets killed one of our warriors and that traitor to our people, Cutshamakin, raced forward and scalped him before our warriors could drag his body away for burial.

"That night they burned all the wetus and cornfields at that place and crossed the river and did the same on the other side. Then, without waiting for Sassacus and Monotto, they sailed away.

"At the mouth of the river the winds blew two ships back towards shore, near one of our villages. Some of their soldiers waded ashore and went into the village, returning with armfuls of corn. Our warriors caught up with them and began firing arrows. They dropped the corn and formed two lines, long muskets in front and shorter ones behind. They loaded and fired the big muskets into the air, but we were hiding in groups behind trees, taking turns firing arrows at them. Cutshamikin told the English to collect our arrows and so by nightfall we had to retreat, our ammunition spent.

"Taking our corn, they then left.

"When Sassacus got back, he sent his war captain to Canonicus to get the Narragansetts to join the Pequots.

"The war council went on for many sleeps. The Pequots said the English had violated their own treaty by sending troops into Pequot. They said the English were not acting honorably and their demand for wampum and Pequot children was unreasonable. They said the tribes should lay aside their differences for awhile and join together.

"While the council was going on, word came back to the Pequots that Roger Williams was coming to the council. He was talking against the alliance in every village he came to. Sassacus told them not to kill him for he was the friend of Canonicus, who had given him Oldham's lands on chibachuwese island.

"When Williams arrived, he managed to turn the old sachem against the Pequots by saying the Narragansetts would get their lands back if they joined with the English and drove the Pequots back across the Housatonic river.

"Canonicus sent the Pequots away then and sent word to the English that they would help them fight the Pequots.

"During this time, in Cowesit, three Narragansetts were killed by a Nipmuck and two Pequots but Masasoit sent word to Canonicus that their alliance was not worth breaking for the actions of a lone Nipmuck. This Nipmuck was related to me.

"In the time of the quinnekomuck (longhouse ceremony moon - October), two of Canonicus' sons, Mianatonomah, two Narrgansett sachems and twenty warriors went to Boston to seal the agreement they had made with Williams.

"That they were bewitched there by the English there can be no doubt. With Cutshamakin translating, they signed a paper that said they would remain at peace with the English and its allies forever; that neither party would make peace with the Pequot on their own; that they would not let any Pequots live in Narragansett; that they would execute Pequots or turn over to the English any Pequots or any runaway slaves in their lands; that they would receive plenty of warning when the English soldiers needed guides through Narragansett; that trade between the two nations would remain open and that none of their people would go near English settlements unless accompanied by an Englishman or a brave known to the English. The treaty was to last two generations.

"When Mianatonomah left they gave his party a twenty gun salute with their muskets. He brought the treaty to Canonicus and Williams translated. When Mianatonomah told his uncle how the English had shown them great honor and respect, Canonicus signed, declaring himself forever a friend to the English and enemy of the Pequot.

"The magic feather blood had barely dried when my people attacked the hated English at their fort at the mouth of the quonicticut. We had many little battles and captured one of their soldiers who was cutting hay on the island nearby. We tortured him and later burned him at the stake. Another time we followed an English ship as it left the fort and headed upriver. We waited in the reeds along the banks as two men, observing the large flock of ducks in the area, got into a rowboat and headed to shore to shoot some. As the the belly of their boat slid onto the riverbank, we jumped out, surrounded them, killed one and brought the other to camp. We tortured him for three days, cut off his hands and feet and forced hot coals into his skin. He was a true warrior and never cried or asked for mercy so after three sleeps we gave him the honorable death he had earned.

"Throughout the winter we remained close to the fort, setting fires to their storehouses and haystacks, butchering their cattle and dressing in the clothing from the men we had killed, making the cries they had screamed when we tortured them to draw the soldiers out of their strong fort.

"During the winter the Narragansetts began warring on us, so many left the fort to help defend the villages to our east. When the snows melted, the captain of the fort, a man called Gardiner, accompanied by soldiers, began setting fire to the fields around the fort. This caused the ones hiding in the grass to run, then turn and shoot arrows at the English , who ran back into their fort.

"A while later we learned that an Englishman named Thomas Stanton had sailed though Niantic and was let inside the fort. We tried a trick then and called him out to talk about declaring a truce. Gardiner and Stanton came out to sit in parley with us, their cannon aimed at our breasts. One of the warriors was wearing the English coat from the man we captured in the hayfield. He asked if the Engish were at war with the Niantics as well as the Pequots. He said he was a Niantic and wanted to go inside the fort to trade but Stanton said the English couldn't tell one tribe from the other so they would trade with no one. Such disrepect for his tribe made the warrior furious and he spat out that he was Pequot and since the English killed Pequot women and children, we, too would kill the English women and children. He bragged he was wearing the coat he had taken from a dead Englishman. Stanton stood up and ordered one of the soldiers to kill him but but Gardiner said it could not be done under the flag of truce. He then called us cowards: womankillers afraid to fight men.

"This made our warriors angry and they got up, breaking off the talks. As we got near the trees, the English fired at our backs but we ducked and stayed under cover until they went back into their fort.

"Shortly afterwards, Miantonomah attacked the Mohegan villages where Pequots were living and captured 27 Pequots. He cut the head off the sachem and sent it and the prisoner with 20 fathom of wampum to the English in Boston to show he was keeping his word. Our people brought to Boston during the war were stripped, branded with hot irons and put on ships to be sold as slaves. The attacks by Miantonomah made Uncas realize that his people would either have to join the English and Narragansetts or be treated like Pequots.

"The English on mauntowak (Long Island) were massacred and Wiadodme, sachem at the mouth of the Mohawk (Hudson) river was ordered to kill the sachem responsible but he refused for the sachem was a powerful powwow.

"We then laid plans to attack their settlement at pyquog (Wethersfield). Because we knew the English would retaliate in kind, we sent most of our women and children to an island fort for safety.

"Then we attacked, letting them have a taste of their own war. We killed everything we could catch and then set fire to the village. Sequassen took two English girls prisoner and we sentenced them to death by fire at the stake but Sequasen's wife Winicombe claimed her right to intercede and took them. Later she ransomed them to a Dutch captain.

"That was our last victory, for we learned Uncas and the Mohegans had joined the English. We learned from Ninigret that an army was marching through Niantic on their way to Pequot and then a Mohegan captured Sassacus' spy outside the Saybrook fort. The Mohegans were like the Mohawks in war. They roasted the spy then ate his flesh while our warriors watched from the woods. It was one thing to fight the English who hid in forts and stood in the open with their muskets. It was another thing to fight one's brother who knew our hiding places and our trails.

"The days were very hot and we were wet with heat as we used English hatchets to cut down trees as big around as our legs, then dug holes and placed them close together with an entrance in the east and another in the west. We made two forts. Sassacus' fort was farther away from the river. The pallisade of the one most of us stayed in was on top of the hill encircling what the English would have called twenty acres of land. Inside it the women planted acres of corn and the warriors built rows of wetus. One morning as we slept in this great fort near the mystic river, mother earth shook and knocked our hanging pots down. Our powwows got together and said it was a bad omen but they couldn't agree whether it was bad for our people or our enemies.

"As the fish came upriver to spawn, we gathered at the fording place on the river and gathered much fish to take to our forts nearby where it would be dried. When we had finished, we returned to the fort and held our nahmoskeeswush (Fishing Moon - May)) ceremony. We ate our fill of fish stew and sang and laughed as the dogs played with the fish still flopping in a little water at the bottom of the birch-bark buckets.

"The wind had picked up and was blowing the clouds over the moon in the eastern sky when we finally settled down to sleep. Just before dawn we heard a dog barking and then the sentries shouting 'Owanux! Owanux!' ("English! English!").

The old man's throat locks up and he has to stop, overcome with tears.

"The Pequot traitor Wequash Cook had led the Mohegens, Narragansetts and English to our fort . They shot their muskets through the logs and then overtook the sentries at the eastern entrance. At the other entrance my cousin fought them off. Before we knew it they were inside, poking their muskets into the wetus, shooting, shouting. Most of the people inside were not warriors. Our old people, women and children screamed as they ran away, first to one area then to another. I and the other warriors grabbed our bows and began shooting back but then their leader, a captain Mason, set fire to one of the wetus. The wind whipped the flames and everyone panicked, trying to get away from the exploding wetus. The air was so thick with smoke we couldn't see or breathe. The heat from the flames cracked our bowstrings and we had to throw them down and fight off the English hand-to-hand with our knives. The English had gotten through the western entrance so a group of us ran over to drive them back. Suddenly the English withdrew and my people began scrambling out the entrances. But the English had formed their own pallisade around us and shot whoever escaped the flames. We charged their lines and a handful of us broke through. One of the sachems yelled at me to run to Sassacus' fort and get the others so I did.

"I covered the distance down the hill and through the swamp swiftly, meeting the others half-way. We separated, chasing retreating English warriors through the woods. But when we came to the fort it was too much for our warriors. Their friends and relatives were blackened corpses. Our warriors let out bloodcurdling screams and rushed towards the English guns. One by one they were shot and joined their loved ones in death.

"Those who could still fight rushed the English at a small brook as they headed toward their ships. Then we returned to the burned fort and wept. Such total destruction we had never seen. We couldn't move for the horror of it. We couldn't think. We just walked around, staring, numb.

"We left the dead there. The fort where they had lived was now where they would sleep in death.

"Afterwards, Sassacus called a great council together at his fort. Six councillors sat on either side. Behind each sat six more. The speeches went on and on, each speech ending on a raised note. Women brought in a huge kettle of meat stew with a large wooden bowl ladle and each ate then passed it on. The councillors ate last.

"After a while, the sachems sentenced all Mohegans living in our swamp fort to death. Sassacus was then criticized by sachems who said he had not been wise in sending most of his best men to the mystick fort the day before. The talking went on until day became night. Sassacus told his councillors the Pequots only had three canoes left to paddle now. One would take us into Mahican territory on the Hudson; the other would take us to the Connecticut where we could attack the three English settlements and the third would lead us east, to Narragansett where we could try to attack and conquer the Narragansetts then move into their lands. No shouts of 'ho, ho!' followed his speech. These were sad words.

"Although Sassacus wanted to continue the fight, most of the sachems wanted to flee west. Their spirits and their hearts were broken. So we packed our possessions and then burned everything left behind so the Mohegans couldn't have it. After we crossed the quonicticut one band turned back. They said they would rather die in Pequot than face the unknown enemies in Mohawk territory.

"The rest of us went on, through quinnipac and wepawag. Our feet and bodies ached from walking, walking. We ate berries, plants, dug roots and shellfish, but kept on walking. At one village we forced the sachem there to give us food and let us stay for a little while. While our people rested, five sachems and a few warriors went with Sassacus and Monotto up the river to ask the Mohawks to take us in but we were ambushed. Monotto and our group barely escpaed with our lives but Sassacus and the sachems were killed.

"When we made our way back to the village where our people were, we found them gone. The sachem and his braves had been captured, too. The English had tied the braves up, taken them out in a ship and dumped them in the water. The soldiers, led by Captain Stoughton, took the women and children to be sold as slaves. Uncas' warriors captured and killed those fleeing, including three sachems. He recognized one as the sachem who had driven him out of Pequot and, after torturing him, cut his head off and stuck it in the crotch of a tree near pashevesauke (Saybrook).

"We went on to the place where the others were and told them they were in great danger. We took them to hide in the swamp and it was there my people made their last stand. For days we held the English off but the last day they sent a messenger through the thick fog to say they would not harm anyone who could prove they hadn't killed English. One by one our old people emerged through the fog but we warriors refused, shooting arrows at any English we could see. Wincombe led the women out with their children and the English went away.

"The rest of us went to live amongst the other tribes. I went to lower quansik and it was there I heard that most of the people who surrendered had been sold as slaves.

"The English then began bothering the other tribes who had taken us in. Some were surrendered but Massashowell and the Wabbaquasetts let me and my family stay in maanexit.

"At this time horses were very valuable to all our peoples. Only the wealthiest sachems had horses. One was Pomroye, brother to Ninigret. During the skirmishes, Uncas killed his horse and Ninigret complained to the English about the damage because his people were neutral. The English told him they knew he was harboring Pequots and ordered him to give them up. This made him very angry but later he agreed when they said if he did they would give him 20 fathoms of wampum to replace Pomroye's mare.

A pungent bitterness wraps the old man's last words,

"So this was what my people, once a great nation of warriors, were worth in the end. Many of us sold for the price of one horse."

Chapter 14
(A re-telling of Pynchon's visit to tantiesques and of events in the 1630's)

An old woman rises, taking the talking stick in her hand. Her bent body, clothed in soft brown doeskin covered with finely embroidered flowers and vines, casts a crooked shadow over the listeners. In contrast to Many Winters Bear, her voice is gentle, poetic. It, too, suffers from age and occasionally wavers. Her black eyes shine from the firelight and pierce the eyes of her listeners as she speaks.

"I am known to you as SpiderWoman. This was not always my name. Like most of you, I had no name when I was a child. My mother and father and relatives called me "nippaamoose", little girl, little doe, when I was little and as I grew older, I was known simply as She Who Lives Near the Brook.

"When I was a girl, my village was near quabogud in a place called tantiesques. My parents lived in a wetu in the village near the pond. Like most villages, it was at the place where the pond flowed out so when we washed our pots or bodies the dirt washed away into the river. Our pond flowed into the quanepaug. Not far to our north were small ponds leading to the big quaboag pond, into which the quaboag river flowed. The tribes here were were called the Potepogs.

"Our area was called tantiesques because it was between two breast-shaped hills. As a squaw, I always felt very close to our earth mother, for her shapes were everywhere. A distance to the west, there were the waddaquadducks, the long hills. I thought one of the mountains looked like a maiden lying on her side, its middle dipping down like the curve of her waist. Our cornfields, too, were full of soft breast-shaped mounds, and when I was little my mother told me she had heard that corn had grown from the body of Flint and Sapling's mother. She said corn had sprouted from her breasts and that is why the kernels have milk in them.

“As I grew older, I spent many hours gathering plants, for my mother was known for her knowledge in herb-gathering. Even shamans would visit her and ask her about plants.

“The plants reminded me of parts of the body: some were kidney-shaped, which meant they helped people with dark urine or trouble passing urine. Others looked like the lungs and were good for coughs and chest pains. Some were the color of blood and would help those who had bad spirits in their blood or heart or women with mooncycle trouble. My mother taught me how to talk to the plants, to ask them how they could help our people. She taught me that plants sleep like humans, and that we should remember that all their energy goes into their roots when they sleep, so the best time to pick the leaves is early morning. She said the best time to dig up roots was when the moon was out and the best time for the stalks was just before dark when the energy was flowing through them down to the roots. She taught me to talk to several plants before picking their sister, telling them we would only take what we could use. Always we thanked our sister plants for their gifts when we picked them. And always we left a gift of tobacco for Mother Earth.

"The men would gather sumac and sassafrass leaves to add to their tobacco mixtures. We gathered boneset (Joe Pyeweed) and meadowsweet to help with winter illnesses, headaches and fevers. The roots, leaves and bark of poplars and willow trees helped relieve toothache when chewed. For old age joint problems we gathered bull thistles, poke root, prickly ash, black cohosh, sassafrass and witch hazel. On long walks we chewed on bear's ears to take pain from our legs. When our insides locked up, we used raw clams and mussels, which were also good for sores inside and out. Other cures for bowel troubles were butternut bark, mayapple (mandrake), slippery elm and wild yams. The last was very good for pregnancy nausea. I preferred to use water lilies, cohosh, pine tar, blackberry leaves or cattail heads for water in the bowels.

"Cocklebur root helped stop chest and stomach pains but turnip root and pokeweed berries were also good for this. I thought the wild yam root worked best.

"Cranberries were good winter food and helped calm nervousness. They and juniper root or wintergreen leaves helped problems with water. We also used sassafrass, butternut bark and passion flower

flower.

"We had many treatments for skin problems, including yarrow leaf juice in bear fat, sweet acorn oil and yellow plant (which also helped sore throats if we made a tea of it). We also used cattails, balsam fir gum, bloodroot for fungus infections, pink root for vermin, poke root, sassafrass, wild (false) indigo and spotted alder (witch hazel).

"Usually herb healers settled on a few favorites and used them for almost everything. The leaves might be good for one thing, the bark or sap for another and the root for another still.

"When I was young, many plagues swept through our villages. These illnesses could not be cured with my mother's plants or by the powwow's medicine. People got a fever, turned yellow all over, vomited, passed bloody stools and yellow water, bled from the nose and died. Our brothers to the east and north were killed in great numbers. Whole villages died, leaving no one to bury their dead. We were lucky because our villages were not near these, but were in the hills. But Gentle Rain's small village to our south perished completely. Afterwards, we avoided it when we traveled south and no longer fished in its pond so the disease's spirit would not attach to us and follow us into our own village.

"As a female, my life was concerned with planting and drying the three sisters, gathering berries and nuts, making the meals, butchering the animals the men caught, cleaning and drying the fish, cleaning and curing the hides and making clothing for the people. I also learned how to weave baskets, mats and bags and how to make clay pots.

"My education began at a very early age. When I was old enough to be taken out of the cradleboard, I began helping my mother and relatives by bringing them things or carrying a stick or two of firewood when we went to the swamp to our south. As I got older, I could carry water and more firewood.

"I learned how to pick the blueberries, strawberries, raspberries and blackberries that grew close to the village. Many hours were spent with the other children gathering these berries. Of course, we ate as many as we gathered! We also gathered the soft-skinned chestnuts and the harder nuts.

"We helped our mothers pound acorns with the stone pestles on the big stone mortars then helped bring the mashed meats in tightly-woven, covered baskets down to the river and let the water wash the poison out of them. Afterwards, the paste was spread out to dry. It would keep a long time as a powder and we used it to thicken our stews with. It had a nice fat and nut flavor. The chestnuts were dried whole for winter food.

"Nut gathering time was also bear-fattening time and often we would have to run away from a grove of trees when a bear lumbered in. From a safe distance we would watch the big bears sit on their fat haunches and take each little acorn or chestnut one at a time, eating it daintily like a piece of popped corn. This amazed us but also annoyed us for the bears took a very long time eating this way and we would have to find another stand of oaks or chestnuts.

"We also gathered birch bark to make wetu articles with. I was taught to sharpen my knife on my hair when I cut birch bark. I learned that for cooking vessels, the bark had to be turned inside out so it wouldn't burn. Birch bark strips were valuable as tinder to start our fires in the morning and I learned how to use small wood and corn cobs to keep the fires low to the ground in the wetu's cooking pit so they wouldn't burn the wetu down.

“Although I am fat now, when I was little, I was always skinny. This was so for most of my sisters. We got fatter as we got older unless we married a lazy man who wouldn’t hunt. But if that happened, we could just tell him to leave and go back to his parents’ wetu. I heard a white man who visted our village say the older women looked as fat as partridges. This was good, for it showed we had plenty to eat.

“In my sixth winter I began to learn how to sew moccasins. My mother put my foot on the floor of the wetu and took a piece of charcoal from the fire to trace around it. She showed me how to make the right shape and explained that everyone’s moccasins were made just for them. There were regular moccasins, she said, without lining, and winter ones which had rabbit fur linings. These were larger to allow room for the fur. Sometimes cattail down was used instead of rabbit fur. The moccasins were rubbed thoroughly with fish or bear fat to keep water out of them. She showed me how to take a dried ligament strand from the long muscles of deer and other large game and how to thread it into a hole at the end of a sharp bone made from the deer’s front leg or the even smaller ones from birds' legs. The larger bones were used when we sewed the large hides together. Each adult woman had a mantle made from two whole deer hides, fur still on. We wore these inside out (fur against the body) in winter to keep us warm. Women each had a pair of hide strips that went over the tops of their winter moccasins and were laced above the knees in winter so we could walk through the snow. I was shown how to slice strips of doeskin to make the laces that tied the mantles together or wrapped around the moccasins.

"But our clothing was never as important as that made for our men. For our lives depended on how well they hunted. If a hunter went out without a spare pair of moccasins or without a warm hide to cover one arm and chest, or without warm leggings, his mind could not be on hunting.

"That spring I helped with the planting for the first time. After the men burned the fields, I helped carry the baskets of little fish from the streams to the fields, my feet becoming black as I walked across the still-warm ground. At every mound we stopped and our mothers used a pointed stick to dig out a hole in the top, into which we placed a fish, deep enough so brother raccoon wouldn't smell it. Afterwards, we planted four corn seeds in each hill, one in each direction, and outside them four bean seeds then four squash seeds. This was so the beans could climb the corn as it grew and the large squash leaves could keep the water around their roots.

"All the time we worked, we sang songs to Creator, thanking him for everything. We sang a corn song, a bean song, a squash song, and whatever song one of the women made up as our moose shoulderblade or clamshell hoes dug up weeds. Since I was still young, my mother sent me home each day when the sun was directly overhead so I could watch my little brother and sister and stir the stewpot. My older brother was with the others in the small, mat-covered structures that sat on high poles above the fields. Their job was to scare the crows away by shooting untipped arrows at them and making noise. The old men's job was to watch the boys and to keep an eye on the woods for enemies.

"Yes, we had many enemies before the white man enemy . Some of our villages would get raided by the Mohegans or Narragansetts, who would kill some of our men and take women and children away, to live out the rest of their days as slaves in their villages. But we feared the Pequots to our south and the Mohawks to our north the most. The Pequots we called the grey foxes and the

Mohawks were known as man-eaters for they not only killed humans, but they ate their flesh.

"For this reason we always had young braves on the hillsides in horse-shoe shaped stonewall enclosures. Their job was to watch below, to scan over the valley and hillsides to warn of enemy approach. And also to let us know if anyone was coming along the trail that led through tantiesques from east to west. Because the men burned off the brush every autumn after the first snowfall the area was full of grassy meadows and there was not much underbrush in the woods so they could see a long way off. The deer thanked us for making their travels easier by often coming near our villages and offering up their lives to us.

"In the time of the falling leaves just before my twelfth winter, the winter when I became a woman, the braves sent out an alarm as we were gathering in the dried corn from the slopes. When we ran to the village we found three white men in front of the sachem's wetu. With them was a Pequot. The men, through the words of the Pequot, told our sachem that they were following the trail to the quonicticut river because a sachem there by the name of Wahginnicut had asked for protection from the Mohawks.

"As is our custom, we always offer visitors food so we women made much to eat. We roasted eels the men brought from the river; we offered samp mush from the dried, pounded corn, and we offered a stew made of different meats, squashes and bear fat. The white men were not gracious about our feast and ate little. The Pequot said they were used to bread, so we made some of our appon, corn cakes, cooked in ashes. These they ate.

"They had many questions, but mostly about some of the black rocks my mother had brought from the hill nearby. The black, shiny rocks were pounded and used for body paint, or mixed with clay. This made our clay pots much harder when they were cooked and they didn't break as easily as the others. My mother used to feel good when the Wabbaquasetts would offer to trade some of their fine mats for her fine pots.

"Some of the men took the white men to the black rocks and let them pick up some to take with them to show to their sachem in Pautuxit. This was the first time I had seen white men. I didn't care for them much. They stunk of dirty flesh and had hair all over them. But I was curious about the stuff they made their clothes out of and they left some of it behind, for our sachem. It was wonderful warm stuff, easy to sew. It was dyed the color of the leaves and when it got wet, it did not drip, but kept the water in so the surface felt dry. The Pequot said it came from an animal they had in their villages of England, across the great sea. We called the woolskin etouwawayi or kopocki (thick cloth). Their thin cloth we called wassoppi. Colored cloth was called sucknuit if black, mishquinuit if red and wominuit if white. We did not like the white or light-colored cloth for it stained quickly and looked bad.

"They also gave our sachem a steel knife and all the men had to ask to handle it and try cutting things with it and throwing it. Unlike our knives, which had sharp obsidian or other stone blades, theirs had a shiny metal blade that was very sharp and very hard.

"The English visitors fired thundersticks into the trees and killed many ducks with one thunder. These sticks frightened us, but our men were curious and asked many questions about how they could get some.

"This visit left us wondering about their strange ways and articles. We began to feel a hunger for more of the wool and for their steel blades. Our sachem said that with metal hoes we could plant and clear more land than we could with our stone tools and he said that having metal tools would be a good thing for our people. He said their thundersticks would allow our men to kill more animals and would help us protect ourselves from our enemies. My mother and I wondered about the strange pots they cooked in, also made of metal. They did not break when dropped and they had metal handles to carry them with. She told my father that she would not mind having one of them some day.

"My thoughts soon turned away from the white man for I had my woman ceremony at the time of nikkommo. I was frightened a little bit by the blood my body was shedding, but my mother told me women had very strong medicine in them and if it wasn't used for growing babies, it had to be returned to Mother Earth. She brought me to the small wetu outside the village and the women in there told me many tales about a woman's magic. We could take a warrior's magic away with it and he would not be able to catch anything, they said. So to protect the men in our village from such a thing, we withdrew and returned the magic to the holes we dug in the floor of the wetu. We covered them often with fresh earth so the wild animals wouldn't be attracted by the smell of blood. The women laughed much and told many funny tales in the darkness of the wetu, so the time passed quickly. I was to come to enjoy these times when I became a mother and needed a little rest every month. We shared secrets and often knew things the men didn't because we had this special time. Of course, the men had their purification hut, too. It was the sweat lodge. They could not shed blood but when they got very hot their sweat dripped like blood onto the hot rocks.

"Because of our destructive magic, women do not become powwows or sit in council with the warriors and elders until they become old and the magic dries up. It was after my magic dried up that I became a medicine woman for my people, but that is further on in my tale.

"After my entry into womanhood, I began to learn how to embroider the designs of our people. I learned to make squash blossoms and vines and other plants out of porcupine quills that had been soaked in water dyed from different plants.

"I learned that berries and alder bark made nice red dyes; that sumac, blackberries and ocher made black dye and that their afterwater made grey; that oak bark, onions and acorns made brown dye; that paint brush and globe mallow made orange dye and that golden rod, clover, snake weed, and rabbit brush made yellow. We also made green dyes from grasses. Of course, all these were pale colors and not as bright as the white man's dyes, which were set with vinegar. The white man also had a blue dye from a plant to our far south. This we all admired and were able to copy a little with a tall beanpod plant called wild indigo. But the blue would fade out after several washings.

"Our pots and bodies were painted with powdered white chalk, the silver-black rocks and the black, yellow and red clays.

"We learned that for ceremonial dress and items our people had four colors and that they represented the four directions.

"We had quills but the white man had the beads we are all wearing now. After the Narragansetts began making it, we had white and purple wampum beads, but they were only for the sachems and the sagamores. Families like mine did not have any wampum but it was considered an honor to be asked to help sew belts of wampum for important ceremonies. Our sachem was not rich but by the time I was thirty winters, he had two strings of white wampum around his neck plus a necklace of pounded copper beads. Our people traded with the Mahicans and Montauks for this copper metal. These could be used to buy things from the white men, but mostly we traded beaver furs for wool, tools and guns. But this was not until much later.

"We could sew small shells into the ceremonial clothes we made and sometimes we peeled flakes of the shiny rock (mica) and sewed them on, but they often crumbled and had to be replaced. I was told Mishalisk had a pair of ceremonial moccasins with little pieces of mica sewn into the soles so when she sat in council, the fire-light made her feet shine.

"We also sewed raccoon, ounce, wolf and fox tails to our men's furs so that they would hang down one arm. This signified that they were important.

"Because it was not easy to get enough skins to make new clothes, in all but the coldest weather the men and older boys would only wear a strip of the softest doeskin between their legs, tied with a leather thong around their waists. We women wore an apron of doe-skin over our upper legs. We only wore our moccasins when traveling over rough ground or in areas of snakes. Then, we would also add leggings or strips of doeskin up to our knees, for even though we respect the asunk, he often doesn't return the favor if he meets us. Fringes on the leggings would warn our brother of our coming so he could avoid us.

"Once, when I was traveling southwest to the reed marshes near the path to the Skipmunk's territory, my brother stepped on a rattlesnake at the bottom of a hill. My mother had a little bit of powdered snakeroot in a small leather pouch and she immediately made my brother eat it. He gagged and threw up, but the next morning he felt better. His leg was swollen and splotched with purple and black so we had to carry him home, but he did not die. This plant will kill a man if he takes it any other time. This was one of the things my people knew. We knew where it grew and every mother kept a little in case someone in her family should need it. We also used the yellow and orange flowered hawkweed. It has purple veins like a rattlesnake so that meant it could be used to treat the poisonous snake bite.

"After the snake bit my brother another squaw followed it, blowing smoke towards it, praying and chanting as she tried to appease it. We thought this bite was a bad omen and our shaman spent many moons praying and fasting over my brother to remove the curse.

"In our wetu we sprinkled the herbs that made the snakes stay away.

"The time my brother was bitten we were headed to mashapaug. There, we would gather bundles of reeds and tie them together with the rope the women twisted from stringy roots. This Creator taught our ancient grandmothers to do by showing them how vines twisted around small trees.

"We would carry many bundles apiece on our backs to our village so we could weave mats to line our wetus with, to cover our bed frames and corn stores and weave bags to carry or store things in. Although I learned how to weave and how to make rope, I never really enjoyed these tasks. They were very monotonous and the only way I could do them was in a group with other women, for we would tell stories and laugh and sing and the time would pass quickly.

"I also learned how to sew covered containers with the white birch bark we gathered. These would hold dried seeds, quills, shells or powdered things. We would make them during the corn growing time and later, in the middle of winter , we would decorate them. Besides quills, we would chew designs in the bark (before sewing them together) and smoke them in the fire to turn them brown. A brave valued a squaw who could create beautiful designs on his clothes and objects.

"We learned how to make simple bark buckets and how to clean the bladders of animals to carry water in. However, if an object needed to be carved from wood, such as the bowls, cups or spoons we used, the men would go out into the woods, find a knot or burl in a tree and bring it home to make the utensils. This was winter work inside the wetus. For larger items, such as the canoes, the men would find a tree that had been felled by lightning or burn the base of a tree to fell it, then use fire to char out the middle. They would also char out the middle of a tree stump and make us a thick club so we could crush the dried corn kernels into powder. Many times it was the younger boys or the older men who did these things as it seemed the men in their best years were always out hunting or fighting.

"The men also made the musical instruments we used: rattles from turtle shells or gourds and pebbles; drums with deer hides stretched over heat-curved frames and the flutes that sounded like bird music. The flutes were used by the young men in courting. They would hide in the bushes outside of a wetu and play their music until the maiden they were playing for came out to see them.

"After such courting, I married a fine man when I was in my 14th winter. He lived in Asquoach and was of the wolf clan. I am of the snipe clan so it was permissable for us to marry. We get our clans from our mothers and people from the same clan cannot marry. The other clans are the bear, the deer and the hawk. Each village has a clan mother, usually the oldest member of the clan. She and other clan mothers keep track of the marriages and are grandmothers to all in their clans. Clan mothers have much authority in council, for they can speak for their whole clan. They are responsible for telling the legends of the animal that their clan is named after, so deer people know that they have the swiftness of deer and the hawk or snipe the keeness of eye for hunting and so on. When a boy from a clan enters manhood, a man from his clan guides him and helps him understand these qualities and how no one man has all, but together, all of us make a whole, all of us make a complete circle. This helps us to keep from thinking that we are the best and do not need each other. He then learns the dances of his clan so he can call upon the help of his clan totem and thank it after a good hunt.

"As you know, the Oneida have more clans, and it is up to the clan mothers to decide if all bird clans are one and all wolf, coyote and fox clans are one when our people here marry. Our Oneida brothers also have beaver and heron clans. Clan mothers were also the ones who would punish children who had disobeyed their parents, for it is not our way to punish our own children. Usually the punishment was be intended to humiliate the young brave or squashes in order to teach them a lesson.

"The summer before my marriage, I began making the things I would need in my own wetu. My mother and I followed the path to the south near the village of siog (Holland) pond to the black rock place to gather some rocks so my clay pots would be very hard. Then we gathered clay near the stream to the west of the path and took it a short ways uphill to the place of the ovens. Here many women were working, coiling wet clay and layering it into the shape of pots. They used paddles to smooth out the coils and also pressed designs in the tops with sticks, grasses or rope. As I wanted to impress my future husband, I fussed with the designs, so many days passed in the making of my pots. As the clay got dry, we poured more water over it until we were finished. Often our ovens were right next to the water, scooped out of the stream or riverbanks.

"The pots cooked in the ovens until they were hard and dry. They had a groove near the top so a thong could be tied around them for hanging over the fire. Others were slightly pointed at the bottom so we could place them directly into the coals. I knew that every year I would return here with the other women to make more pots, for hard as they were, one day they would break when little hands tried to carry them to the stream or when one of the dogs knocked them over. And it was good to have extra in case a trader came to the village.

"I loved the feel of the wet clay in my fingers. I loved squishing it and rolling it and even loved the smell of it. The clay and my hands were almost the same color, and when I made my pots I felt as if Mother Earth and I were one.

"The night of my marriage, my friends came to my wetu and told me my husband was in love with another squaw. They made up all sorts of tales and even though I knew it was in fun and we all did it, I admit I felt a little angry and jealous. But my husband had eaten the bitter cake I made for him of corn and ashes, so I knew he loved me the best.

"As the sun rose the day of my marriage, I saw the powwow going around the sacred circle burning sweetgrass, his voice telling the bad spirits to depart as he stopped in each direction. He sang thanks to Creator and magic songs that only he understood.

"Wetolechen, the sachem of tantiesques, stood before the sacred fire in the middle of the circle and smoked deeply from his soapstone pipe. He blew the smoke up into the heavens as he offered the grandfathers a smoke and let the delicious scent drift upwards to Creator. He chanted a song of praise and our drummers began to sing a song asking Creator to bless our marriage. The women entered the circle and danced around, their feet covered with decorated moccasins, gently touching Mother Earth. They too, sang a song, but this one was of the fertility of the earth.

"My husband and I entered the circle and danced side-by-side to where the sachem stood. He looked us both in the eyes and said that it was a good thing for braves and squaws to marry, for they would make many strong braves and squaws and so the circle of our people would continue.

"We danced to the music and others joined us, dancing round and round, all happy. Afterwards there was a feast, the food provided by my family. And then my husband and I entered the wetu he had built just outside the others in the village. I rejoiced in my heart, for I knew the man I married was a good man and would take care of me and our babies.

"Such was my life in the early days when our white enemy lived to the east. But the first winter of my marriage saw the beginning of the changes that swept through our land. A moon after the Pequots were driven out, the trader called Pynchon got permission from the Agawams to settle a group of English near their fort on the quonicticut. Because he was now chief sachem of the river tribes, Wrutherna got two coats more than the other sachems for signing the paper they called a deed. Afterwards Pynchon's trading post at what they called Springfield brought many English traders through tantiesques from the coast."

Spiderwoman's eyes shine even brighter. She slowly shakes her head and puts her hand to her breast as she says,

"My heart is too heavy with sadness now to go on. I have spoken. Later I will speak again."

Chapter 15
(A re-telling of events from 1637-1644 and the Narragansett-Mohegan war))

An old man rises to address the group. There is something different about him; his hair is cut in the Mohawk style and he wears a red calico print shirt fringed with ribbons over his buckskin breeches. His eyes are hard, like steel tempered in fire.

"I am John Tattawaban ("I know not where the wind is", i.e. Windwalker). My father was a Natick and was respected as a trader. I used to be called Wee-grammomuet and then later, Kennummet (he who carries a load along the path). I was born in the same year as Wamsutta. I was related to Shatookquis for I married his eldest daughter Star Dancer. I had often stayed in Asquoach with my father in our travels from Natick to the quonicticut river and then later to the trading post in Podunk. My father, Waban, became a Christian and married Tasnunsquaw, a daughter of Naddawahunt, so he, too, was related to Shatookquis.

"I was still a boy when the Pequots were destroyed by the whites. Never had our people seen such a thing. Not even the Tarrantines were so brutal. The whites trapped the people in their swamp fort and then set fire to it, burning them all alive. This was not the warrior's way to do battle. Our warriors would usually plan raids during the winter, go near a village, fight a battle and maybe capture some of the women to bring back as wives or slaves to our wives. Even the Mohawks didn't kill entire villages or tribes. But they were the best warriors and we all feared them. More fearsome than their thundersticks and clubs was their practice of eating their victims. This gave them the soul of whomever they had killed and that person would not go on to Cautanowwit's garden in the Southwest. We had heard they liked to burn little children, mix their ashes with water and drink them to make them braver. The tribes living along the upper quonicticut and housatonic rivers lived most in fear of the Mohawks, but as tribes began trading with the English and Dutch, they too began to fear the Mohawks, for they were allies of the French one minute and the English the next.

"I met Pequots, Mohegans and Wappingers during their wars and often accompanied my father further on, to montauk island. I was with my father in the village of coquit when Sassacus, Monotto and forty warriors fled west to the Mohawks to try to get them to avenge the horrible massacre of the Pequots. But the Mohawks cared only about their fur trade with the English on the rivers and instead killed most of them, sending Sassacus' scalp plus those of five of his sachems to the English on the quonicticut to prove they had killed them.

"This practice of taking one's knife and slicing off the scalp of one's enemy was new to our peoples. Before this time we had only cut the scalplock of hair from our fallen brothers so we could attach it to our belt. But the white men wanted the whole scalp, skin and all, as proof of the kill. Other times, they wanted the heads, so they could place them on poles outside their villages. This was a terrible thing, for it meant that the fallen warrior could not receive a proper burial and that his spirit would not be at rest.

"After the Mohawks killed Sassacus, the Narragansett sachem Mianatonnah, who had taken in those Pequots fortunate enough to have survived the massacre, began warring on the people of the Mohegan sachem Uncas. At this time the whites in Boston were visited by Uncas, who gave them 20 fathoms of wampum, which was quite a fortune, as a gift, but it was actually to keep them from from demanding the Peqouts he had. They gave him a red coat and corn and believed him when he said he had no Pequots living amongst his people, even though six of the braves in Boston with him were Pequots. When the English said they planned to exact annual tribute for each Pequot, he told them the Niantics and Narragansetts were the ones harboring all the Pequots. Uncas knew how to lie to the white man and he knew how to lie to his people. He was a fox who wanted to have everything he saw.

"A short while later the English in Boston told Miantonomo that the Narragansetts could right the wrongs of his cousin Ninigret, sachem of the Niantics, who was stealing from the former Pequot (now Mohegan) tribes and demanding tribute.

"Then both sachems were called to their English village called Hartford in Podunk. On the path from Boston to the river , Miantonomo heard that the Mohegan-Pequots had attacked the village of wannushowatchkoogs, killed many people there and destroyed 23 fields of corn. This made him very angry and by the time he arrived at Hartford, he wanted to go on the war path. But the white men and the sachem of Hartford insisted that he meet with Uncas and take his hand in friendship. Uncas sent word to the Narragansetts that he would boil Miantonomo in a kettle if he went to Hartford.

"A moon later the Narragansetts received a sign, for the stone people, who are the oldest of our brothers on this planet, held a war dance beneath the surface of the earth that shook the lands closest to Miantonomo's people. Some of the powwows said they were dancing with the Narragansetts while others said they were dancing against.

"What turned Miantonomo against the English, who had been his allies, was their demand of tribute from him and the Mohegans for the Pequots each captured and now held as slaves. The Narragansetts, most of whom had not liked the English and had not been happy with Canonicus and Miantonomoh's alliance with them, argued bitterly that the English had no right to claim tribute. The English did not own the Pequots, they said, even if they were the ones who forced them to surrender.

"Miantonomo had entered into the alliance in the hopes that the English would help him drive the Pequots and Mohegans out of what had been ancestral Narragansett lands. Then he and his people were going to turn on the English and kill every one of them along the quonicticut tiver, in their inland settlements, and along the coast. But Uncas had been playing his own game, which called for the English to be his friend and help him drive the Narragansetts out so he could have all of Narragansett territory.

"Around this time, Massasoit's federation began to fear that the war between the Narragansetts and Mohegans would involve them, so Ousemequin went to Plimouth, bringing a gift of 18 beaver skins from him and Uncas' sachems to show him that the Wampanoag federation was not at war with the English.

"My father and I were staying with Canonicus at the time and we saw the white man Williams visit the great sachem along with Miantonomo. The Narragansetts had deeded aquidneck to Williams in exchange for his help as a mediator between the Narragansetts and

Wampanoags a handful of winters before. We could see that Miantonomo had come to like this white man and even listened to him when he talked about his god. My father and I were also curious about this one god who was more powerful than all our gods. We learned he had a son whom he sent into the enemy camp and that the son died an honorable death without begging for mercy. He was a great warrior who won battles with words and not arrows or thunder-sticks. He spoke of love and of all brothers living in peace. I suppose he sounded a little like Deinganda, the great Iroquois speaker who united the Iroqouis into the five great nations of the Huron, Seneca, Onondagona, Oneida and Mohawk. Although we valued a man's courage and valor on the battlefield, we admired more a man who could bring peace with words. Massasoit was such a leader. He would tell people that he had seen so many people die from the plague that he was afraid if brother killed brother, there would soon be no people living on the land Creator had led our ancestors to. Yet he would lead a war party to avenge a wrong if words failed.

"This Williams of the white man's god would never fight, though. He had the power to win others through putting a spell of love on them, which we thought was powerful magic.

"Perhaps because of Williams' words, Miantonomo agreed to sign a peace treaty with Uncas during the harvest moon. It was at this time that Massasoit's second son, Pometacomet, was born and Wamsutta changed his name to Mooanam.

"Around this time the river sachems called a great council and deeded land to John Pynchon. Caccarant, Secouusk, Wenepawin, a Woronoco, and Mishalisk signed for parts of agawam and skep. Also signing were Nippasumsuit of wollumansuk (red earth country) whose main village was near uncanoonuc (breast - Mt. Dumplin) and the narrow place along naultag brook. After much discussion and for extra coats, Wrutherna deeded north of pecousic, north of masaksicke (Longmeadow) and up the chicopee river to usquacoh and nayaset. Niarum, tamashim of Coa, signed also. The sachems told their people they would allow the whites to come into our area so their cannons could drive the Mohawks away. But they also wanted to be able to trade for the English muskets and goods.

"My father and I spent much of the following year in Natick, where Ninigret was staying. We sat in when a pniese named Mason came to Ninigret and demanded that he pay the long island people for his previous thefts from them. The white man entered the wetu where we were smoking, grabbed Ninigret and put his knife to his chest. This was the first time we had seen such an attack without warning and the whole area became alarmed that the whites were going to war with us. But Ninigret did not strike back. His eyes became slits and his voice deadly quiet as he agreed to send payment to the tribes, who were bitter enemies of his cousin, Miantonomo.

"I saw then the smoke of the fire that would burn in his breast towards the English, a fire fanned by their treatment of Miantonomo that summer.

"Knowing his hatred of the Pequots, the English sent a Pequot interpreter to Miantonomo to answer charges that he and Ninigret were plotting to war on the English. Miantonomo refused to talk with the Pequot, as he was still warring with their remnant. But he agreed to travel to Boston to deny the charges. When he got there, the English forced him to speak through a Pequot interpreter and treated him worse than we would treat one of our dogs. As was fitting for a sachem, he showed no emotion, but the fire raged within his breast, which made him , like Ninigret, determined to drive the English out.

"Ninigret was next called to Boston and he told the English that he and his Niantics wouldn't hurt the English if they came into his territory to pursue enemies. Around this time, Ninigret and Miantonomo learned that many of the long island tribes were selling land and inviting the English to settle in their territory. These tribes were enemies of the Narragansett federation and such news made them very uneasy, especially since the whites were also getting deeds to the area across the bay in quillipiac (New Haven) from the Wappingers.

"Most of my time was spent courting Shatookquis' daughter, so I often took my birch bark canoe down the quinabaug (Charles) river then portaged across to the pewonganuck (Mill) river and followed the quaboag's swift current to tantiesques, where I portaged to the quinibaug river and then sailed into lower quansik. I took part in their deer hunt that fall, helping build a funnel-shaped run of cut sapling spears into which we herded the deer after other braves flushed them out of the thick woods north of Quaboag. But my favorite form of hunting was to lie low in a canoe near a river bank at dusk. We would make noises like deer and soon one would come forth to investigate, for deer are very curious. If it were a buck, we would then bring it down instantly with a well-placed arrow as it drank. The does we did not kill unless it had been a very bad hunting season and our people were starving. This was also the best way to hunt moose. We preferred moose skins for summer wear and our women would spend many hours scraping the hides with a sharp flat stone and then decorating the skins with earth pigments for us.

"What I liked best about the canoe method was that it was almost always successful, whereas a hunt in the woods might only drive the deer deeper into the forest.

"The winter of my marriage, we heard that Ousemequin's pniese Hobbomock, whom he trusted like no other and who had been living with the English in Plimouth, died. He had taken up the ways and the god of the English. He had tried to persuade Ousemequin to give up our 37 gods, but he refused to listen, saying their god was not the god of the Wampanoags. That year, Ousemequin sold many lands to the whites near sowams. As was our custom, he sold the land conditionally: his people could still hunt and fish where the white man would live.

"Marriage talks were begun by Massasoit and Corbitant regarding Massasoit's sons and Caunbitant's daughters. Although it wouldn't happen for ten winters yet, his son Mooanum (Wamsutta) would later marry Tatapanum (Weetamoo), Corbitant's daughter, after her first husband died, leaving her squaw sachem of Pocasset. And later, Philip would marry her younger sister. This would allow Ousamequin to finally consolidate all of the tribes around him.

"A winter passed when all was quiet. My father and I were very busy bringing the fine, thick inland beaver skins to the trading posts, where I would trade for guns. These we brought back to the inland tribes, which were now collectively called Nipmucks by the whites, for they lived along nippemaug, the fresh waters. The people also wanted more hoes, knives, hatchets and iron kettles. The wool skin cloth was valuable, especially the thick blankets, which the tribes to our north made into winter robes. Occasionally we were asked to find a horse for one of the warriors and when we did I would ride it along the river, keeping pace with my father's canoe, which was always heavy with goods. We would use the horse to pull the canoe over dry areas. Our trade was mostly from the English towns on the coast to the Nashaways and Quaboags, for we found the white people very eager to trade for furs, which they sent back to their chief sachem across the great sea. They were also eager for land and my father was invited to the council when his father -in-law , Naddahattawants, then living in musketaquid, sold a large piece of land on both sides of the punkatesset (Concord) river to the whites. Naddahattawants had taken on the white man's god and his son, John Tahattawan, was sachem of a village near Nashoba for those who had taken up the new god and white man's ways.

"A short while afterwards the sachems Kutchamaquin and Massaconomet signed agreements to live with the English under their laws in exchange for protection from the Tarrantines. Ousemequin went to live with Naddawahunts for a while at Magnus Hill after these things happened.

"There were many men acting as full-time traders by this time, but my father and I were still the best-known. Many hides and furs had lead tags bearing our mark on them at the trading posts. We could travel in the Mohegan, Narragansett, Quansik and Wampanoag territories without fear of attack for all were eager to obtain the muskets we could provide.

"As you have noticed, much of what I have told you was news I heard or saw in my travels, for such was the life of a trader. We didn't do much hunting, fighting or fishing, for we were too busy carrying goods back and forth. For our safety, as well as to know how to get the best deals, we always kept our ears open. We acted as much as traders of news as we did goods and wherever we stopped we were always welcomed. Even the white traders treated us as friends and not as competitors, for we had the pelts they wanted.

"We were in Narragansett country when we heard that a son of Canonicus had died and that the great sachem was inconsolable. He burned everything he owned - his longhouse and all his possessions - to appease the gods.

"This would have been unusual in the other territories, who had gotten away from the sacrifice rituals, but for the Narragansetts this was a normal custom. Of all the tribes, they had been the ones to keep the rituals and the old ceremonies. Our powwows said this was why they had been spared the first plagues that had killed off so many of the other tribes.

"The next year when we went to Narragansett territory, we heard that Miantonomo had hired one of Sequassen's men to kill Uncas, but the man had only wounded him. We also heard that some of the white people had been sent out of their villages and that Punham, sachem of mishawomet (Warwick) had taken one in.

"At the time, Miantonomo and Canonicus were returning from Mohawk territory where they had gotten some of the sachems to agree to fight with the 3,000 warriors who had pledged to fight with the Narragansetts against the English. The Mahicans, Sokokois and Susquehanas to the north wouldn't join for they said the Mohawks were now friendly to the English, having broken off their friendship to the French. They were also friendly to the Dutch who built a trading post-fort at Montreal. Ninigret sent news of the plot to a sachem on long island but Wiandance's older brother, sachem of Shelter Island, intercepted the messenger. The message said, 'For so are we all Indians as the English are, and say brother to one another; so must we be one as they are, otherwise we shall all be gone shortly, for you know our fathers had plenty of deer and skins, our plains were full of deer, as also our woods, and of turkies, and our coves full of fish and fowl. But these English having gotten our land, they with scythes cut down the grass, and with axes fell the trees; their cows and horses eat the grass, and their hogs spoil our clam banks, and we shall all be starved.'

"As He Who Has Crossed the River will tell you, travel by boat in the sea is never an easy thing, and the boat carrying Ninigret's messenger crashed into rocks off Shelter Island. In defiance of Wianadance, his brother let the messenger return to Ninigret, for he was afraid of the Narragansetts as he had heard their powwows were casting poison spells on Miantonomoh's enemies. Wianadance was not afraid and told the English at Saybrook of the plot. Uncas had heard of this, too, and rumor was that his powwows were also working the same spell on Miantonomoh's people. The fear grew stronger as Wiandance died of poison and his people started dying from a plague. The tribes began to whisper that the Narragansetts had sent the plague amongst all of their peoples, too, and the powwows began to cast protection spells, even in the inland villages. Wianadance's brother also died after he had executed those living in his territory who had killed English during the war.

"But the thunderstick was more powerful than spells against the English, and the long island tribes allied with Miantonomo and drove all of the white people from mauntok (Manhatten) to mahockemo (Stamford) off their land. They killed the white outcast woman Anne

Hutchinson and took her daughter prisoner. Punham had taken in the English outcast minister Samuel Gorton and on capawack (Martha's Vinyard) Hiacoomes became a Christian and took in Thomas Mayhew to preach to his people. In Quaboag, the Englishmen Thomas King and Nathanial Norcross signed a deed with Naddawahunt to settle in part of Nashaway (in Lancaster).

"Mianatonomo also began to listen to the ministers and because of his new affection for the English god, he (and Canonicus) then sold mishawomet (Warwick) to the minister who had been banished from the white man's villages. He was then called to Boston, where they told him had no right to sell shawomet for it belonged to Punham, who had pledged his submission to them, so it was actually English land. They told him that Uncas and Sequassen were fighting and warned him to keep his men close to home. Miantonomo thought his forced visit to Boston might be a trick by Uncas and the English, so he refused to eat any food unless Winthrop ate some of it first.

"As soon as he returned to Narragansett, Miantonomo and 1,000 warriors went to Sequassen's aid. There were 400 men with Uncas, who had worked out a signal with his followers that when he went to meet Miantonomoh face to face they would attack. Miantonomo had obtained a metal coat like the one Standish wore so he felt that he had strong medicine. When Uncas' men began screaming and shooting arrows, the Narragansetts fled, for they knew their Mohawk allies were only a day's sleep away and they wanted to wait for them before facing the ferocious Mohegans. Miantonomo couldn't run as fast as the others because of his heavy suit of armor and a Mohegan named Tantoqueson captured him. During the battle, two of Canonicus' sons were wounded, adding to his grief.

"There were two Narragansetts with Miantonomo who wounded him in order to show Uncas they were on the side of the Mohegans. Uncas was outraged that they would do such a treacherous thing to their sachem and had them executed on the spot. He sent word to Hartford that he was bringing Miantonomo in but on the way Miantonomo proposed that they call an end to their war by the marriage of Uncas' daughter to him. He also proposed to have his brother Pessacus marry Aime, Ousemequin's daughter, and thereby seal an alliance with that federation. He told Uncas that if all three federations were united, they could easily drive the English away and back into the sea from whence they had come.

"Uncas was considering such an alliance and had sent word out that the Narragansetts could ransom their sachem by paying a large price of wampum. But the English came to him and made him promises. They told him in secret that he must execute Miantonomo, so as soon as he had his prisoner in Mohegan territory, Uncas, who was walking behind Miantonomo, buried his hatchet in the Narragansett sachem's skull. Afterwards Uncas denied ever having offered to trade Miantonomo for wampum although his braves had accepted some already from the Narragansett sachems Chimough and Weetowisse and two war captains Pawpiamet and Pummumshe.

"As traders, we were aware that the Narragansetts and Montauks spent their winters now making wampum, for it was what the white men took for trade. We knew the Narragansetts were rich with this, and so did Uncas.

"After Miantonomo's murder, the white men held a meeting and declared that Miantonomo had started the war. When Williams told him this, Canonicus became very angry and took a stick and broke it into ten pieces. He said each represented a lie the English had told his people. Williams said he would intercede for Canonicus with Boston but never went there, instead he went to long island and made peace with the Mohawks and Dutch and then got on a ship and sailed back to their great sachem in England.

"Around this time Ninigret adopted Tom Pequin's relative, Poquin, a Mohegan war captain captured by his people. He gave Poquin some of Miantonomo's Cowesit lands near lower quansik, which were now part of Ninigret's lands. Kienemo sent Weetowisse, Pawpiamet, Pummumshe (Pumbushe or Pambussa) and Chimough to Boston to complain that Uncas stole their wampum. They signed a treaty with the English stating they would not war on Uncas.

"Pessacus then sent a message to the English asking them to remain neutral so he could avenge his brother's murder. After a long delay, their messenger finally returned from Boston to tell them the English wouldn't agree to such a thing.

"Pessacus, Meika and Ninigret then led a war party into Mohegan territory. With the help of the Narragansett squaws, who often traveled between villages to visit, they found out which wetu belonged to Tantiqueson, who had captured Miantonomo. He was surpised, attacked in his wetu, the way he had attacked Miantonomo. Then they seiged Uncas and his warriors in his fort.

"All these events made the inland tribes nervous, for the memory of how the whites had totally wiped out the Pequots was still with them. But when they heard a rumor that the Mohawks were thinking of joining forces with the English, Ousemequin, Cutshamekin, Squaw Sachem, Masconomo and Nashawowam called a council in Mishalisk's territory and signed a treaty with white messengers in which they agreed to ten conduct commandments. The Massachusetts sachem Josias Passaongassit also signed a treaty with the English.

"By the time of the burning moon, the rumors had reached Narragansett that the English were gathering a huge army of Mohawks to help Uncas. The English told the Narragansetts that if any tribes came in and signed a peace treaty they would not attack them. Wittawash, Awasequin and Aumsaquen were the first to go in and sign. Later Pessacus, Meika, Canonicus and Ninigret visited Boston. Pessacus gave the English a stick and said the disposition of the war was in their hands. The English said that if each nation agreed to send 2,000 fathoms of wampum to Boston every year as tribute, they would not war on them. This was a high price to pay for peace, but the sachems agreed and signed the treaty. Cutshamekin and Weekesanno were also present, as well as Josias and Cullicut. The Massachusetts sachems served as interpreters, but they had a personal stake in the matter for a war with the Mohawks exposed them to much danger from northern attack.

"When neither the Narragansetts or Niantics had sent the wampum to Boston the English sent a war captain to Narragansett. Pessacus fled inland but the war captain found Kienemo (Ninigret) and held a gun to his head while demanding that he pay. The Niantics said the Narragansetts hadn't supplied their amount yet and the Narragansetts claimed it was the Niantics fault. In reality, neither had much wampum, for with all the warring and uneasiness, their people had not gathered enough shells to produce the amounts they had been making before the war with Uncas. And they had lost the many fathoms they had given to Uncas' squaw for the release of Miantonomo.

"So the English exacted a very high price for peace that autumn. Their greed and impatience to collect their tribute would cause the Narragansetts to forever hate them."

Chapter 16
(A re-telling of the leadmine at tantiesques, 1644 - 1658)

This time a younger man stands up and takes the talking stick. The food ketttle has been pased around and many lie back to listen, their stomachs full.

"I am a Pequan also. My name is George Tahanto. My family moved north to my mother's territory of quansik after the war. We settled in Pambussa's territory near hassanamessit (the place of many stones - Grafton). I married a daughter of Quequaquonset and moved to a village on siog pond, part of her territory.

"My cousin Konkowasco spoke of the visit to our area of the Englishman John Oldham. After he saw the black rock, others came and Wetolechen, sachem of tantiesques, sold them the rocks. One of the men who came was a printer and it was he who first showed my cousin James how to make their words appear all at once on paper.

"After the war, we often saw Pynchon and other white men traveling along our path on their horses. Sometimes they had wagons attached to the back and they struggled to keep the wagons from getting stuck or breaking on the rough sections of the path. We used to gather and watch as they yelled to each other and whipped their horses or oxen to get them back on the path or around a steep bend. We had a better system of hauling goods. Our women could carry heavy loads in their large hempen bags and travel farther in a sleep than the white man's wagons. But we enjoyed watching such things. As children we had watched the creatures in our world. We watched for hours as ants built nests or bees made hives. We would lie in the grass and spend long hours watching the birds, fish and beavers. Such watching helped us understand our brothers better and often amused us as well.

"So we watched our white brothers. We thought they made

things hard for themselves, wearing layers of heavy clothing and hot face hair. Even their way of walking, in which they turned their feet outwards with each step, made their journeys longer, for we knew the best way was to swing the foot in front, pointed straight ahead. In this way a man needed only a very thin path and did not tire as quickly. They also wore very thick boots and shoes that got wet and caused blisters. But these shoes were nice to have in areas of nettles or brambles, for a brave hated nothing worse than to be running through the woods and step on something sharp. Our moccasins were not thick-soled like the white man's shoes and boots and often got pierced, even if they were lined with rabbit fur.

"For many winters the white man did not stay more than a sleep or two at the black rock place. Then one day Pynchon rode into quansik with two other white men and a wagon filled with goods. Tied to the back of the wagon were two of the animals they called cows. Inside its bed were crates with chickens and small pigs.

"By the time they stopped on the hill near the pond, many of my people had gathered around them and their Pequot interpreter. Since the war that killed most of my people, many Pequot men became the white man's tongue in exchange for the right to live as free men amongst them."

"Pynchon told us the two men with him would be living there and would need help constructing some buildings and cutting wood. He said they would pay firewater for such help. The next morning he left them and went towards the village to trade with those there.

"We did not understand at first, for we did not cut firewood. Our squaws would just gather dead, rotten wood from the swamps or forests near our villages. To chop a living tree down and then cut it up and split it into pieces was new to us. The Englishmen became angry with us when we watched them doing this. Some of our people also became angry for the English did not ask permission of the trees before killing them or offer tobacco to the tree spirits. Our powwows said this would turn our tree brothers against us someday.

"Being a Pequot Mohegan, the Siogs weren't very friendy to me. I was an outsider of sorts. My wife began to listen to her people and told me she did not want to be married to me anymore. I had to leave the wetu I had built for us and live outside the village. So when the English wanted to be friends with me I was quick to respond. After I brought them some fish I caught in the pond we called quassuck (pond-all), they asked me to stay and work for them. They wanted to get the metal lead from the rocks , they said, but first they had to heat up the rocks with the firewood they were cutting. They were living in a rough shelter near the pond and I built them a wetu. They gave me a steel-headed axe and I learned how to chop the trees they felled and how to use another metal tool to split the logs so they could make a fence to keep their animals from getting lost in the woods.

"Throughout the summer we worked hard everyday. They built a small four-sided house for themselves and their animals while fires burned on the rocks. They would keep adding firewood until the rocks got a whitish color and then they would throw water from the pond on them. This made the rock people angry and they made a tremendous noise as they split open. The noise made the great serpent in the middle of the earth angry, too, and it sent many snakes to where we worked.

"The Englishmen would dig out the soft black stuff inside and then throw the remainder of the rock aside. I began to build a circular stone house with these. It was wide at the bottom and grew closer together at the top. Over the whole thing I put mud and tree boughs so when the winter came I had a very warm wetu.

"Although I had become friendly with these men, there were two things about them I did not like. One was their love of firewater.

"At first I loved it and would grab for the jug whenever they offered some to me. It made me feel like two men, stronger and taller and braver than I was without it. But when they drank it they became angry and argued amongst themselves and even fought with me, threatening me with their knives or muskets. They called me a dirty savage when they drank and would say insulting things about my people. Then they would do the second thing I disliked. They would feed firewater to our young women and then take them into their beds.

"I spent many hours talking to the sachems of the neighboring villages, telling them to keep their people's daughters away from the white men but some of the girls still came, for they too, loved the firewater.

"For my help at the lead mine, the white men gave me a big piece of one of the pigs they slaughtered.

"They later sent me to the surrounding villages to trade pig for maize when their tan powder called wheat corn ran out.

"The following autumn I helped them load the black powder rocks into the wagon and accompanied them to the white man's village called Springfield on the quonicticot river. The road from the mine to the path was very steep and full of sharp rocks. We lost some of the crushed rock along the way but it was quickly collected by my people, for it made a fine face and body paint when mixed with bear grease. The women also liked to put it in their clay, but by this time they were making less clay pots and making more items to trade for copper or iron kettles, which were now being made at a foundry in saugus. They found that the English liked their baskets the best, so mothers and daughters spent less hours dragging clay from the streambanks and more hours gathering bullrushes in Wabbaquassit and splitting ash limbs into splints for the sturdy baskets the English liked so well. For fancy baskets they would twist some of the strands they wove to create a raised texture or they would take berry juice and a feather and paint designs on the sides. The women learned that by doing these things they could get more wampum for their baskets from the traders.

"In their greed for the white man's goods, the braves began killing more animals than could be eaten fresh They now killed many foxes, muskrats and beavers just for their skins and so my people ate less deer and more of these small animals. The beavers were seen less and less as they took their families farther away from our hunters.

"One of the things I traded for in Springfield on our trips with the ore was the white man's sugar, which came in hard cones like our maple sugar, but which tasted sweeter and didn't have any pieces of soot in it. I traded for beads for my mother and sisters to use on their clothes and for the food they called green peas. Our peas were red and tart (cranberries). I traded for gunpowder and musketballs for I could hunt better with a musket than with a bow and arrow. My mother would ask me to bring back some of their cloth or some of the blue stuff called indigo for dye. She sent herbs and baskets with me on my trips and the braves from siog sent many pelts, each wanting certain goods in return. Some wanted firewater but most of the people wanted English steel or sugar.

"On one trip to their village of Springfield, I observed a very strange thing: a shaman of theirs, a man called Hugh Parsons, was tried for what they called witchcraft. They said he was consorting with the spirits. This confused us all very much, for how could a man be a shaman if he could not talk to the spirits? But this was just one more strange thing the English tribe did.

"Now I will tell you how the trips were made: the path the English later called the Bay Path ran from the quonicticot to the village of mishawam, on the shore of wechakum. It was just north of the lead mine, running through metewemesick (Sturbridge), and quassuc (Sturbridge). Once on it, we forded the quinebaug river then went uphill to Wetolechen's Puttipoog valley. We went north of little alum pond past the oak trees and south of big alum, then north to quaboag old fort. We went over the waddaquadduck with the steerage rock and went west, to the sandy plain then on to numksceenaganees (Elbow)brook. Our people had no problem crossing the brook, but with the wagon, we had to cut logs and make a rough bridge. The oxen did not want to walk on the logs so it took us a long time to get across. This was a good place for corn storage and the women often buried large supplies in the sandy knoll near the brook. We followed the bend of the quaboag river and we crossed little streams as we made our way through the oak forest. There was lots of good- burning dry wood full of resin in this place. We called this wood wegumantig, the English called it candlewood. After it we again had a problem when we started uphill and had to ford the chicopee brook. Afterwards the path ran on good hard meadow ground away from the quaboag. The path curved around the rocky place and then we crossed near the head of the small pond nayaset (near Twelve Mile brook). This was swampy and full of poplars and chestnut trees. Next we went over a branch of the chicopee again in the area of red and white oak trees. The path took us uphill to the place of the pine trees then downhill to a stony brook beyond which was a large cedar swamp and a little pond (Nine Mile). From this pond we went around the base of a hill, through a gravelly area and then skirted the south of kwonokamaug (Loon) and another little pond (Five Mile). The path then went sharply south towards the quonicticut, crossing a little steam before ending at Wrutherna's (Wequaquan's) big fort on the hill overlooking the river. All along the way the people came out to meet us, wanting to trade, but the English were impatient and often refused the food and drink offered.

"My last trip took place ten winters after the white men first came to the lead mine.

"While in Springfield we heard that Weetamoo went to Plymouth asking for her land back. She told them Wamsutta (Alexander) had made a mistake and that the land he sold to John Cooke was not his to sell, but was hers. She was within her rights to claim this, but to go to the English against the wishes of her husband was a very bold and proud thing to do. Sometimes the clan mothers would speak in council if they thought we weren't doing what was good for the people, but Weetamoo thought nothing of contradicting Alexander in front of his councillors or making decisions without speaking to him first. She was the type of wife a chief sachem didn't want to have and I wondered how soon Alexander would take another wife.

"While we were in Springfield the overseer at the mine, William Diens, hired some white men to accompany them back as I was the only quansik male amongst the Siogs, Potepaugs and Quaboags who would cut wood and haul rocks and water for them.

"After he returned with his new English crew, I was no longer treated like a white man. I was ignored and not offered firewater when they sat around and drank it. These things made me angry and when they were all called back to Springfield the following year I was not in any mood to go with them.

"I continued to live at the mine, though, for the fishing was good in quassuck and I kept looking for the silver metal the English said was in the rocks. This metal, which they made into little flat discs with pictures of pine trees on them to trade with, would have made my people wealthy and they could have bought many muskets and English goods with it.

"After a while I stopped looking for the silver. I married one of the girls who had visited William and the other men and moved into her village north of siog near the swamp. She was darkskinned, related to Tuspaquin's people. Because my mother was also related to Tuspequin (but light-skinned), she had to consult many of the old clan mothers to make sure we weren't of the same clan before we married."

Chapter 17

(A re-telling of the Mohegan attack on Quaboag, 1645-1646)

A woman who is old but not aged rises and takes the talking stick. She is tall and her back is straight. Her long, thick black hair is worn in two braids that hang down her front. She wears a white man's broad-brimmed hat. Her hands are hard from long hours of work.

"I am the daughter of Shatookquis. My name is Little Dove, which the English say is the symbol for peace. I was born ten winters after my brother, Konkowasco. We have the same father but my mother was a tantiesquies squaw called Red Flowers on the Path.

"In the Hunting Moon of my fifteenth winter, I remember the white man called Winthrop staying in our village on his way to the quonicticut. He and the men with him were going to travel all the way down the great river to the sea, he said. He had purchased munnatawkit island (Fisher's Island) off the coast and was talking about trading with our people. Our sachems told him we could not trade that winter. They said they could not take the quinebaug down to the sea because of the war between the Mohegans and Narragansetts.

"Most of the braves in quaboag did not fight for the Narragansetts or the Mohegans. We hoped only for peace. Yet the worries of ambush kept us from traveling far from our forts and in asquoach we did not move down near the pond in the summer. We kept boys in our lookouts on the hillsides and as we women worked we anxiously expected to hear the deep booming of the large, balanced rock near the fort that would warn us to return at once.

"That year and the following one, we planted more corn than we needed and stored it in more locations than usual, for we lived in fear that we would have to abandon our homes and flee. Our men hunted close to the fort, on the waddaquadducks. They did not venture to moose meadow or to the seashore.

"Some of the younger sachems said Ousemequin and Naddawahunt wanted peace because they were old men, but we knew why my grandfather and the great sachem wanted peace with the white man.

"Both men were contemporaries of Passaconaway, the pow-wow sachem to our north, and both men had been present at his gathering when he had a vision that made him say that the people who attacked the white man would be vanquished. They saw the truth of his vision when the Pequots were destroyed for their murder of Oldham and his crew. The only way our people would drive the English out, he said, was if the English drew first blood.

"It was one thing for Ousemequin to keep peace in the east, but our people were sitting on the Mohegan and Narragansett borders. Before the troubles with Uncas and the Pequots first began the Narragansetts raided the Wabbaquasetts and the villages in siog and asquoach. They had forced my uncle and the other sachems to pay an annual tribute of beaver skins and corn. During the war, we had been left alone but when we heard about the tribute the Narragansetts would have to pay, we knew it would not be long before they would be bothering us again.

"A year passed in this way but we weren't prepared for the surprise attack by the Mohegan named Nowequa during the time of the *kepenumminamun* (Ripe Corn - September) moon.

"I was helping dry corn in the warm afternoon sun. The men were mostly off hunting although a few were lolling in the sun, their bodies drinking in the last warmth of summer. Our corn fields were a distance from the village for we didn't want the mice and rats that lived in the fields to come into our wetus.

"While I bent over the mats on which we were spreading corn, I was aware of how everything had a heavy scent. From the field I could smell the ripe grapes and overripe leaves in the forest. I smelled the musty tall grasses around the cornfield and the smoke coming from the fires where hides were being tanned. The whole world smelled like squash just before it turns rotten. It was heady, and I, a young maiden in love, was drunk with the beauty of the golden and red leaves and the deep blue sky.

"I often stopped and peered across the hill in the direction of quabogud, half-expecting to see the young brave who had been courting me since we met at the fishing weirs that spring. I loved how tall and straight he walked. I loved his lean face, his dark brown eyes, the way he wore his hair. But most of all I loved how he made me feel like I was the only squaw in the world. When his eyes looked into mine, I felt as if the whole world were framed between his lids.

"So my mind was elsewhere and I sang a song to Grandfather Wind as I turned the corn that had been placed on the mats a few sleeps before. These ears were whole, leaves and all, so they had to be completely dry before storing or they would develop mold and the whole cache would go bad before they could be eaten in the middle of winter. Most of our corn was husked and the kernels removed. The corn kernels would later be scraped from the ears with clam shells or deer jaw bones. This corn kept the longest and we used it in our samp mills to grind into corn meal or cracked corn to add to our stews. But the corn with the husks tasted better and could be added whole to the stew pot. By drying it this way, the milk inside the kernels didn't dry out so much, but it did loose the sweetness of fresh corn.

"We harvested corn at three stages. When the first thin ears were ready, we picked green corn. This was made into succotash with fresh beans and was a treat. We usually held a festival called *micheeneekesos* and gave thanks to Creator during this time.

"Next we harvested ripe corn and ate it on the cob, steamed in its husks. We especially liked it steamed with clams or fish from the pond.

"Our third and most important harvest was this, the harvest to dry and store our winter food. There was a sadness to this harvest, for we were saying goodbye to summer and getting ready for the coming cold.

"Already we were smelling the cold in the air when we woke up, hugging our furs. But by the time the fires cooked the first meal of the day the sun would be shining, bright and warm. The sound of the bees gathering pollen from the woundwort, purple and white boneset, wuttabaug (swamproot) and the birds gobbling chokecherries and grapes and the squirrels busily gathering nuts from the wild beechnut and chestnut trees in the forest was the sound of urgency, for they knew that soon all would be covered with snow and Mother Earth, which was soft now, would be hard and cold.

"In the other direction, I could see the geese on the pond. Every day more arrived and soon we knew we would hear their wings beat together, filling the air with a rush and honks as they headed south. I always marveled at how they took the shape of an arrrowhead in their flight, as if they were the tip of a giant arrow that Creator was pointing.

"Every woman in our village worked harder than usual this time of year, some gathering reeds which they would make mats with in the winter; some gathering nuts or cracking and washing the acorns to make nut powder to thicken our stew with; some plucked the quills off porcupines so they would have them to use to embroider the clothes we would make in the winter; others harvested corn or dried the tubers of the tall sunflower ground nut (Jerusalem artichoke) that grew in the meadows near our corn. Any berry or nut we could find that we didn't need to eat that day got stored away by the women.

"The boys were busy fishing in the ponds or hunting raccoons, turkeys or squirrels. Many small pelts were drying on poles leaning over the small fires. We used only certain types of wood for drying our hides, for some had an odor that would get into the hide and never leave. One such was maple, which we valued for its sap, but we didn't want to go around smelling like sugar. Our men were most particular, for if they thought a hide would be smelled by deer or whatever they were stalking, they would bring it back to the squaw and throw it at her feet. Such a thing would cause her shame.

"Our men didn't bother us too much about other things, but hunting was a deadly serious matter to them, much as tending the crops was to us. For each man and woman had a job to do in our society. We had to work together to support the whole. I would no more have thought of my family as separate from the group as a bird nesting in the treetops would have thought itself separate from the flock. If one person in our village was without meat, a brave would go out and catch two oppossums or a large deer and invite them to share in our meal. My brother reinstituted the give-away and every year at *nikkomo* we would place our best goods on a hide in the middle of the sacred circle and those who needed things would ask the owner for it. This kept us from loving material things too much and kept us from being too proud to ask our brothers and sisters for help. It pleased the gods, for we had not been visited by the plague since I was a little girl."

The elder closest to Little Dove takes a deep pull on his pipe.

He offers smoke and prays, then she continues,

"Now I return to the afternoon I was telling you about. The shadows were beginning to stretch across the hills and I could smell the smoke of the wetus wafting from the ravine where quaboag old fort was. I missed our summer village near the shores of the pond, but knew that until the Mohegans and Narragansetts smoked the pipe of peace our lives would not return to the way they had been. We thought peace would come soon for news had arrived a few sleeps past from a traveler along the east-west path that there had been a great battle on Montauk (Long Island) that might end the war.

"Saying a prayer of thanks to Creator for the glorious day, I sat back on my heels and closed my eyes, my face turned towards the sinking sun. I could hear the sounds of the children playing on the ridges of the hills near the fort; I could hear a squaw nagging her old husband to walk faster. But most of all, I was listening for the gentle strain of my brave's flute on the wind.

"I heard soft footsteps in the hay behind me and smiled, thinking it was he.

"Suddenly, a man grabbed me from behind, his arms wrapping around and pinning mine to my sides. I opened my eyes and began to struggle, kicking and yelling, but I saw that there were many warriors and they were holding my sisters the same way. The thought "Mohawk!" kept racing through my mind, making the blood rush like fire through me and making my heart beat so hard it hurt. I tried biting the black and white painted hands that held me and tried to squirm free, but this warrior was too strong. Suddenly, he threw me down and my face hit the ground with such force that I got a mouthful of hay and corn dust. He pulled my arms behind me and knelt on me, his knee in the small of my back. I tried to look up, but all I could see was the bottoms of the cornstalks and the ground. He tied a thong around my wrists and then pulled me to my feet. I then saw my sisters were also bound and were were being pushed back into the trees.

"Wildly, I looked around for the men, for the children. Then I saw an army of these strange men, armed with thundersticks, at the top of the ravine.

"Somehow in the panic, a brave remembered the rocking stone and now I heard it calling our men back from their hunting as I was herded with the other women into the woods and we were shoved together and told to keep walking. Some were crying, but I was too stunned to cry. It had all been so sudden, so fast.

"I kept seeing steel knives and thundersticks as the men holding us talked amongst themselves in an agitated way.

"I heard a thunderstick roar from the direction of the fort and then a tear formed under my lid. I had little brothers and sisters down there. I had parents and my brother. My whole life was there, beneath their thundersticks. I tried to look back, but all I could see was warriors, pushing many women along towards the direction of the quonicticut.

"One of the older women in our group spoke up and asked them who they were and what they wanted. They told her to shut up and for all of us to keep quiet, but she whispered to us that they were Mohegan and not Mohawks. This made us feel a little better, but not entirely, for we had heard that Mohegans also sometimes ate pieces of their victims. We had heard that when Uncas killed Miantonomo he had eaten a piece of his shoulder and said it was the sweetest meat he had ever tasted. Others said they had not heard this, but now it came back to my mind and I was frightened for my father. If anyone would be eaten it would be the sachem.

"That night we were hidden in a cave north of the path. There were bats that flew out over our heads when they shoved us in. It was dark and stunk of bat feces. We were offered no food or water, but told to keep quiet. The next morning we were awakened by the sound of voices outside the cave. I saw some of the large hempen baskets our women made heaped with things from the village. Wampum strings lay beneath our copper kettles as well as many furs and skins. I knew in my heart that my people had been killed and everything they owned stolen.

"Then the baskets were carried away, followed by the warriors. Two stayed at the mouth of the cave and refused to let us go into the woods to pass our morning water. We had to walk to the back of the cave and squat, our feet slipping on slimy bat feces and sharp rocks as we saw large black spiders crawling around in the thick mats of spiderwebs on the sides of the cave. We could smell snakes and that made us even more miserable. This ability to smell snakes was something our women had and it was so keen that when we went berry-picking, a mother could tell right away which paths her children should avoid.

"As it got dark, first one guard and then the other left. We slowly crawled out of the cave, half-expecting an ambush, but the men were nowhere to be seen. It only took us a minute to cut each other free and run back to asquoach, each carrying a fear in her breast of what she would find. I heard many mothers calling their children's names as they ran, their faces wet with tears. I felt their sorrow, for we knew warriors often used children like clubs, swinging them from their feet as they smashed their heads against something hard.

"The village looked like it had been struck by strong winds. Things were scattered all around, clay cooking pots were tipped over, cracked or broken, their contents eaten by the dogs. There were ashes everywhere and where the hides had been drying were now only bare stakes in circles around the dead fires.

"Our men greeted us with hugs and affection, asking many questions, then went into the longhouse in war council. We learned that the Mohegans had shoved everyone into the wetus, posted guards outside the doors and ransacked the village.

"Over the soft whimper of the children we heard pieces of their words in council. Nowequa. Mohegans.

"We began to straighten up the village, sweeping debris away with brooms made of branches tied together. We restarted the fires and the broken pottery was put in a pile, for once ground up, it would be good to add to our next batch of clay.

"The fine hides and the furs from inside the wetus would be sorely missed, especially as the nights were growing colder. But they had not taken our corn, squashes or beans, so we knew we would make it through until spring. Food stealing was one of the worst crimes a tribe could commit against another and it was rarely done except by the Tarrantines, who had a short growing season in the north and were always trying to trade for corn. All the tribes had been incredulous when we learned that the English had burned or trampled the corn fields of the Pequots. But their burning of the entire village overshadowed the destruction of the food.

"My grandfather and other Quaboags from quabogud were in the longhouse. I could hear Naddawahunt's deep voice silencing the others as he urged the Quaboags to remain neutral. He said the Mohegans wanted to draw us into war for then they could claim our lands if they won. They didn't like the way we paid tribute to their enemies so they took anything of value, especially the 35 fathom of wampum my people had, so we could not help the Narragansetts pay the white men tribute.

"My father agreed that it was best if we did not retaliate. My brother said we should go through the white man's court, for the white man would make the Mohegans repay us. He said Uncas wanted to be on good terms with the English and would do anything they demanded.

"My brother's voice was drowned in argument by the younger braves, who had been eager all along to enter the war. Because of his many trips to Lancaster and Natick and his association with the white minister John Eliot, my brother was considered to be someone walking in two worlds. Some felt he was more powerful for learning of the white man's god and others thought he was foolish or bewitched. I loved Konkowasco but I, too, could not understand why he had to spend so much time with the white man.

"It was very late before the voices died down and the council rested. Their arguing continued for many sleeps until a messenger from Ousemequin said that the great sachem favored my brother's plan of neutrality. He said if we entered war his people would also have to enter, for they were our allies. He said that the English in Hartford would deal with Uncas and we should keep our neutrality with the warring tribes and the whites.

"So the matter was settled. Our men had to hunt long into the winter to replace the furs and hides stolen from us and we women missed the nice metal cooking pots we had grown used to. We spent many long hours that winter making extra things so when the traders came through we would be able to buy new pots and wool blankets. The men spent many nights away from the village searching for beaver dens, for they, too, were eager to trade and to obtain as many thundersticks as the Mohegans had. Because of these troubles, I did not marry that winter, instead marrying in the spring when the fish ran. My husband, Two Crows, came to live in asquoach and I felt safer knowing he was amongst our men to protect me and the children we would have.

"We learned that Nowequa had acted without Uncas' knowledge and that he had stolen from some of the Mohegans at the same time and had also broken the canoe of the white man Winthrop. Uncas had been at the white man's court in New Haven at the time to answer charges that his people had been moving into Pumham and

Sacono's lands. The English ordered Uncas to keep his brother Nowequa under control. Then we heard that a war party of the Mohegans attacked Wequash's people and that Uncas was now in more trouble with the English. This made us happy for his tricks were finally being turned on himself. Like the long island sachems before him, Uncas now lived in fear of poisoning and witchcraft from the Narragansetts.

"This was good, Konkowasco said, for the Narragansett pow-wows were second only to Passaconnaway. But he also said the white man's god was strong and a moon after our attack by the Mohegans he was back with the man Eliot.

"And so ended my last winter as a maiden and began my life as a wife and mother. My carefree days had been cut short, robbed by the Mohegans under an autumn sun. Somewhere along the path or in the cave, I had changed inside and was no longer the girl I had been."

Chapter 18
(A re-telling of Passaconnaway and John Eliot, 1646)

Konkowasco again rises, his antler bone necklace clicking as he uses the talking stick to help him up.

"My sister was not alone in not understanding why I sought the white man's god and the friendship of John Eliot.

"I first met John Eliot through Waban, who had invited him to stay at his wetu near *pitchgusset* (Watertown) hill. John had a house and congregation in the white man's village but he had become friendly with the Naticks and was eager to learn more about them. A Pequot named Cockenoe from Montauk taught Eliot how to speak the tongue of our peoples. This was not new, for the man Williams knew how to speak to the Narragansetts and Wampanoags and many white traders had picked up a crude knowledge of our speech, as we had theirs. What was different, was that John was translating his medicine knowledge, contained in something he called a Bible, with the help of Job Nesutan into our tongue, so we could also have the power of their god.

"Waban had heard him speak to Cutchmakin's people near Dorchester and had invited him to Natick, where his brother-in-law, my uncle, John Tahattawan, lived. He sent word to me to come to listen to Eliot and so I did during the *peppewar* (late October) moon.

"I had seen a few Englishmen by then, so I was used to the clothes from head to toe and the pale, unshaven faces. I think I had even grown somewhat used to their scent. The scent of John was that of sweaty horse, for like most of the Englishmen now he rode on the large beasts when traveling from town to town. My people were a little in awe of these beasts and how the English could make them go wherever they wanted. We were also in awe of the large beasts they called cows. The English charmed them and kept them near and could get milk from them when they wanted and the beasts would let them lead them into a building and even let them kill them. This was powerful medicine. Our people were afraid of these beasts and when they would crash through the brush fences around the gardens our squaws would run away. The damage they did to our people's crops near the English villages was a constant source of trouble between the English court and the sachems, who said it was stealing and therefore violated the treaty Ousemequin's federation had signed with them.

"They had another beast called the pig that they would let run wild near their villages. These we were afraid of, too, for they were mean and would chase my people. But they ate the hated sesekq (rattlesnake) so we didn't complain about them too much unless they got near our clam beds. And their flesh was full of fat and tasted better than bear meat.

"Because I had not married, I traveled more than my brothers, especially through Massachusett, for Passaconaway had taken me on as his life-long pupil. This was an honor, for most powwows learned from a powwow in their own tribe or nearby and once they became older stopped learning from others. But Passaconnaway was not your average powwow. He was more like a god come to earth and to be taken on as a student was more than a powwow could hope for.

Konkowasco pauses. He lights a bundle of dried sweetgrass in the fire and begins smudging its smoke over the faces of those sitting in the dark. His voice takes on a strange tone and his eyes burn like little fires as he says,

"Now I am telling you things that only powwows know, and what I tell you no one is to ever remember unless he takes up the way of the powwow.

"Passaconnaway told me there had once been a great powwow from my people in quansik. He was so loved by Kitchtan that he didn't die. He was taken up into the starry sky on a flaming sled drawn by a team of wolves.

"He taught me the spell to say over a bowl of water to make a dark cloud and thunder appear. When the thunder and cloud passed, there would be a clump of ice on the top of the water. This was especially impressive magic to do in the summer.

"Another time he took an adder and held it in his hands, changing it into a worm. He could also take a dried up snake skin, and by saying a spell and stroking it, make a live snake appear.

"He said in his youth he could speak a spell, take a deep breath and swim underwater the whole width of the cabassauk (Merrimac) river on one breath.

"Through the years he showed me how to make fire appear on the water, how to make rocks and trees dance and how he could turn himself into a flaming tree. The last thing I never mastered.

"Passaconnaway showed me how to make green leaves appear on a dead branch in winter and how to speak the spell over ashes and water to turn them into a green leaf.

"He was such a great powwow he could bring forth a large seagull from his mouth, put it on the water to swim, then take it back up into his mouth again.

"He told me the words to make warriors immune to arrows, hatchets and bullets and how to chant over a bullet, swallow it and have it reappear out of my belly hole.

"He said my ordeal visions had been very powerful for the power of the thunderbird (eagle) is the greatest power a powwow could have and that it was related to the power of the rattlesnake. He told me if I prayed and fasted I could ask the thunderbeings to guide me to a thunderstone - a black stone dropped from heaven or an egg-shaped stone with crystals inside. This I did.

"Passaconnaway told me that to dream of a snake meant an enemy was trying to kill you. He said the only way to prevent this was to find a snake before the sun reached overhead the next day and kill it. He said to be careful when approaching it, for its eyes could hypnotize me. He said if you blew smoke into its face it would go to sleep and then could be killed. Passaconnaway had taught his warriors how to kill rattlesnakes and squeeze the poison from their fangs so they could dip their arrows into them when fighting the Mohawks. This knowledge he had received in a vision from *chingachgook*, the great snake at the center of the earth. This was just one of Passaconnaway's spirit helpers.

"This spirit also told him to tell the women that they must drink snake blood while they were in labor so the baby would slide out easily, like a snake. It told him that a person who had swallowed a baby snake while drinking in a stream should fast for several days, but keep food in front of his mouth, which would draw the snake out. This often happened to our people so this was a good secret to know.

"Passaconnaway wore rattlesnake rattlers tied around his leggings just below the knees and he made a noise like a rattler when he walked.

"I had already learned to always wear a necklace of braided sweetgrass, for its scent was sweet in the gods' nostrils. All powwows use it to blow into the ear, mouth or nose through narrow bone tubes, or to use it when sucking out poison spirits from sick people. But when I went to stay with Passaconnaway after the plague, he told me that nothing would help, not sweetgrass smoke, not tobacco or sassafrass smoke, if Kichtan was angry with the person.

"Passaconnaway knew how to cut holes in the heads of sick people to release the spirits making them ill. This was a skill he had learned from a colorful feathered serpent god in another vision. Passaconnaway said this god's people lived far to the south and were covered in gold.

"He told me that a screeching hawk circling the village after sundown meant that someone would die that night. He said to dream of black animals or birds was a bad sign. My people knew that to hear a dog howl meant death, but Passaconnaway said a black dog's howl meant the death of a sachem.

"He said that to avoid nightmares and to keep from having one's soul snatched while it was wandering in the land of sleep, one should turn one's moccasins up before going to bed.

"Passaconnaway kept a giant snapping turtle in a bark container of water in his wetu and when someone wanted to know the answer to a question, he would consult it. If the turtle were friendly to the questioner, the outcome was good, if unfriendly, he or she was advised to change the course of their actions.

"Passaconnaway wore a headdress of a foxfur, with antlers on either side. From the tips of them hung strings of red and yellow human hair. These were powerful magic and hc never said how he came to own them. Most of us copied this magic, but had to use black hair and paint it with yellow and red ochre.

"All around Passaconnaway's face hung long eagle, hawk, crow and turkey feathers. His cloak was made of turkey feathers and the feathers of a little yellow bird. Everything he wore was a symbol of the animal spirits he commanded.

"Passaconnaway showed me how he made fire appear in the snow. He took me high up on monodnock (mountain) and showed me how he called the spirit of the thunderbird down, through him. He turned a glowing white as everything else turned dark and he caused tremendous thunder and lightning and great winds over all the valley. He could strike his staff and the snake spirit would send up scores of poisonous snakes from the bowels of the earth. He could talk to Creator and kill a man with a look.

"I learned some of his medicine, but never had the power he had. I could concentrate and send myself into an enemy village disguised as a panther, listen to their plans and then return from my trance to tell the war captains what I had heard. I could conjure up wind storms against the enemy or fog, but never bring down the thunder and lightning the way the great Passaconnaway did. This was why I wanted the white man's god. Passaconnaway had no need of its power, but I wanted more and I felt the man John Eliot would teach me so my people could protect themselves against its spells."

Konkowasco begins to chant, shaking his turtle-shell rattle and smudging again. He ends with "A Ha!" and the children listening seem to awaken from sleep.

"There were many people gathered on the hill the first day John Eliot spoke. He was a tall man and easily climbed a large rock overlooking those of us sitting on the grass below.

"Job Nesutan and Cutshamakin climbed up next to him to help him when he couldn't find the word he wanted to say or to explain about some white man thing that we had never seen. These men had been with the English soldiers during their attacks on the Pequots. They had lived amongst Englishmen for years and knew their ways and speech. They told us that John Eliot was not like the soldiers or their sachems, that he was a man of peace and loved us the way a father loves his children.

"Many sachems attended the event. Besides Cutshamakin, the Massachusetts federation was represented by Mascononamo of Agawam, who brought his family and councillors. From Hassanamesitt came Petavit, the second husband of Squaw Sachem (my grandfather' sister) and his young son Wattascompanum plus Kattenait, who later took the first name Job. Another sagamore from that area, Quanohit, brought his young sons, whom the English later named James and Thomas. Gunrashit, another sachem of the

Hassanamesit area, attended. There were other children present who would later become followers of Eliot's god- among them were the boys who later were called Peter Ephraim, Andrew Pityme and Peter Jethro.

"From Weshakim my uncles Muttawump and Shoshonam (Sam) were there as well as David. Others there were Apequinash, who later took the name John, Old Jethro from Natick; Matoonas from Packachoog; Tom Dubler and Peter from Nashoba and Pottoquam, who took the name Simon, came from Wachusett. Even some Wabbaquasetts had made the journey, among them Nontratouso, Keehod and Willymachin. From Nashoba came our chief sachem Nahattawahunt of Nashoba, and his son John Tahattawan. Caleb of Tatumasket was there and from Nashaway came Monoco. Noticeably absent was my father, Shatookquis, and Ousemequin. Both wanted nothing to do with the white man's god.

"Most of the people there had grown up knowing the white man and so they did not think Eliot's ways strange. In fact, I think many looked up to him as a man of great medicine. I partly felt that way, for the English seemed to get whatever they wanted from their Creator. Of course neither I nor my friends stopped to think of how the white men were always fighting amongst themselves- the English against the Dutch and French and against any who did not worship the way they did. We were there to obtain some of the whiteman's god's medicine. And John Eliot knew how to keep our interest, for he would tell us things we had never thought about and we would ask many questions.

"Eliot spent the week telling about how they thanked their god every day for all he had given them, which we also did. He told us their god had given his people ten laws. They were similar to codes we knew, except for one that said they could only marry one wife. This one caused the sachems to ask many questions and we found it difficult to understand. Many told him that the people were happy with our system, for a young wife would help an older wife and would continue to give the sachems children so they could send them out to their villages to continue the royal lines. If a man could support more than one wife, why did this anger their god?

"Eliot said they didn't know why their god had given them these rules for it wasn't their way to question his wisdom. To do so was considered an evil thing, he said. He told us that their god was always at war with the devil, who was similar to Hobbomock. This devil had once been one of their god's most beloved councillors and had sat with the great sachem in the sky as a brother. He had much medicine, but he wanted to be the chief sachem and he led other gods in a battle. God won and sent the devil into a place called hell that was always burning. But the devil was always trying to get men to become his subjects and lose the love of God. He would trick them and make them do terrible things, Eliot said, and the only way to defeat this devil was to keep thinking about God and the things God wanted us to do. Their book called the Bible gave people the instructions on how to walk the good road and how to recognize the devil's temptations.

"This was very strong medicine to my people. We knew about evil spirits and powwows such as myself knew how to win them over so they would help us in healing or working our magic, but we did not know how to keep them from bothering us when we didn't want them to. I especially wanted to learn how to recognize their tricks, for if I could outsmart them, I could control them whenever I wanted. I became hungry for the secrets in this Bible, but at the same time other powwows began to boast that they were more powerful than the white man's powwows, such as Eliot.

"Their boasts and showing off led the English court to pass a law forbidding them from coming into the English villages or even from practicing in their own villages. They also passed a law forbidding our people living in their villages to worship our gods.

"Many powwows had come to hear Eliot speak because of this. They wanted to learn how to use this god so they could be friends of the English. However, most left feeling that Eliot asked too much. He said they believed their god out of faith, and not because they had seen him working. This did not make sense to us, for we knew what our spirit guides could do for us. Eliot said that even if their god didn't seem to answer their prayers and give them what they asked for, he had answered them and given them what he wanted to give them.

"Many of my fellow powwows laughed at this in the privacy of our wetus. What good was a god that didn't give you what you asked for? How could we use this god to help our sick or stop a drought or flood? Our people would laugh at us if we conducted ceremonies and called upon this god, offered sacrifices and chanted and sang only to have the god not help us. We would lose our status quickly, we knew, and no longer receive gifts from our people for our services.

"This was strange stuff to us, but still I chose to learn more, to see if I could learn the magic words to outsmart the spirits.

"Eliot said a man who had this god in his heart would always know what God wanted him to do and the right path to follow. We had our Great Spirit who did this same thing. But as a powwow I felt it was my responsibilty to learn about as many gods as possible, so I decided I would listen to Eliot again the next time he spoke."

"A while later I accompanied my grandfather Naddawahunt to the village the English called Lancaster in Nashaway. He had been persuaded to sell the lands to the English by Thomas King, who had visited us with Nathanial Norcross in tantiesques to get a deed for the black rock place (the lead mine). They had said it would be good to have a Christian village near his people but when we visited we found the minister was not as holy as Eliot was and the people were rowdy and drunk. My father said Eliot had told him he would like to create separate towns just for my people who wanted to be Christians. No bottled spirits would be allowed in these towns, he said.

"And no powwows, either."

Chapter 19

(A re-telling of the Narragansett skirmishes, 1647 - 1650)

Shatookquis (Firehawk) rises. His face is deeply lined from his losing battle with the lung disease. He coughs into the pile of moss in the small basket he carries and then takes a sip of the slippery elm tea his daughter offers him.

"After my daughter's kidnapping, the Mohegans went away but my people did not know peace the following year. It was no longer safe to walk the path from the Nashaways to the quonicticut. I moved to the congomond lakes but returned when my father told me he needed me in quansik.

"That year three travelers were killed between Quaboag and Agawam by warriors who left no sign to identify themselves. They had been carrying beaver pelts to the trading post in Springfield, so at first we thought it was the white man. But others said it was the Narragansett, who stole the pelts because they were desperate to raise the wampum needed to pay the English. Some said it was the Mohawks, for the Narragansetts now had them fighting with them against the Mohegans. Such an alliance put us in a dangerous position.

"A while after the first murders, five more braves were murdered on the path from Nashaway to Quaboag.

"My father sent many messages to Ousemequin during this time, pleading with him to try to act as mediator to make peace between the Mohegans and Narragansetts but Ousemequin sent Wamsutta to tell him the English would end the mattter when their army went to Mohegan to fight with Uncas. He knew our hatred of the Mohegans, made more poignant from their attack the previous year, but he said he had pledged to be the white mans friend and to fight with them and not against them.

"But when his eldest son Wamsutta visited me and my brothers he swore us to secrecy and then told us that once the Narragansetts were subdued, their lands would become part of the Wampanoag federation and others would become part of the Mohegans'. Then our people would combine and drive the Mohegans out, he said. We had to be patient. His people, too, were being harrassed by the Narragansetts, especially those living in the border areas, but it was best to just let the English deal with them. Why shed the blood of our people when the English were ready to shed blood in battle? Once the war was over, there would be less English, Mohegan and Narragansett warriors for us to fight.

"Wamsutta told us we should wait, building up our armies, until the time was ripe. Until that time the whites must never suspect that our peoples were anything but friends. His father was not to know these plans, he said, for Ousemequin was very old and wanted only to live quietly.

"To our south in Niantic, Ninigret married his daughter to Sassacus's brother in-law to gather the Pequot remnant into his federation. This angered his long island allies, for they hated the Pequots.

"Then, in the time of *towwakeeswosh* (when they hill the corn-June) moon, the great sachem of the Narragansetts died. Canonicus was a contemporary of my father and Naddawahunt and our sachems sent wampum to his heir, Meika, to show homage.

"Shortly after, Wequash died and Uncas told the English he was poisoned by the Narragansett and Mohawk powwows.

"But Uncas himself had to answer charges by several Pequots who said they had paid him money for asylum in Mohegan and that he had taken 100 fathoms of wampum from them but had then threatened to turn them over to the English. They were appealing to the Boston court for permission to live in English territory as free men and not as slaves because of alleged war acts. Uncas claimed the wampum had been sent as homage following the death of one of his sons the past winter.

"While Uncas and his councillors were at the court, Pessacus and Ninigret were ordered to come and bring the tribute they had promised. Pessacus sent word that he was sick and could not travel, but a moon later Ninigret appeared with some of the wampum. The English were not happy and pressed him for all of the wampum, which made the sachem of the Niantics very angry. He asked what right had they, the newcomers to Turtle Island, had to demand such payment? Why did they demand so much? His people and the Narragansetts had been much affected by the war, he said, but the English said they didn't care and would war on them if the wampum weren't delivered.

"These words scared the Niantics, who said they would send the sons of Ninigret and Pessacus to live with the English as a sign that they would pay them in two weeks, or fourteen sleeps.

"Of course the children they sent were not royal sons, for who would be so foolish as to risk losing members of the royal line? When the sleeps passed and they couldn't send the money, the English soldiers marched into Narragansett and tried to exact it in person. Desperate, Pessacus took a war party into Mohegan and tried to rob one of Uncas' villages, but he was driven off and the English did not receive their tribute.

"To get even, the English told Ninigret that Pumham and Sacono owned the area they had sold to the man Gorton, who had returned from their sachem in England with permission to settle there. They also bought part of noantum (Sudbury) from Kutshamakin, Cato and Jojeunny and their pniese Standish bought land in nameunkquasset (Bridgewater) from Ousemequin.

"While the whites were busy grabbing land from the Wampanoag federation, one of them called Peter Stuyvesent said the Dutch sachem had given them permission to settle in the Wappinger and Montouk lands.

"This caused a rift between the Niantics and those tribes on long island who had been allied with them. They argued over the wampum Ninigret had demanded from then and then paid to the English. They attacked the Mohegans first, then the Niantics. Their sachem was more determined than ever to drive all the English out and Ninigret and Pessacus began to gather an army to join them.

"We in Quaboag became involved when Squaw Sachem's enemy to the north, in alliance with the Mohawks, attacked our villages and demanded tribute. We were still poor in wampum and so they didn't bother us much, but her villages were repeatedly raided and all of Quaboag was afraid that the Mohawks and Tarrantines would ambush us.

"Ousemequin refused to declare war on the Narragansetts and I became impatient with his insistance on peace. We became caught in the same quagmire as the Narragansetts and Niantics and had to send our boys and girls off to find shells so we could manufacture wampum. Even the Mohegans had to pay the whites this material, for they told Uncas he owed them for every adult male and boy Pequot he had kept after the massacre. There was a lust for this stuff that pitted tribe against tribe and English against our people.

"Our gardens weren't tended as well as in the past for our children were too busy searching through the bottom of the ponds for clam shells. Our wampum was not considered as nice as the wampumpeag made at the seashore from the whelks, so we had to make more of it just to keep the Narragansetts from robbing us of furs, kettles or other things that they would then trade for wampum.

"My warriors had not accepted the Narragansett harassment without a struggle, but the Narragansetts had better thundersticks and more of the pellets. We often had only small stones to put inside the muskets and very little of the black powder we needed to make the thunder. Our braves had to use their thundersticks sparingly and had to spend more time hunting for they needed beaver pelts to keep our southern neighbors happy.

"But we were not happy and I spent many hours in council with my brothers talking about joining the plot being formulated by the Narragansetts, Niantics, Wappingers and Montauks to drive the English out. They were weak now, they said, for their sachem Winthrop had died. What would we have to lose, we asked? Yet my father urged us to remain allies of the whites. He said they would be the ultimate victor. We didn't know what to do- all we knew was that we didn't want to end up like the Pequots, who had no country of their own now.

"I remember that winter as very bleak. Before the snows came there were caterpillers everywhere. We found them in our beds, in our food, all over.

"Travel was dangerous so we had few visitors. Food was scarce for the Narragansetts had taken corn as well as beaver pelts. As sachem, I was constantly being challenged by the braves to kill the Narragansetts the next time they visited. But I was also under oath to Ousemequin that I would not attack them, even the renegades living in Hyems and Mesea's territories. Many families left Asquoach that year and went to live with the Nashaways, so only a handful were left to defend us from the repugnant raiders. I was full of sadness that winter. My people had spoken. They did not like living under the thumb of the Narragansetts and in danger from Mohegans and Mohawks. They did not agree with my desire for neutrality.

"At the next harvest time we heard the Mohawks had warred on the Hurons and had won. It was said they were conspiring to kill all the Dutch "when the ice was on the water." There was to be more trouble in Iroquois. The Senecas attacked and then incorporated the neutral tribes and then the Mohawks attacked the Susquehannucks but weren't able to conquer them.

"As I showed my youngest son how to carve spoons and bowls from burls and knots of hornbeam, elm, white oak, hard maple or basswood, charring them then scraping them out with a shell and polishing them with a beaver tooth, and how to make arrows and chip flint and quartz for arrowheads, I knew I was teaching him a way of life that was passing. He and his brothers wanted muskets, not bows and arrows. But I taught them that muskets can get wet or run dry and fail but a sturdy root ball club would always work. I said the white man was new but the ways of our people were ancient and would eventually prove to be the true ways. They listened repectfully but I knew they laughed about me and my resistance to change behind my back.

"During that winter I had my first battle with chest sickness. My son and my squaw spent many hours beside my bed, chanting, singing and giving me skunk cabbage tea to drink. I had fever and walked often in the spirit world. My grandfather visited me and told me that my father was right, that we would gain nothing by fighting. But then he said our people would never win in a battle with the whites. "Your son will be the bird of peace," he said. "You must help him be the peace bringer so you can save your people."

"I also suffered much with the toothache that winter. This is the most horrible of all pains and I took a variety of medicines. When they didn't help, I sent for Konkowasco and he tried willow bark. When that didn't work, he mixed powdered white hellibore root with raccoon grease and stuffed it in the tooth hollow. This finally quieted the pain I had felt with every breath, drink and bite.

"As spring returned to our hillsides it brought back my health but Konkowasco went away again on another spiritual quest for knowledge."

Chapter 20
(Shaman training and the Praying Villages, 1652-1653)

Konkowasco helps his father down. The longhouse grows quiet as Shatookquis recovers from a coughing fit. Konkowasco then takes the talking stick and begins:

"I spent the next few winters with John Eliot. Since the gathering in Natick, I had been in touch with John Tahattawan and others who wanted Eliot to establish a village where our people who wanted to worship his god could live. This was needed, we agreed, because those who renounced our gods and accepted Eliot's god were treated cruelly by the others in their villages. They were spat on and their wetus ransacked while being challenged to fight. Eliot had told them that his god would not allow them to fight, for they had to "turn the other cheek" to their enemies but this was a hard thing to do when they were always being picked on. Some said they felt like the little chickens the English raised, chased about by the others and pecked at. This new god was jealous of the other gods, the Bible said, and if one wanted his love one had to give up all the other gods. The other powwows said this would make our gods angry and said the followers of Eliot would bring trouble to their tribes so they were told to leave and build new wetus outside the villages.

"Eliot knew of their troubles and obtained a grant of land from his government in Natick on the Charles River so anyone who wanted to could move there and live in peace. He said that in his people's history Christian people had often been mistreated and punished for loving God, but that God never stopped loving those who loved him and that he had blessed the English with all they had because they loved him.

"The new village in Natick was built like an English village, in straight lines. There were three rows of streets with small square houses and a house where they could learn about God's words. Those who lived there were given names from the Bible and Eliot began to teach the people how to read and write the white man's language. The most popular names for the men and boys were Simon, Benjamin, Andrew, John and David.

"While this village was being planned, John Eliot came to see me. He said he understood I was a close friend of Passaconnaway's and asked if I would take him to see the great sachem/powow.

"Although I thought Passaconnaway would never consent to such a thing, I told Eliot I would send a message to the great sachem of the Pennacooks to see if he would receive a visit from him.

"I was surprised when he sent word that he would see him, for he had avoided the English before, fearing that they would bewitch him.

"Passaconnaway's village was located on a large island in the middle of the mommock (or cabassauk - Merimac) river. His braves met us at the shore and ferried us across the rapid current. Because it was *towwakeeswosh* moon (June) the water level was not as high as in the spring and there were many rocks. The Pennacooks knew this river and deftly avoided the rocks. Our canoes approached a hillside covered with pines, turned against the current and moved in, coming to rest in a sheltered cove. Some of his Passaconnaway's people came out to see us, helping us pull the canoes to shore. I was greeted warmly by many, for I had spent much time there while learning things from Passaconnaway and was considered a Pennacook brother.

"Eliot was also given a friendly welcome. He had a way about him that made people want to be his friend. He was not pushy or gruff like many of the Englishmen and he stopped at each person, looked them in the eyes and said, "Netop" as he gave each a small gift - a bright blue bead, a bit of ribbon, a bit of salted pork or cheese wrapped in cloth, even a few musketballs. And he brought Passaconnaway a thick blanket made of what they called trading cloth. One thing Eliot never brought to the people but other white traders did, was the firewater. When pressed for some, he would tell the sachems that their god did not approve of it. This made him uncomfortable as sachems would tell him their ministers at Plimouth and Boston drank it and said it was good. Eliot said the Bible often warned men about drunkenness and that his followers did not drink the fruit of the vine. He said much sin had happened because of fire-water drunk by people who were like children and not used to it. The

Plimouth and Boston fathers were used to it, he said, and knew how to drink it without becoming drunk. He said it was like the herbs powwows used. They knew how to chew a little to obtain their vision, but they did not chew so much that they died.

"Of course, he would then add that such visions were the work of the devil and that we shouldn't chew any herbs at all or seek after any vision except those sent by God.

"Passaconnaway offered a feast of salmon and fresh meat to us. He introduced Eliot to his elders and offered him his long, carved redstone pipe to share. This redstone was precious for it came from the west and could only be obtained through trade with the Iroquois. Eliot watched the singing and dancing Passaconnaway's people did for us and accepted any bowl that was passed to him. Unlike the whites who semed anxious to leave as soon as they came into our villages, Eliot was relaxed, hugging the children who came over to him to touch his beard or his clothes.

"The following day Passaconnaway took Eliot for a walk on the island. We stopped at the top of a hill that looked out over the Pennacook land to one side and the Nashobas on the other. Further away through the summer haze we could see the blue hills of the Massachusetts and the tree-covered mountains to our west.

"Passaconnaway motioned Eliot to sit by his side.

"He said,

"'I have heard you are a great powwow of your god.'

"Eliot said he was but a servant of his god.

"Passaconnaway then asked, 'Can you make the stone people talk?'

"When Eliot said he didn't understand, Passaconnaway stood up and struck the ground with his staff. The hillside shook and there was a loud rumbling from below. Those with us fled into the trees, yelling out in fear. As it stopped, Eliot, who had also been afraid, regained his composure and told Passaconnaway his god had done such things for his people. He said he had made a whole city wall fall down when trumpets blew and had made a dry path through the red sea so his people could cross it.

"Passaconnaway looked at Eliot for a long time then told him to call on his god and make the river around his island stop so they could walk to the other side.

"Eliot replied that it was not in his power to ask God to do such a thing and Passaconnaway grunted in disgust. He silenced the interpreter and said to me that Eliot was a fraud and not the great powwow he had heard about.

"But Eliot had our tongue and knew what he said. He told him how his god had sent a plague of hailstones and had rained frogs down on a people in a place called Egypt and how he had turned a river greater than the one below into blood and how he had sent a plague of snakes upon the Egyptians and then killed all of their first-born children.

"Passaconnaway listened and then asked if Eliot had seen any of these things with his own eyes. Eliot replied that they were written in their Bible and that every word in it was true, for it had been sent from God.

"He then told Passaconnaway that he would not engage in a contest with him to show who had the most power, for that would be considered tempting the lord his god. He said what Passaconnaway and the rest of us powwows did was evil and made god angry.

"I felt ice form in my stomach as Passaconnaway stared at him. I braced myself for the death he would send to Eliot, but instead Passaconnaway said he had had a dream a while ago and Creator had told him he must not hurt his white children for they would someday be as wise as his people. They just needed time to grow up, Creator had told him.

"Eliot said such words would make most Englishmen angry, but he said he believed we were all god's children and that he believed my people had once lived in the deserts written about in the Bible. He said one of the tribes had become lost in their wanderings and he thought the people on Turtle Island were lost Jews. He said that made us a member of god's chosen nation. He said he thought we once knew god but then we fell alseep and when we woke up we had forgotten him.

"Passaconnaway said we were Cautantowwit's chosen people and the English were now *his* adopted people.

"Eliot asked him many questions about Cautantowwit and Manitoo plus other gods and Passaconnaway told him as much as he would be able to understand. Eliot said he knew we were this lost tribe because our Keepers of the Stories knew of the great flood that god had sent to punish sinners. He said we would not have known such a thing if we had not once known god.

"Throughout the day and into the night, Passaconnaway listened to but did not argue with Eliot. He indulged him, smiling at his words, but I read the frown in his eyes. He told me later that one must never listen to them without putting one's mind on something else, for they could hypnotize one with words. He told me the secret was to sing a song to one of my spirit guardians in my head and heart while listening with my ears.

"Passaconnaway said we had a powerful magic in this ability, but it was so powerful he was afraid a man would succumb to it while trying to master it. He warned me to be very careful and gave me a piece of a smooth red rock. I held it up to the light and saw fire dancing in it and he told me there was a huge rock of this in his territory, that it was a place of great manitoo and someday he would show it to me. He said whenever I listened to the white man about his god, I must hold his rock in my palm and call upon its spirit to protect me from being hypnotized.

"Passaconnaway also told me he had taught the Mohawk powwows how to poison their enemies from a distance by visiting them in their sleep and placing a spell on them so they would carve their spoons out of the poisonous laurelwood root. He said he feared they were now teaching the long island people how to do this to the Narragansetts and Mohegans. He told me how to counteract the spell so I could protect my people. He then said even a great powwow sometimes makes mistakes.

"I knew his people had a good relationship with the Mohawks so was not surprised to hear that he had given them a spell to cast on their enemies. What surprised me when I returned to Quaboag was the information that the Narragansetts, Mohawks and Mohegans were now getting guns from the Dutch at Fort Orange (Albany), because they wanted to fight with them against the English. Also to our north and west the Senecas, Cayugas, Onondagas and Oneidas were asking the French at Quebec to intervene and to call a truce between them and the Hurons at Montreal.

"We thought the Narragansetts hated all white men plus the Mohawks and Mohegans, so thought it strange that they should now accept their alliance. Waban told us that there were different tribes and Meika was just playing the tribe called the Dutch against the tribe called the English. The Mohawks had been using the white man this way to kill their enemies for some time. Waban said the

Narragansetts and Niantics hated the English so much because of their treatment of them regarding the wampum that they would do anything to drive them out.

"But such talk was soon replaced by the news that Ousemequin's eldest son, Wamsutta, had married Corbitant's eldest daughter. This was not a first marriage for Wetamoo, for she was a widow and now sachem of Pocasset.

"Such a marriage made Ousemequin's federation stronger for he no longer had to fear that Corbitant would stab him in the back. The Narragansett threat to his north had finally been solved, not by warfare but by love.

"That winter we heard that Ninigret had gone to Manhattoes (Manhatten) to be treated by the shamans and Dutch doctor there for a persistent problem, thought to be a spell cast on him by the long island and Mohawk powwows. But we also heard that while he was there he spent much time in council with Dutchmen.

"As the Narragansett-Niantics and Mohawks were making plans with the Dutch white men, the English were busy buying more land from Ousemequin and Wamsutta. In the time of *wapicummilcum* (the February) moon Wamsutta sold chisawannock (Hogg island), off the coast to an Englishman. A moon later he and his father sold a part of sunkunke (Rehoboth) to the white man. At that event, Wamsutta did something that surprised Ousemequin and showed the white man that he was wise to their ways. Instead of wampum, he asked for the metal coins the white man used. Wampum was only good at the trading posts, he told his father and councillors. White man's metal coins were good for trading anywhere. But a while later he sold some of Weetamoo's lands to the English, which marked the beginning of troubles between him and her.

"To our south Hyems sold a large area called quinebaug to the English. In Quaboag and Wabbaquasset this caused much worry, for would he then try to sell our lands?

"The Mohegans led a war party into Niantick territory that spring and robbed much wampum. This made Ninigret crazy, for the English were constantly bothering him for the wampum they said he owed them. A piece of wampum had become more precious than blood in Narragansett at that time. The English then sent a messenger to him demanding that he answer questions about the plot with the Dutch that Uncas had told them about. Ninigret was full of rage and began all-out war with the Mohegans, Wappingers and those long island bands who were not his allies.

"This brought the English army against him and the Dutch. They sent ships and seized the Dutch trading post on the quonicticut at Hartford. In quansik such matters made us very nervous. Our trade was disrupted and our paths saw so few travelers that grass grew over places where many bare feet had once touched Mother Earth.

"My friend Eliot sent word to me that a friend of his, Thomas Mayhew, had opened a full-time school on Martha's Vineyard where he was teaching the Christians there to read and write. Another school was opening at the place they called Harvard in Cambridge and Ousemequin's youngest son, Sunconewhew was to be its first student.

"My grandfather was very interested in this thing, for he knew the white man played tricks on our people with their magic scratchings on hoosick, their white skin called paper.

"He asked his youngest son if he would like to go. He also asked Nassawanno's young son if he would like to go to one of these schools, for the boy was very smart and could understand some of the white man's tongue.

"So I brought the boys, who later were called Andrew of Quabogud and Nassowanno's son, who later was called Lawrence, to Eliot so he could take them to the school he thought best.

"Eliot decided to take them on in Natick. He had a Hassaminisso boy named James there who was going to Harvard to learn the language so could become a printer and make copies of their god's book, the Bible, to give to people who knew how to read. James was the son of the asquoach sachem Noas who had recently given Eliot 1,000 acres of land near his village for a Christian village. His uncles were Tukapewillin and Anaweakin, both Christians in praying villages.

"Many small battles took place between the Narragansetts and our southern neighbors, but quansik knew a winter of relative peace.

"I had a pupil of my own by then, a boy called Crawling Turtle. I took him to the ancient ledge where our ancestors had carved the figure of a deer and then a short distance to the stream where there was the ancient stone shaped like a mother. This place had much manitoo and was used by our women when they wanted help getting a child. It also had many fine quartz crystals, which had manitoo. I taught him how to find a good-sized one and how to look into it to see what others were doing. Such a thing was often asked of shamans by sachems or war captains during time of war.

"In the same area beyond the waddaquadducks to our south was a place we called Hobbomock's bowl . We spent many sleeps in the different seasons lying on our stomachs in the small cave in the belly of the bowl as we watched the horizon. I pointed out to him the notches made by Creator that framed the rising sun when the spring was coming so we could tell our people when to plant. There were other marks on the rim of the bowl, some made by ancient shamans of piles of rocks, that told us when the snow would soon come and I showed him how to watch two piles of such rocks when the sun was setting, for when it set precisely between them, the days would begin to grow longer and Grandfather Sun would return to our people. As powwows we had to observe these things, for if the sun did not rise or set as it should during the right moon we would know that Cautanowwit was sending us a message that he was changing the great circle of life for Turtle Island.

"At night we observed the clusters of stars. One night in the time of the *papsaquoho* (December) moon, we observed a very important event. The moon shone blue in the black, bitter cold night. As we observed this strange thing, ten shooting stars passed overhead followed by ten more. While sitting at our fire on the hillside under steerage rock, I had a vision. Creator came and sat down with us. He said many changes would happen on Turtle Island to our people in the next twenty winters. The moon was the color of water, the color of our tears, he said.

"I asked Creator how I could help my people avoid these things. He took me to a place where there was more snow than I had ever seen. There were no trees, no rocks, only great walls of blue and white snow and deep, black water. I saw a red wolf running, its tongue hanging out of the side of its mouth, the drool frozen to its muzzle. Under a blue moon it ran and ran, its eyes full of that desperation an animal gets when it knows the hunter is winning.

"I tried to see what it was running from, but all was an eerie black and white darkness. The wolf appeared to live in a world where nothing else existed, but it was afraid, it was being chased.

"Suddenly at the crest of the hill behind it, I saw its hunters. They were riding on a great bird, a huge dragonfly. I heard the crack of a thunderstick and saw the wolf fall, its body rolling over and over in the bloody snow. The huge flying thing flew over it and then flew away, leaving its twisted, dying body on the snow. Then I saw its spirit rise and join the spirits of its pack and they ran and played without fear in the snow under the spirit moon.

"As I blinked, raising my eyes from the fire, I felt tears on my cheeks for brother wolf. Below I saw our valley, its rows of snow-tipped hills glowing under the blue moon. Creator had told me in my mind that my people would become like the wolf. No matter how far we ran, the white man would come after us and hunt us down, leaving our bones to rot where they lie. As with the pursuit of the wolf there would appear to be no reason for it. Such a concept - killing an animal for no reason - I could not comprehend.

"A melancholy moved into my soul that night, a melancholy I have known every day since.

"My brothers and sisters, we have traveled far from quansik, but as long as we live, we will be hunted like that wolf. As long as we do not look like the white man or talk his language, we will be chased. There will come a day when you must learn to be quansik only in your heart. When that day comes, the land we hunted and fished in will not be recognized as quansik to any who do not have it in their heart. But Creator will give your heart eyes in which to see the salmon swimming in the Englishman's dammed rivers; the ears to hear the hawk above the noise of their machines and the ability to see our grandfathers and grandmothers dancing and singing around our sacred fire circles where their square houses stand. To the white men we will be like the wolf lying dead on the ground. But all who have quansik blood in their veins will know our people still live. The spirit of our people will never die.

"This was something Creator taught me later. The white man's thundersticks have no power over our souls. Their god can take them, yes. But their bullets: they cannot pierce what they cannot see."

Chapter 21
(A re-telling of the emergence of a new generation of leaders, 1654-1658)

John Tahatawaban rises, his eyes moist from Konkowasco's words.

"Around the time of Konkowasco's vision, the sachem Potok of nianticut (Pt. Judith) had a similar vision and realized how dangerous the white man's soulstealers could be. He forbid his people from learning about their god and wrote a letter to the English asking them to stop sending Christianized Massachusetts braves into his lands. He didn't want his people to listen to their words, he said. They were happy with their gods and wanted to be left alone.

"But the English were like a flooding river that could not be stopped. If they were blocked in one place, they flowed even stronger in another. The next summer the English bought squantum (Quincy) from Old Ahaughton, his son William Ahaughton, William Mananiomott, Josiah, Daniel, Job Nassot and Manuntago. These were all men who had been hypnotized by Eliot and the white man Gookin's words.

"The English again started trouble between Ousemequin and Pumham by telling Pumham if he claimed the rights to mishawomot (Warwick) they would send troops to fight with him. This made Ousemequin so so angry he came close to raising his tomahawk against the whites. Nawwashasuck, who was living in sowams at the time, worked out a scheme and Pumham was stabbed before the English could join his men. And so the Pokanokets decided the matter and not the English. To make peace, Ousemequin visited Plymouth and asked the English to give his two oldest sons English names. The oldest was named Alexander and Metacomet was named Philip. Ousemequin was told these had been great warrior-kings who had conquered many lands and built an impressive empire, so he was proud to have his sons named after them.

"The next year he finalized the sale of chisawannock (Hogg Island). Sunconewhew was learning much about the white man's ways and values and he spoke often with his brothers. They told his father the English wanted his lands so much he could do almost anything and they would not fight with him. They told him all he had to do was sell them a piece of land and they would forget all about the wounding of Pumham. Philip and Alexander were very shrewd about these things. Unlike their father, they had grown up with the white man and were not afraid of him. They understood that the Plymouth English did not like the Salem English and they both did not like Roger Williams or Samuel Gorton. And that all the English did not like the Dutch or French. They advised against allying with a particular tribe of white man, but Ousemequin said he would always be a friend to the Plymouth English, for he owed his life to them.

"But I was not concerned with Pumham as much as I was by the new thing the English were doing on the shore of the housatonic River near weantinook (Derby). By now there were many floating islands coming from across the sea, each one bringing more white men. We saw flocks of these great canoes in the harbors near Boston and Salem and at the mouth of the quonicticut and long island. They were a common sight at the English villages of Hartford and Springfield but we had never seen how they made them.

"I traveled to squontock (Derby) so I could watch this mystery.

"I had often made birchbark canoes so I knew boats needed ribs and a spine but the English ships were shaped differently. For one thing, they built their boats inside huge wooden buildings. In one place they made rope and canvas for the sails and hewed tremendous larch beams for the hulls. I had never seen the insides of such huge ships before and it was fascinating to watch.

"I stayed at this place for a moon then traveled to their fort at Springfield with Toto. I traded with Wahginnicut's people in agawam. Then I went on to Nassawanno's village in wombemesseck at the place where the three rivers met. While staying there during the coldest part of the winter, we heard that the great sachem Masconomo had died. He was buried on the hill overlooking the bay along with his musket. His widow was now afraid the English would make her leave her home, so she asked them for permission to stay where he had fenced in.

"This outraged his nephew Nassowanno. He said it was a lesson to us about becoming too friendly with the whites. He said he was glad his son was learning their laws, for he would protect them if the English came to quansik seeking land.

"But they did come that year. That was when the first white man moved into quansik at the black rocks in tantiesques. Our brother George Tahanto told you about this.

"Around this time the nine English families at Lancaster received their first real minister. His name was Joseph Rowlandson. Up to this time, the people living there had wanted to go back to the Salem area, but the English would not let them leave. They said they would lose their grant if it weren't occupied so they stayed but they were not doing much. Monoco and Muttaump's people paid them little attention unless they wanted a drink of cider. But this new minister was very strict and began making rules. No longer were our people free to intermingle with the whites. They were told to stay away because they were a bad influence.

"This made the sachems burn with hatred. One thing we cannot tolerate is to be insulted. If it hadn't been for Naddawahunt's intervention, the entire village of Lancaster would have been destroyed that year.

"By now the English were establishing a number of villages along the path from the quonicticut to wechakum. The men Ephraim Curtis, Thomas Day and Thomas King were settling around wachusett and quansigamond in Simon Pottoquam's territory. As I moved along the paths trading, I saw more and more white men living on our lands. Most didn't have permission from their king but had permission from the local sachems because they thought the white men wouldn't war on any tribe that had whites living with it.

"It was around this time that Wetolechen died. His son Wascomos took over sachemship of the asquoach area. Naddawahunt's son Nascowanno and Mishalisk's son Muttaump took over chief sachemship of quansik. Both Naddawahunt and Mishalisk were getting old and were chief sachems in name only at this time. The same thing was happening with Ousemequin. His son Alexander was really the one in charge.

"So now a new generation of rulers was coming to power. A new generation that had not made pledges to the English."

Chapter 22
(1659 - 1661)

Konkowasco rises, pulling his robe tighter. The robe is made of raccoon hides with a layer of hawk feathers at its shoulders. The colors of the hawk feathers and the raccoon fur are almost identical, which led to the naming of his robe "Bird Cat" by the Oneida children.

"I was in contact with Eliot's Christian people around this time and received a page of print from James Printer, who was now working as an apprentice to Samuel Green. In Pocasset John Sassamon began working with Eliot to translate the Bible for his people. Sassamon spoke the white man's tongue so well that he was often asked to go to Plymouth or Boston to serve as an interpreter and Ousemequin had him look over the deeds he signed when he sold land rights to the English.

"But Sassamon was not liked by the other Pocassets, for he had helped the English destroy the Pequots and had taken as a reward Miantonomoh's young daughter. This had angered our people for royal captives were not given to commoners as slaves. If a royal male were captured, he was entitled to an honorable death at the hand of a sachem of equal or greater rank. His children were entitled to kind treatment by the conquering sachem's family and were not given to common warriors as booty. Many felt Sassamon had become too English and no longer cared about the ways of his people, for amongst our people it was considered a grave offense to think of oneself as of greater status or rank than one actually was. We accepted any brave who truly was what he said he was, but if a warrior claimed to have counted five coups and had actually counted fewer he would be scorned. If a visiting brave said he was a councillor and we found out he was nothing more than a common villager, he would be scorned. Perhaps this was because we had no way of knowing who a man was except by what he told us when he came amongst us. If a man lied the first time he came amongst us, we would soon find out and he would not be welcome again. It was better to say one was not important than to pretend otherwise.

"Sassamon had violated this and now thought of himself as the white man's tongue. Like Squanto, he claimed to have knowledge that others didn't have. Amongst the white men he was given status and Eliot made him a preacher to the Christians living in the village of Natick.

"During this time Uncas began to demand that our people join him against the Narragansetts. He first attacked Josias' village, for this son of Chickataubet had been the one who encouraged the inland peoples to become allies of the English. His uncle, Kushamikin was very friendly to the whites and often served as a witness or interpreter at their courts. He had sold packooge neck and was receptive to Eliot, other reasons Uncas singled out Josias Chickataubet for attack. But the main reason was that Uncas' allies the Mohawks did not like Chickataubet's people. We did not join them but later heard that during a battle Uncas and the Mohawks killed eight of Josias' people and twenty-four were carried away into Mohegan territory.

"Then Uncas sent a Pequot named Obechiquod to my father's village and told them if they fought alongside Uncas they would once again be free and no longer have to pay tribute to the Narragansetts. My father and I argued against such a thing as Uncas' troops marched into my grandfather's territory in Pocumtuck, for the Pocumtucks were an enemy of the Mohegans' ally, the Mohawks.

"Our braves were angry with Ousaemequin and his peace talk. They were angry with Naddawahunt for his peace talk. They said while the old men spoke of peace the Mohegens and Narragansetts were picking us off, like weasels raiding a white man's chicken house. They said the quansiks had waited too long for the white man to punish the Narragansetts. They said the white man liked Uncas and would never punish him so he was the one they wanted to be allied with. The said the white man would destroy the Narrgansetts and Niantics the way they did the Pequots and that because we paid tribute to the Narragansetts we would be attacked, too. And they said it would be wise to be allies of and not enemies of the Mohawks. They said the Pocumtucks were no longer the strongest federation and it was now time to change. These words infuriated my father and grandfather and almost split quansik apart.

" Then Mohegan war parties began to be seen in our hills and we knew it would only be a matter of time before they came and demanded corn for their troops.

"Naddawahnunt sent word to Ousemequin about this situation and Alexander sent a party of warriors to asquoach to defend our fort. They skirmished with the Mohegan braves and sent them back into their own territory.

"Around this time Crawling Turtle and I went to hear Passaconnaway for the last time. We had heard that he was dying and went to see with our own eyes if this were true. I loved Pasaconnaway like a father and hoped it was just a rumor. But when we arrived at amoskeag on the shores of the cabassauk (Merrimack) river, we saw many campfires. Passaconnaway and his eldest son Wannalancet came down the river and his sons lifted the frail old man from the canoe. He was reclining on a light bed of thin branches and soft hides and they carried the whole bed, with him on it, to a waiting wetu. My heart bled when I saw how tiny and old he had gotten and I went over and took his bony hand, looking right into his eyes as I greeted him.

"The next day he had us bring him to the top of a hill and he spoke to the many, many people below. Since his voice was weak, his sons repeated what he said and in this way his words echoed through the crowds.

"He said, 'I am an old oak that has lasted the storms of many winters. My eyes are dim and my limbs tremble. The scalplocks that dried before my wetu told the stories of my victories over the Mohawks who invaded our hunting grounds. Then, in their place, came the palefaces. The lands of our forefathers were taken from us.

"'I tried the magic of my sorcery in vain. I, who can take in my palm as I would a worm the rattlesnake, I who have seen Cautanowwit in dreams, and talked with him awake, I, as brave as the bravest, as strong as the strongest, as wise as the wisest, I am like a reed before their tempest.

"'Now, my children, hear my dying words. The oak will soon break before the whirlwind.

"'I commune with the Great Spirit. He whispers to me "Tell your people: peace. Peace is your only hope. Your forests shall fall before their mighty hatchets. At your fishing places, they shall build their houses!"

"'We must bend before the storm.

"'Peace. Peace with the white man is the command of Kitchan and the last wish of Passaconnaway.'

"Then he said to his closest advisors, 'I am now going the way of all flesh. I am ready to die. I will not meet in council with you on these shores again.

"'I will now leave this word of advice with you: be careful how you quarrel with the English. For though you may do them much mischief, you will all be destroyed and rooted off the face of the earth if you do.

"'I was as much an enemy to the English at their first coming into these parts as any one and did try all ways and means possible to have them destroyed, at least to have prevented them from sitting down here, but I could in no way affect it. Therefore I advise you never to contend with the English nor make war with them.'

"And so I knew that Passaconnaway had also received a vision of the red wolf. We remained a week with Passaconnaway in his village, but he slept most of the time and even though I prepared flute reed (cow parsnip) tea for him to gargle with, it hurt his throat to speak. So with great sadness in my breast, I left my friend and teacher knowing I would never see him again.

"Now there were only ten families left in asquoach- my father, my brothers, myself and my uncle's widow and the old warrior Ono Pequin and his family. Along with my father he had fought against Uncas many years before and he said he wasn't afraid to fight him now and so had come to live with us to help defend our village. Shattookquis sent word to quabogud that we would need help harvesting our corn and we received some squaws from Naddawahunt's villages and from the villages of my uncle Nassowanno, who owned the lands west of quaboag pond.

"Around this time Eliot talked to Naddawahunt and my father and convinced them to sell a piece of land near quabogud for an English village. Ousemequin, who was now living in weshakim, said if we sold all but a little piece of land to the English we could still hunt and fish on our lands and be protected by the English. The Mohegans and Narragansetts would not dare attack the English the way they did us.

"This land sale made many of our braves angry and they went to live with the Nashaways, who were talking about joining forces with the other tribes. My uncle Muttawump came into quansik and challenged the sale, saying his mother Mishalisk owned the land and, as chief sachem of her northwest holdings, he had to agree to the sale. He and my father had words and my father moved south of the lead mine in mashapaug near Wabbaquaset.

"The English only fined Uncas ten fathoms of wampum for attacking the Pocumtucks, so the Narragansetts under Canochet became bolder and four of Meika's braves fired into English houses in Mohegan.

"The English immediately summoned the Narragansetts to council. They told them that they were going to declare war on the Narragansetts unless they turned in the four braves who had shot at the English houses or paid them 595 fathoms of wampum. This was a cruel thing, for the English knew the Narragansetts couldn't even come up with the wampum they still owed them. Then the English did a clever thing. They told Meika (who was now married to the squaw sachem of Niantic) and Ninigret's representatives that they would not send their troops against them if they signed a piece of paper that gave them more time to gather up all the wampum. The paper said that if they didn't pay the wampum, the land would become the property of the English. To buy time, Canonicus' grandsons Quissoquus, Scuttup and Quadqueega, sons of Magnus, and Neneglund signed this thing they called a mortgage and returned to Narrgansett to gather their army together.

"By this time, like his contemporaries Ousemequin and Naddawahunt, Ninigret was living in seclusion, in poor health.

"To counterattack the agreement with the English, Potok complained to them that their people were illegally settling at nianticut (Point Judith).

"As had happened before, when Uncas learned that the Narragansett owed the white man wampum, he attacked my people to make sure we didn't help them raise the money.

"This time it was Naddawahunt's village of quabogud that was raided.

"The Wampanoag braves were staying in our fort. We were all very cold that winter for our squaws were afraid to go far from camp to gather wood. Winter had come early and snow had covered the piles of corn cobs our squaws used for fuel. They found some of them, but other piles were hidden under the snow that would not melt. Our old people went to quabogud to live that winter, for the village had more braves to provide meat and they had more firewood.

"We woke up one morning in the time of the *squocheekeeswush* (January) moon to find another arm's length of snow on top of the other layers. It had blown into our wetus and it took us some time to scoop it out of the way with bark pails, baskets and metal cooking pots so we could go into the woods to pass our morning water.

"Crawling Turtle, who was living with me, then helped me and Alexander's warriors dig the others out. I had heard my people say that the severe winter was a sign from Creator. Others were worried about how all the snow would flood our lands when it melted in the spring. But neither I nor Crawling Turtle had received any visions or signs. We told them that the snow was also making it hard for the English, whose ships couldn't move on the frozen quonicticut river.

"As I went to the spring and broke the ice so I could scoop out some fresh water, I heard a crackling of branches and huffing sounds coming from the direction of quabogud. I pulled back behind a large maple tree and waited, my tomahawk in hand.

"The sachem called Pambussa (Piamboho) came into view, his face contorted with exhaustion as he struggled to run in the deep snow. He wore only a loincloth and no leggings. I shouted for the others and ran to him, pulling the mantle off my shouders to wrap around his heaving chest.

"We carried him into my wetu and the squaws began rubbing his feet, which were a dusky blue color. If the weather had been a little warmer we might have been able to find a rattlesnake to kill so we could wrap its warm hide around his feet. As it was, we had to mix bear grease with wild indigo for a poultice on his frostbitten feet. I sent Crawling Turtle out to get some wood from the trunk of a white pine tree. Shavings of this mixed with the shavings of wild plum and wild cherry could be boiled, mashed and then put on his feet to draw out the poisons.

"'It was Uncas' son and about 70 warriors,' Pambussa panted, 'They attacked while it was still dark. I sent my squaw and children into the swamp and loaded my musket, aiming at the door flap.

"'But they did not come in. I stuck my head out to see what was happening and saw them come out of another wetu, wiping their knives on the snow. I raised my musket and aimed, but they ran off before I could fire. Then I heard my squaw and children screaming and ran in the dark to find them. The wind picked up and the snow was falling so hard I couldn't see in front of my face. I searched all night for them and then went back to the village, hoping they had found their way back.

"'There I learned three of our people had been murdered because they wouldn't give the Mohegans wampum or goods. Besides my family, three others were missing. We found some footprints near the ice but the snow covered their tracks well.

"'I wish I had not sent them out' Pambussa kept repeating as I made him drink a tea of wild ginger that would bring some warmth to his cold limbs.

"Two of the Wampanoag warriors put on their snowshoes and winter clothes and set out for quabogud to find out more and the others went out to see what they could find near the fort. We knew that even with some of Alexander's best men, we were no match for 70 warriors. The thing that made us safe was our location, for any approaching warrior could be seen from the ridgetops. But not if he approached in the middle of the night during a snowstorm.

"Towards dusk a party of warriors went out to the caves nearby and uncovered some of our corn caches and brought the corn closer, to the cavern near the booming rock.

"The next two hands of sleeps we spent in anxious expectation. Pambussa's feet turned deep blue and he was racked with fever. Taking care of him took up most of Crawling Turtle's and my time. We kept applying mashed jack in the pulpit root and corn husks steeped with wild mustard juice to his feet and fingers while calling on our spirit helpers to come and pull the cold from his flesh, which was now a purple color and breaking open in spots. I soaked corn husks in hot water with tobacco and applied them to the sores but didn't think he would survive. While he slept, Crawling Turtle and I watched to see if the light appeared over him. If we had seen it, we would have taken him out of the village to die. The thought of him dying in the snow made me remember my vision of the red wolf. I saw now that the snow was actually white wampum and that it was the Englishman's greed for this that we could not run from.

"Then Pambussa's squaw and children appeared back in quabogud. The Mohegans had allowed her to return to tell

Naddawahant that Uncas' son Oneko would release the other three if the Quaboags sent 25 pounds worth of wampum, two guns and two blankets to him. This was all the remaining wealth in quabogud, for though there were more guns, only two worked.

"Ousemequin heard this and sent Quaquequanset with the details to the English. Ousemequin refused to let my people send the goods requested, for he said my people did not owe tribute to the Mohegans. He told the English that the Quaboags belonged to his federation, not to the Narragansetts as Uncas claimed. Then another of the prisoners escaped and found her way back to Quaboag. She said Uncas told the English his attack was against his enemy Ono Pequin and not against Naddawahunt.

"As soon as the snow melted and the mud dried up Ousemequin moved to quansik, to my aunt Nawwashawsuck's village of Quabogud. He said the English would protect us from the Narragansett, Niantic, Mohegan and Mohawk warriors and English soldiers with muskets were sent to us from Lancaster.

"Ousemequin encouraged his son to sell more land to the English that spring and Alexander sold them some land adjacent to montop and then sold land in sapowett to them. He said this made his position with the English stronger and they would protect any people who belonged to him, such as the Quaboags.

"That fall the English ordered Uncas and Okeno to return the two Quaboags they held and to repay my people what they had robbed them.

"This was Ousemequin's last contact with the English, for a few moons later the sound of a black dog howling was heard outside his wetu and the great sachem of the Wampanoags died in his sleep.

"Alexander had been acting as sachem, but for all matters of importance, our sachems went to Ousemequin. When he died, the peace with the English died with him. I think my grandfather Naddawahunt knew this, for he died the following summer.

"After his death his son Sam ruled Weshakim, John ruled Natick, Nassowanno ruled Wombessuck and Mishalisk's sons ruled the rest of Quansik and Squakeag. Hyems, Allumps and Messea ruled southern quansik.

"Now my father, Shatookquis, and Wequagan, Squaw Sachem and Mishalisk were the elders of quansik. The wattawessu (shining torch) had been passed."

Chapter 23
(A re-telling of Alexander's coming to power, his death and Philip's succession, 1662)

John Tattawaban again rises. His voice is strong and he speaks fast.:

"Alexander's birth as chief sachem of the Wampanoag federation was not an easy one. His father's grave was no sooner heaped high with stones by those who loved him then Alexander's first challenge came - from Weetamoo.

"Weetamoo was not happy with Alexander, this much all knew. To prevent her husband from selling any more of her land, she deeded some to the Englishmen John Sanford and John Archer.

"But Alexander wasn't interested in selling more of her lands or those of his father. He had paid a visit to Canochet in Narragansett and wherever I went to trade the talk was that the Wampanoag federation would soon be entering the war as allies of the Narragansett and Mohawk. The tribes were all angry over the treatment of the Narragansetts by the English and of their excessive demands for wampum. Like a fire that begins with a spark and then smolders, a resentment against this injustice was spreading amongst the tribes.

"This war between the English and Narragansett federation had been a strange thing, for the Mohegan were sometimes friendly to the Narragansett and then at other times would go behind their backs and tell the English about their plans. Uncas, who was by now getting old, refused to be linked solidly with any group. He was like an eel caught with the hands, always squirming to get free.

"Because I wasn't sure if his people would be friendly or hostile, I stopped going into Mohegan to trade. Instead, I concentrated on working the coastal area of the Massachusetts and the Wampanoag peoples as the English were now looking for fish to export instead of beaver pelts. And they were looking for silver instead of wampum, which meant much trading to get to the point where coin changed hands.

"The best area for this coin was in Narragansett - Niantic and Mohegan along the rivers. The English had a new sachem called Charles the Second and he favored this area.

"At this time the English above Quinebaug considered themselves different from the ones below. We thought of them as two federations now and besides these there were other, smaller tribes - those of Williams and Gorton plus the English on long island and then the Dutch. As a trader, it was important to keep them straight, but this was not an easy thing to do so I just kept to the English federation above Quinebaug.

"On the river, Wequagon and his son Squompe were approached about deeding the wild lands south of coasit (Hadley) to the whites. They met in council with Joseph Crowfoot, who lived across from these lands in a fort on the other side of quaniticot.

"While they were in council, I was in munponset, trading near the ponds where Alexander and his councillors were hunting. The corn was growing tall in the long, hot days and nights and many people were at the seashore fishing. All was slow-paced. Even the flying insects seemed to work as if in a trance, droning softly amongst the grapes and over the cranberry bogs.

"Alexander and his men were resting inside his wetu, their guns leaning on the outside, when a troop of Englishmen rode into the camp and ambushed them, pointing their muskets into the flaps. They said they were sent by Winslow to tell Alexander he was to appear before Winslow and his court to answer charges of joining the Narragansett enemy.

"This was Alexander's second challenge. The English would never have treated his father in such a way. They accorded Ousemequin the respect a chief sachem deserved, but Alexander was treated without such courtesy.

"Alexander argued with the soldiers and refused to go until John Sassamon's brother Roland said he would accompany him to speak for him. He said if Alexander did not go, it would be interpreted as a sign that he had already joined the Narragansetts and was an enemy to the English. He said the English were like hungry dogs drooling over Alexander's lands so it would be best to go and pretend friendship. In confidence, Alexander's councillors told him the time was not yet right for declaring war: they did not have enough guns and he did not have the support of the Massachusetts and many inland tribes.

"So, in spite of the blistering heat, Alexander went, his eyes burning with the rage of the insult with every step he took. The soldiers offered him a horse, but he refused, preferring to walk beside Weetamoo and the others accompanying him.

"I asked to join the group for I thought my connections as a trader and my knowledge of the white man's tongue could help Alexander in Plymouth but was asked instead to go to sowams and tell Ousemequin's youngest brother Akkompion and Alexander's brother Philip of the event.

"They knew who had told the English about the plot and the name "Uncas" was spat under more than one breath as they continued their arduous walk.

"We did not normally walk in the midday heat of the Burning Moon, preferring to do our traveling early in the morning before Grandfather Sun leaned too much on our backs or later in the day when the sun passed to the west. But that was not a good time in this area for the mosquitos that bred in the swamps and salt marshes ate a person alive then.

"The English messengers committed a serious offense that day. You see, it was the custom of our people carrying non-urgent messages to arrive, take a meal with their hosts, spend the night and then set forth in the morning. This was the proper way to come before a chief sachem. One did not ride into camp, point a gun at his chest and order him to drop everything and follow. This was what warriors did when they attacked and took prisoners.

"Philip was in Corbitant's village, where he had been living since his marriage to Wootonekanuske. This was Corbitant's youngest daughter and sister to Weetamoo. Whereas Alexander's marriage had been to consolidate the two sachems, Philip's marriage was made out of love. Ousemequin had hoped to marry him to Naddawahunt's daughter but there was a problem with the clans. So, even though the marriage did little to solidfy the federation, Ousemequin had given it his blessing since the two were in love. He did think it a good idea for Philip to live in Pocaset and, because of his proximity to the Narragansetts, Philip had been his link in his recent talks with Canochet.

"Philip (Pometacomet) came out of his large wetu to meet me. He was tall like Alexander and carried himself proudly like one would expect the son of Ousemequin to. Philip and Alexander had sat in on council after council with Ousemequin from an early age. While other boys were playing in the streams he and Wamsutta were learning how to be like their father, how to listen to the white men and to the councillors. He knew many English words but could not read them as well as John Sassamon or his younger brother Suneconewhew could. Both he and Alexander relied on a councillor they called a secretary to write letters to the English and to review the wording of land deeds.

"Pometacomet's brows pulled straight over his narrowed eyes as he listened to what I told him. He invited me to join him and we waited in the shade for his councillors to arrive. Wootonekawuske brought me a ladle of water and a bowl of boiled sea bass and corn samp flavored with bear grease. She was very young and also very beautiful with none of her sister Weetamoo's hardness.

"Later, when Akkompian arrived, Philip's men went into the longhouse to speak in council. I was present to answer their questions.

"Akkompian urged Philip to be careful. He advised them to go to sowams to talk to Alexander when he returned so the next day we set off for Pokanoket.

"But Alexander did not return. We heard a taggamut running into camp a few days later shouting, 'Our chief sachem is dead!'

"Weetamoo and the others arrived the next day. I saw then that for all her hardness, she had truly loved Alexander. She had painted her face black, but it was broken by two long streaks of flesh color from her tears. She kept wailing and the other women joined her in the mourning wail.

"'Our sachem was poisoned by the English!' she screamed over and over. She said they had been cruel to him and when he began to get sick they refused to let him return to sowams so his shaman could find out what was causing his illness. Weetamoo said this proved they were guilty, for they didn't want the shaman to learn what they had done.

"Through her sobs we learned that they had repeatedly accused Alexander of planning to make war against them and had refused him water or sleep until his head ached and he burned with fever.

"When they finally let him leave, it was too late, she said. As they carried him home on hides stretched over two poles, he complained of a severe pain in his head and then he died.

"'Their shamans poisoned him with laurelwood juice!' Weetamoo cried. She said she would not rest until our shamans poisoned all of them.

"So came Philip to power.

"He no sooner took over then the English summoned him to Plymouth to swear his loyalty to the English. Weetamoo begged him not to go, but he, Akkompion, his councillors Pumposa (Nimrod), Punkquaneck and Aqeetequesa plus the sachem Francis from Nauset went to Plymouth.

"Akkompian had Philip's ear and he told him he should do what his father did whenever the English were breathing on the back of his neck: sell them some land. This was all they wanted, Akkompian said, and when they threatened war it was because they were hungry for more land. So Philip sold them wollomonopoag (Wrentham) and they left him alone for a while.

"To help him with this sale and future ones, Philip asked John Sassamon to be his secretary. This thing made many of Philip's subjects angry.

"Although Alexander had been from the loins of Ousemequin, he didn't have the charisma that the old sachem had. There was something about Ousemequin that made people stop what they were doing or thinking when he spoke. His peace talk was always stronger than the thunder of muskets. Philip had some of this charisma, but he didn't talk of peace.

"My father and the other old men were now ignored in councils. The younger braves liked Philip and were ready to put aside peace talk in favor of bullets and arrows.

"Around this time the Massachusettts tribes rallied around Josias and went to war with the Mohawks to avenge the murder of Josisas' people. This gave many of the younger braves an outlet for their anger and Monoco and James Quannapohit brought armies to join in the war."

Chapter 24
(A re-telling of the growth of English villages 1662-1670 and the Massachusetts-Mohawk war)

George Tahanto finishes a pull on his long, white clay pipe then speaks:

"After Alexander died, affairs in quansik became very confused. The Narragsanetts in Hyems and Allumps' territories took advantage of Ousemequin's death, terrorizing the area so much that many people began to move away. Ninigret died and someone told his mother Montuntuck that some of our people spoke his name so she sent 300 Narragansett warriors into quansik to capture those who had insulted her son. Our braves were out hunting at the time but the warriors forced our women to give them clothing, kettles, traps, wampum, guns, deer skins and pigs. They said it was tribute that should have been paid to Ninigret. I moved my family to Weshakim, for there were many strong, aggressive braves there and leaders who were not afraid to fight.

"Unlike Quaboag's older leaders who cried peace all the time, Nashaway's leaders were finished with walking the patient path. They were constantly meeting with the other sachems in Massachusett and with Philip's representatives to talk about a war plan. But most weren't ready to join the Narragansetts, for we didn't trust them. They were too strong and powerful and we felt they would turn their guns against us as soon as the English were on the run.

"The Massachusetts sachem Josias was not afraid of the Narragansetts and he began to go from village to village speaking in council with the sachems and the elders to raise an army to war with the Mohawks. For Josias it was a revenge war, a war of honor. But for most of the young braves who threw their spears into the war fire, it was adventure: action after many years of waiting. I threw my war stick into the flames for I was frustrated with how the Mohawks and Narragansetts were making it hard for people to travel or live in peace.

"The younger braves knew little of battle and even less of the ferocity of the Mohawks, but we older warriors knew just what we would be facing and it could make one's blood turn cold.

"For the next eight winters our warriors gathered and led raids into Mohawk territory. Those eight winters took many lives and made many widows.

"Our first foray was begun with high spirits. Josias was well-respected among the troops. He and James Quanapohit had collected a good supply of corn meal from the Nashaway and Massachusett villages and some of this we buried along the trail for our return trip.

"We left the hills of Nashaway in late fall before the snow but after the harvest. My squaw had made me sturdy deerhide leggings and a robe with the fur turned inward to protect me against the bitter cold we would be fighting in. I had lined moccasins and plenty of extra thongs to repair my snowshoes and moccasins with.

"Our women traveled in the rear, protected by the older warriors such as myself. The younger warriors could walk faster and see sharper so Josias kept them with him up front.

"We left Nashaway and took the trail that led around the northernmost part of wachuset mountain and then across the hills through Poquag and on to Pocumtuck. There we were joined by an army of Pocumtuck warriors, for they, too, had a score to settle with the Mohawks.

"We crossed the quonicticut by night and spent several sleeps near the great falls beyond, our warriors doing a little fishing while they waited for the band that had climbed the great mountain (Greylock) to return and report what they had seen. Despite my age, I climbed that mountain because I had heard the view was better there than that from steerage rock in asquoach."

"The Hoosacs met us as we neared the next river and some of their warriors joined our growing party. We left our women and children with the Hoosacs, for even though our women were brave and would fight fearlessly, Mohawk territory was no place for them to be.

"From the Hoosac territory , we turned northwards. The Mohawk's large village of schagticook (Albany) lay due west but its approach was well-guarded. By now the snows had come and we knew the Mohawks probably knew about our army, so we traveled silently by night in canoes up the great river. By dawn, we would find a secluded place and pull our canoes out of the river slightly, covering them with spruce or cedar boughs. We'd set up camp in the woods and our best bow hunters would obtain fresh meat for us. Our fires were kept low and wherever we went we would either walk on rocks or sweep our snowshoe tracks away. Our advance party would find good vantage points and look for smoke from Mohawk villages or hunting parties.

"Our destination was a village north of schagticook. This was the village where the war captain of the party that attacked Josias' people lived.

"But the Mohawks found us first.

"We were dipping our paddles into the black river, careful not to lift them in such a way as to cause noise. We came to a section of high rocks and slowed our canoes down so they wouldn't drift against the sharp edges that could slit their bark skin and send us into the fast current of the icy waters. Along the shores all was black as the trees grew down to meet the river. It was as if we were traveling in a dark tunnel, floating in darkness. The only sound was the sluggish current, our breaths and an occasional hoot of an owl or howl of a wolf. Above us the stars were pinpoints of brilliance in a black, black sky.

"As we slowed to navigate this section of shallow water and rocks, we heard the animal howls and screams of the Mohawks. The screams were drowned by the boom of their guns and the surface of the water became agitated with bullet-spray. The paddlers worked furiously to get the canoes free as our warriors fired back into the swarm of black figures hiding in the trees.

"Josias shouted for us to use our bows since our musketballs were being wasted in shot at phantoms. Then we began to hear the screams of Mohawks up close, followed by splashes. My canoe got free, but when I looked back, I could see the one behind us hung up on the rocks, the Mohawks fighting hand-to-hand with its occupants. In the growing light I fired at the Mohawks, identifiable in the dim light by the tall roaches standing up straight in the middle of their shaven heads. (Our men who normally wore their hair this way changed it before battle so they wouldn't look like the Mohawks).

"We got our canoes to shore and the fighting moved up the riverbank to the forest. Throughout the course of the day our warriors, dead tired from a long night paddling, kept the Mohawks at bay as we worked our way downstream. With the darkness we regrouped, finding each other through our signal call - the short bark of a fox.

"We waited through most of the night, but only half of our warriors found each other.

"We lost our gunpowder and supplies in the canoes and so returned to Hoosac then back to our villages where we spent the winter in intensive hunting for hides to trade for more musket balls and gunpowder.

"So began the pattern of our war with the Mohawks. Winter excursions followed by hunting and trading while our women planted more corn and made more moccasins.

"During these years Weetamoo remarried- this time to Quequequanchet - but he didn't want to stay in Pocasset so she took another husband, a brave called Ben Petonowet, who was very friendly with the English.

"Philip and Wootonekanuske sold Mattapoisett. Then Philip and others, including his brother Sunconwhew and Uumptack, Isoke, Peebe and Tatamumaque sold lands in acushnok, coaksett, Compton, seacunk (Rehoboth), east of scituate, the area adjacent to Pokonet, acushnet (Dartmouth) meadows, wepoiset (Swansea), the island of askusenag, land around nokathay and pispogutt (Middleborough). Around this time William Tuspaquin and Philip's sister Aime, sold the lands around assowampett ponds and the meadow near them and the Taunton path to the English. In his attempt to obtain more and more English silver, which he was using to buy guns, Philip and Uncompian challenged the deed for Willet's lands adjacent to monthop and they were paid $11 in goods for them.

"Two things happened in these years that our powwows said were related. Eliot printed a copy of their magic book, the Bible, in our tongue, and a huge comet appeared in the sky for two moons in the time of the falling leaves.

"Then, a few winters after Ousemequin died, a Narragansett named Gibbs from Nantucket openly spoke the great sachems' name. This was tantamount to a declaration of war and Philip (riding his new horse, which was a gift from the English) led a war party against the Narragansetts, who paid him a large ransom for Gibbs' life, adding to his supply of arms. Shortly afterwards the Narragansetts sold weequoncett neck to the English.

"Unlike the Wampanoags, the Massachusetts were not selling more land to the English. Watachpoo and Sampson told the English not to bother them for more land for seven winters. Around this time Sassamon left Philip and went to preach in natick. Tom Sawsuett took his place as secretary. But this was a winter of illness in monthop. Tom had severe pains in his back and Philip's sister Aimie took ill. And Philip's wife was also taking up much of his attention for she was carrying their first child.

"In Boston, lightning killed seven English people and the plague called smallpox had been let out of its box once again.

"In quansik we also had illness and Squaw Sachem went into seclusion. She gave complete control of her lands to her sons and went north into Pocumtuck, to her father's village. For years she had refused to ally herself with any tribes or with the English, which made it hard for the Nashaways to protect the path from qunshpage (Mendon) to Quaboag. Her youngest son, Simon Pottoquock, was one of Eliot's devotees and receptive to the English, which were now settling in our area. A group of English had settled on the land sold to them by Shatookquis and Eliot was building more Christian towns in eastern quansik. Eliot was also active in Massachusetts, preaching in the village where Kushamikin, Chickataubet's brother, lived.

"On the river, the white men called their annual court session in Hartford and told the owner of Ely's Tavern in Springfield to stop selling hard cider to our people. Wequash complained to the judges that English pigs had damaged his garden and Robin was accused of selling stolen rings at Ely's tavern. We learned that these court sessions were how the white men dealt with problems. They did not call a council meeting the way our sachems did when problems arose. They would take down complaints and then wait until their court gathered to settle all business. Thus pigs could damage one's corn in June and we would not get satisfaction until the following Spring. Such is the white man's way. They had courts in Boston, Plymouth, Hartford and Providence. Of all these, the Plymouth court treated us best but we had to take our complaints to the court they said was in our "county".

"With the birth of his son, Philip became more anti-English than before. Weetamoo also became aggressive and managed to reclaim the lands Alexander had sold many winters before."

"In the sixth winter of the war with the Mohawks, Josias and his grandson Chickataubet led 700 warriors to schagticook. This was the largest army he had raised so far but we were no match for the Mohawks, who had more guns and more men. We laid seige to the great fort but after Josias and his grandson were killed, we withdrew back to Massachusett.

"Following this battle, their war captains bought three pounds of gunpowder and lead from the English in Dedham. Perhaps because of this English involvement, the Mohawks went to the Dutch and asked them to mediate a peace between the Mohawks and Massachusetts.

"To the north, at the trading post on the piscataway river, Pennecooks killed an Englishman. The Pigwacket sachem Kongkowasco and the Nashoba sachem Monoco held a speedy trial and executed the Pennacooks involved to avoid war with the English.

"We got another taste of English law when Sarah Ahaughton, wife of the sachem William Ahaughton, was accused of adultery. She was living in the Christian village of punkapog and got pregnant by Joseph Wachemakin. Waban turned her in to Gookin who sent her to jail.

"Four moons later, in peppewarr (October), after her nipapoose was born, she was forced to stand on the gallows on the Boston Common for one hour then was taken to the Christian village in Natick and whipped in public.

"Such public humiliation of women was not done by our people. If a husband caught his wife in adultery, he could execute her instantly or choose to divorce her or forgive her. He did not prolong her suffering the way the "Christian" English did.

"Another incident occured to our north that year. A very powerful omen. It occured on property owned by heirs of the hated sea captain Gorges, near kennibunk. The English began digging into Mother Earth and found thousands of clay bullets and a clay musket. No one knew where they had come from and so the powwows said it was a sign: the stone people were making weapons for us to use against our enemies.

"Things settled down in Nashaway for a while and I decided that I had fought my last battle. I felt too old to go off seeking battle. Now I would only fight if attacked. "

Chapter 25

(A re-telling of the hanging of Matoonas' son and Eliot's work in Quaboag, 1669 - 1671)

By now the darkest days of winter had passed. Outside the longhouse the snow was dull and hard from melting and refreezing In this time of the ice bridge's withdrawal Konkowasco again addresses the young people of Quansik:

"I had not fought in the Massachusetts-Mohawk war, though most quansik warriors had participated in at least one campaign. I had been consulted about that war on many occasions by Josias, Monoco and James Quanhopohit and had told them what visions I had or what my oracle, a pet snake, said. Repeatedly, the visions had said that the English would not become involved in helping the Mohawks , and when the Mohawks wanted peace after the English at Dedham became involved, I knew their shamans had been seeing the same things I saw.

"During this time, Eliot was making many converts. He had built more "praying villages" like Natick in the Massachusetts and Nipmuc territory. In quansik, I had helped him obtain the deed for land near asquoach. Wetolechen's son Annoackamor, known as Noas, and my father Shatookquis, who now signed deeds as Nommorshot or Nokin, signed this deed, which allowed Eliot to settle a village near potepaug. They walked the ground with him and my father planted a slab of granite on the western boundary so Eliot wouldn't infringe on asquoach and quaboag old fort and the corn storage areas. Those who know my father will know how much talking it took me to get him to sign that deed! Noas had more authority, being a grandson of Mishalisk, so his permission was the most important. My father was now living in mashapaug. When he signed the deed with his black cat mark, he told me that if it were ever settled, he would leave the area entirely. But I had my reasons for wanting this praying village, as I will tell you later.

"Wherever Eliot went to preach the people came in crowds. His god called on therm to love their neighbor and enemy, to forgive and show compassion. As many people had lost brothers, husbands or fathers to the Mohawks, this was a welcome message. They wanted to learn how this thing could be done, how our people and the other peoples could live together in peace.

"Every household that gathered to listen had lost one or more children or one or more adult members to disease or war in the time since the white man first settled in patuxit. They were weary of all the death, of all the fighting, of not knowing if they would be killed in their beds that night.

"Many of the families who moved to these villages were the grandsons or daughters of the old sachems - the ones like my grandfather who had spoken always of peace. One of my cousins, a sachem named Matoonas, had moved his family to Eliot's village called pakachoog. There, Matoonas was appointed as constable. Matoonas had become hostile to me when I would not give up my spirit guides to follow his god so I was surprised one morning during the *namassack-keewach* (April) moon to receive a message from him asking me to come immediately.

"When I arrived in packachoog, I heard the sound of mourning and upon entering the little square wooden house Matoonas lived in, I saw a group of English-clothed men and women seated in the front room, their heads bent and their hands clenched together in their laps.

"Eliot was with Matoonas and his wife in the bedchamber, praying with them. His face was gentle but when he saw me, it took on a stiff appearance. He asked Matoonas if he had sent for me and the big man nodded, like a puppy caught stealing food.

"I knew that Eliot's feelings towards me had changed when he heard I wouldn't join his believers. But he also knew I was not someone he wanted to have against him, so he was careful.

"He took my hand and said he often prayed for me, then he led me outside. Eliot told me Matoonas' eldest son, who had been a laborer for the English, had killed an Englishman. He had been captured, tried, then executed by the English, Eliot said. He kept saying the brave had received a fair trial. I could help Matoonas, he said, and the people in packachoog if I went back to my people and told them not to interfere, that it had been between the English and this brave only.

"I felt my heart pound loudly as he told me this. So this was what my vision had meant a few sleeps past in which I had seen a young crow attacked in mid-flight by a white-headed eagle!

"Because I still practiced the religion of my people, Eliot told me I was not allowed by law to stay in his village and so I left, unfed and unwelcomed. But I did not go far. I walked down the hill, over the spring, past the freshly-burned corn fields, went into the woods and waited to talk to someone outside the praying village. After dark, Matoonas sought me out and sat at my fire.

"He was dressed like the English with a black hat, black jacket and trousers, but he went barefoot. A turkey feather was stuck into the brim of his hat and the thick, floral-embroidered belt around his waist held a tomahawk and knife. A floral-embroidered strap across his chest supported the gun on his back and he carried a black staff as a symbol of his office. I told him I thought his god loved peace and did not fight.

"'He does,' he told me, 'but others don't, so as Constable I have to carry weapons to protect my people from those who would harm them. To them I am Black Matoonas or Black Staff Matoonas.'

"I think Matoonas knew something was wrong, for his eyes didn't meet mine when he said this. In the dark I heard him draw a long, shuddering sob as I offered him a smoke from my pipe.

"'They hanged him,' he said, 'then they cut his head off and stuck it on a pole outside of Boston. They never even gave me a chance to raise ransom money.' Matoonas said his son hadn't killed the Englishman. His son was a good Christian, he said, not like the ungodly, cider-swilling group of English that had recently settled illegally near manchaug (Singletary) pond (in Sutton).

"As he raised his face, I saw hatred glittering in his black eyes. He pulled the silver badge off his jacket and threw it into the fire, spitting on it. It had been nothing to them. They hadn't even let him see his son before they killed him. They hadn't even let a Nashaway sachem execute him. There had been no honor in his execution. They had hanged him like one would a dog.

"Matoonas asked me to cast a spell on the English, especially on the ones responsible for his son's murder. He knew where he could get some gunpowder, he said. It would be given to our warriors to finish off the English with.

"I was still angry about the treatment I had received in his village and told Matoonas he should call upon his "god" to do this. But when I saw the look in his eyes, I relented and, after smoking with him for a long time, told him,

"'I call upon our stone brothers and sisters to help us and they send a terrible crack in Mother Earth's skin. It frightens the English but destroys *our* paths and diverts *our* streams. I call upon the thunderbird to flood them and he does, but their houses are stronger and higher and they go right back. *Our* wetus, however, are ruined and we must sleep on hilltops exposed to freezing winds. Their storehouses are unscathed yet *we* lose our crops and our buried caches of corn.

"'I summon Grandfather Wind to blow their houses down and instead *ours* are destroyed and our canoes dashed on the rocks.

"'My brother, I cannot harm the English without harming our people more. I send them poison and they sell the poisoned foods to us. Poisonous serpents sent into their midst are eaten by their hogs, who then trample our corn fields. They are like the surface of a sheet of mica- they reflect back anything sent to them. Passaconnaway told me that the only way we could escape their magic was to flee from them.'

"Matoonas then said the only god who could harm them was their god's enemy, the devil.

"I told him I had tried calling on Hobbomock to work mischief against them, but he had not succeeded. Then I told him that since he knew their magic book he must bring it to me and read me the passages about this devil god.

"Matoonas said he couldn't do that for all they had were little pieces of the Bible. Only the white men had the whole book. He said the book was very hard for them to understand and that they had to have it explained to them: one could not just pick it up and read it. I realized then that I should have pretended to give up my spirits so I could have learned more from Eliot. As long as the words in that book could only be read and understood by white men, my people were helpless.

"I returned to Quabogud, where I was now living, and began to try to read the pages through trances. I sent my soul traveling night after night into their villages to listen to their words, to look at the pages and try to understand the words in my soul. I stopped eating and only left my wetu to visit the pit. Such spirit traveling is one of the hardest things a shaman can do and I was near death at the end of my attempt. I had glimpsed pages but the meaning eluded me. There seemed to be a confusion, a contradiction that I could not make sense of. So I resolved to obtain a copy of the white man's Bible in their tongue and enlist a student who could read it. I did not trust the one that Job and James Printer worked on, for it could very well have omitted the words of power my people needed. No, I wanted to have it read exactly as the English read it in their language. I needed to find a white boy who could read and who also knew our language. I decided I would cast a spell on one and enchant him away from one of their villages. This was my plan.

"When I finally came out of my trance vision quest I learned that Matoonas had threatened revenge and had been summoned to Boston to declare his loyalty. Around the same time, Philip was ordered to Taunton to take the same pledge. He gathered a war party together consisting of Tavoser, Wispoke, Woonkaponehunt, Uncompian and Nimrod and camped outside the village, holding a war dance around the fire. War with the English would have begun right then except for Roger Williams, who went to Philip and persuaded him to do what the white men wanted.

"What happened next actually caused the later hostilities. The English demanded that my people turn their guns in. This was like telling the English to give us their coin! Our guns were our wealth - and also were so effective in hunting that they had replaced the bow and arrow for the serious hunters, especially those who traded pelts. Give up our guns!

"Their soldiers went to assoowamsoo and pispogutt (Middleborough) and forced the people there to surrender their guns then they went to the Saconet's territory and demanded theirs. The sachem Tokonoma resisted but Awashonks went to Plymouth and signed a treaty of submission, then later delivered the guns in her territory.

"This infuriated Philip, who had only given a handful of old, broken guns to the English. He went to Awashonks and held council with her but there were many ears that reported to the English and Philip was summoned to Plymouth to answer charges that he was trying to conspire with Awashonks against them. The English sent three men to summon him - Roger Williams and two others known to

Philip. However, Philip refused to go to Plymouth and went to Boston instead to complain to the English there about the war-like ways of their white brothers in Plymouth.

"This was in the time of the harvest moon. Before Philip arrived in Boston, the sachem Tatoson, the Acushnets (Dartmouth) people and even and the subjects of the Narragansett sachem Will Washawanna had turned their guns in.

"I heard that all of Philip's shamans were working very hard on spells against the English at this time and that Matoonas was staying in monthop. All signs pointed to war but my oracle said no, the fighting would not begin.

"Sure enough, when Philip went to Boston they bewitched him and he and Uncompian, Wotokom, Samdama, Wohkowpaheniitt, Wutiakooseeium, Sonkamhoo, Woonashum (Nimrod) and Woopasuck signed a treaty of submission. Philip not only promised his guns, but said he would pay over $100 in English money within the next three winters for his insolence and send them five wolf heads annually as further tribute. This was a king's ransom, literally. It was felt that Philip was lucky to have escaped from Boston with his life. Two moons later Takanumma, Awashonk's brother in Saconnet, also signed a treaty of submission.

"Philip immediately began to send out men to trade for new guns. He found out the English had a new type of rifle that was better than the matchlock muskets they were using - it was called a flintlock musket and his ambassadors went to Mohawk territory to see how they could obtain some. He sent word to the people to lay low, to wait until they could rearm themselves before starting war.

"And so the waiting began. The English bought more lands during this time: the east side of assawamsett to the nemasket falls from Tuspaquin and his son William Tuspaquin. This I thought strange, for Black William, as he was called, was a very powerful powwow. But his father had invited Sassamon to preach to his people and was now under the spell of their god. I thought how wise Passaconnaway had been when he told me that they hypnotized people with words! They put us in a trance and then stole our lands.

"Besides Philip, the sachems Nunkampahoonett, Umnathum, Cheemanghton and Captain Annawon appeared to be under their spell as they sold the English a huge tract of land in Taunton. Woakckompawham (Uncompian) witnessed this deed. Also under their spell was the nephew of Canonicus, Quinnapian, who confirmed the deeds his father had made. And Awashonks sold them more land, this time the field next to punkateesatt, so she could pay the Englishman John Almay $25 the Hartford court ordered her to pay.

"But Philip was being clever. He sent word out to all the sachems that they could sell whatever they wanted and get as much coin and goods as possible so these could be converted into rifles and gunpowder. He said, 'Let them buy the guns that we will use to drive them all from our lands! Let them think they own Turtle Island! Our guns will prove otherwise! They are but the little black flies that annoy us in the *moonesquonimock* (May) moon. They will all be killed or driven away and we will have all of our lands back.'

"Around this time he learned that the English soldiers had ordered 500 of the new flintlock muskets and much scheming went on in an attempt to intercept the delivery.

"Near Quaboag Eliot was creating more of his praying villages.

"He established one in Weshakim and trained Old Jethro to preach to the people. It was at this time when I had Noas send word to Eliot that we would like a village near Asquoach. My plan was to get a copy of their book and to have them send a white man to interpret it. I didn't trust the little bits of it they gave to my people.

"Near Plymouth, Old Tuspaquin was fully under their spell and gave the preacher John Sassamon a piece of land near assowamett neck. Naneheunt and Will Tuspaquin witnessed this deed, which was followed by an even larger deed to Sassamon's daughter Betty and her husband Felix Assowetough.

"This is when Spider woman came to regarding a vision she had received."

Chapter 26

(Spiderwoman tells of more land sales to the English and of SunCatcher's birth 1672-1673)

Spiderwoman rises, her eyes shining like dark black beads wet with rain.

"My people in tantiesques were close to the Wabbaquasetts and the Hassanamisco peoples. We had traveled to quintisset (Woodstock) to hear John Eliot preach from on top of the big rock there and many of our young people were interested in the white man's god. They wanted to dress like the white man and live in square houses and have the furniture like Eliot's fancy carved reed chair and other goods the white man had. Many of our children looked at our little wetus and our hide-covered bodies and said we were not "civilized". They said the English were better because they had more possessions.

"This was how bewitched they were, for such an attitude was completely opposite what Creator had taught us. We had learned how to live with nature, how to be a part of the great One. The English thought *they* were the great One. Anything that wasn't English or from the other white tribes was called inferior or savage. They looked on us as little better than the animals they killed for their pelts.

"Like Konkowasco, I, too, had begun to have visions that warned me of becoming a friend to the English. But my people were on a major trade path and often had to deal with the English, especially those in their new villages called Brookfield, Springfield, Hadley and Deerfield. We were used to their horses drinking from our ponds and the sound of their guns or axes on the land where the black lead was.

"My first vision came after I drank their firewater for the first time. I had made ten fine sweetgrass baskets for the English women and a trader paid me a steel-ended hoe for them. This was considered a wonderful deal and I accepted a drink of the firewater he offered me and my husband.

"It burned like skunk cabbage tea, then felt warm and made me giggle like a young maiden. I felt very hot and began to sweat but drank more when it was offered again. As was our custom, we fed the trader and invited him to stay in our wetu and sleep on our bed with us.

"That night, though, I felt terribly sleepy and don't remember how I got to the sleeping platform. I was in such a deep trance that I never felt the English man's hands all over my body. My husband, too was in a deep sleep and it wasn't until a child was born to us with white features that we realized what had happened. But that is a different story.

"My vision that night was that of a huge black spider with a curious mark on her back. She lived in the bowels of Mother Earth and her web was enormous. Yet she kept spinning and spining all day, the silk threads coming out of her mouth like saliva.

"I watched her but was not afraid. I was fascinated by the patterns in her web. They were the whiteman's patterns, whiteman's things. Then I realized we were no longer in the earth but were up in the night sky and the web shone now along its length like dots of stars. The white man's things glowed but there were dark spots in her web and when I looked closer I saw they were her eggs. They looked like balls made of the red mud we have on the shores of our ponds.

"As I watched, they began to hatch miniature full-grown people that looked like warriors and squaws but had wings. These were not spider eggs. The people walked around on the weblines, signaling to others like them with wings, who flew to the web and were trapped. The big spider immediately began wrapping each in sheets of white gossamer then she turned on the egg-people and chased them across her web, trapping each.

"But she did not chase me. She looked at me and sang a song. 'My children, my children I give you birth but then I destroy you. Run from me, run from me, my children! I am your mother and your death!'

"I felt very ill when I awoke the next morning. My head was full of pain and everything in the wetu swam around me. When I tried to rise off the sleeping platform to make the fire, I vomited onto the wetu's floor and my children started crying.

"The dream wouldn't leave me and after my womb blood had stopped I visited Konkowasco, for his powers as a powwow were respected throughout all of quansik.

"Konkowasco listened to my vision then smoked for a very long time. He asked about the symbol on the back of the mother-spider and I drew it for him. He said it was the mark of the white man's god. I had received a vision from this god, he said, and added that this was the first time one of our people had received such a vision.

"Then he bowed his head. He told me he had a vision of our people trying to run away. He said the weaver of life was playing with us. She was making her own children draw us to our death. Our sisters and brothers in the praying villages were her eggs, he said. They would be our death.

"I was very afraid and showed him my abdomen where the mark of a spider had appeared the morning after my vision.

"He said, 'There is only one thing that can kill a spider in its web and that is another spider. You will now be called Spiderwoman. Your child will have powers that will protect it from the weaver's web.'

"I admit that during those nine moons I was afraid that the child I carried would turn out to have eight legs or be covered with thick black hair. What a shock to find it lighter than my husband and I and with blue eyes and soft, blond hair! Konkowasco visited me after his birth and named him SunCatcher for the way the sunlight shone in his yellow hair. He said he was a magic child and I must let the boy become his apprentice when he turned eight winters old.

"SunCatcher was always noticed by the English when they came through and they asked where I had gotten him. When I replied by magic they would ask more until someone told them I had actually given birth to the boy myself. I think they thought I had stolen him from one of their cribs the way they stole my people to be their slaves. After his birth, I began serving as a shaman to the people in tantiesques for my monthly blood no longer flowed. Instead, its magical powers were inside me and I began to feel spirit helpers telling me how to cure people as they had told me before which plants to pick.

"I would often sit near the stream that ran from quassuck, pond-all, the mother of all the rivers in quansik, and the waters would talk to me, telling me secrets. The small birds would perch near my wetu and chirp words to me as I ground corn on my large, flat stone. So I often knew the news before traders or travelers brought it to tantiesques. I would hear a name from a bird and know something had happened to that person, or the brook would repeat a phrase such as 'Narragansetts kill' and I would know someone had been murdered by them.

"In such a way I knew Tokamona had been murdered by the Narrgansetts. However, why things happened would not be revealed and it was through visitors that we found out what was happening near Plymouth and Boston on our east and Hartford and Springfield on our west.

"By now it was apparent that there were two reasons to sell lands to the English: either because one loved their ways and god or because one hated their ways and god and wanted to buy guns with the goods they traded for the land.

"We suspected that Tuspaquin, along with Assaweta, Tobias and Pewat , sold lands out of love, but his son sold them out of hate. Weetamoo's husband Petonwowitt along with Tatamock and William Isasocke sold swansea near mattapoisett and shomet neck to please the English, but Weetamoo hated them and afterwards she and her brother-in-law, Philip challenged the sales at sopowett.

"Prior to her brother's death, Awashonk's son Mamaneway, who hated the English, challenged his uncle's land sales. Mamaneway said no sale was legal that he had not entered into. He said his relatives-Toloney's sons, Anumpash, son of Pakattawass, Tatuckanna (Tokonoma) and his brother Squamatt (George) were his subjects and could not sell without his permission. But the English refused to listen and replied that the deeds to acushnet were legal.

"Philip now openly hated the English. He told Eliot he cared as much for his god as the button on his coat, which he pulled off and threw in the dirt. The English began calling him *King* Philip. Whereas the title of king was a high honor when they spoke of *their* king, when they said it before his English name, they twisted their mouths so it became an obscenity. Only Philip's high breeding and rigorous training as a warrior made him keep from drawing his knife and attacking the English when he had dealings with them.

"In the time of the falling leaves moon, I was staying in asnuntuck (Longmeadow) helping the women harvest peas (cranberries) in the bogs when a brave rode into camp, his back bare and bleeding.

He said he had been kicked out of the English village nearby because he had entered on horseback. After ripping off his coat and whipping him until he bled, they took his spare coat and told him never to enter an English village on horseback again. We calmed the fire in his wounds by applying a poultice of dried yellow dock leaves and a few sleeps later when he was better, the sachem's wife gave him a good soft, fur mantle. The brave was grateful but he didn't stay. He rode out in the direction of Nashaway where he heard Matoonas was gathering an army to fight the English. So while the wounds outside his body were healing, the ones to his pride grew greater with every breath he took.

"That winter the snows came early and were deep by the time of *quinnekeswash* (the November) moon. The Dutch and English were again arguing about who owned what of the Wappinger and Mauntauk territory.

"In quansik we were settling down into our long, dark winter days, days full of twine-making, basketweaving and hide-chewing to soften doeskins. SunCatcher was teething that winter and I had to feed him warm calamas root and wash his sore mouth with alum root tea. The fungus on the alum root helped the others in my wetu with the watery stools and itching from the little white squash-worm sickness and I often had to go out in the cold and try to dig up some pinkroot for them. I made lots of wild cherry and strawberry root tea to calm the stomach aches in my family.

"Besides his teething, SunCatcher kept me busy with his playing, but often when I looked at him my heart felt a pain as I realized I would not see him grow to manhood in our wetu."

Chapter 27
(A re-telling of Eliot, Gookin and the growth of the praying villages, 1674)

Konkowasco's eyes glinted as Spiderwoman told of the brave's lashing. This winter of remembering was stirring up old wounds, mixing them with the motives for his winter visit to their village in Oneida.

"A year before the war started with the English, I went to see Wannalancet. Upon my arrival in Pawtuckett I noticed the people going towards the new praying village of Wameset. This sat on a neck of land at the bottom of the great falls where the Merrimack and Concord rivers met.

"They said Eliot and Gookin had come to hold a court there and to preach to the people. There was great fishing at that spot and many were going for that reason since it was the traditonal fishing place for the northern tribes as our great falls on the chicopee was for quansik.

"As I approached the village the first thing I noticed was an English-style fort and English-style fields and many cows and hogs behind fences. The meeting was not in the village, but was further away, on the riverbank. A companion told me the village was almost empty now for most of the men had been killed in the war with the Mohawks. Numphow was killed not far from here, killed while fishing for eels in the river, he said. The fifteen families left lived in fear of the Mohawks, who were often spotted on the trail that the Pawtuckets used as they rode horses loaded with fresh salmon towards Boston. The Pawtuckets pickled and salted fish for the English and received livestock and English goods in exchange.

"We passed the falls and it looked like a scene from our own falls this time of year. The boys and men were fishing for eels with spears and gathering salmon, shad, sturgeon and bass from their weirs. The children were splashing in the water and playing on the banks, chasing each other up and down the rocks or in and out of the underbrush. The women were splitting the fish open and spreading them flat on the drying racks, cooking and talking amongst themselves. The papooses hung in their cradleboards from trees nearby, their round black eyes taking in everything. Occasionally an older sibling would go up to the babies and wave a stalk of grass in front of their faces or dangle a flapping fish and the nipapooses would reply with wide, toothless grins.

"The dogs also fished and if one caught a nice, juicy salmon it would take it away from the others to rip it open with its teeth and gulp down the flesh, bones and all. Usually the other dogs would try to get a piece and the grandmothers and grandfathers often had to intervene and stop the fighting before someone got hurt. If a dog got too greedy it would vomit up its meal and then eat it again. Sometimes they got bones caught in their throats and would cough and roll over, rubbing their necks on the ground.

"Everywhere the scent of fish filled the air. From the cooling pots came the odor of boiling fish stew, from the drying racks the odor of fish smoking and the odor of dead fish rotting here and there attracting flies and beetles. The odor would get in your hair and your skin, and for a moon after the spring fishing we all smelled like our brothers and sisters in the water. But we all had full bellies and a supply of dried fish to see us through the winter.

"We went past the fishing party, around a bend in the river and saw a collection of summer wetus near a large outcropping of rocks. On top of the rocks stood John Eliot. With his large black hat shielding his head and the tails of his long black coat flapping gently from the wind rising from the river below, he looked like a big crow. 'Was he sent from Cautantowwit's garden, too?' I wondered briefly. 'Were his words new seeds for us to plant?'

"Wannalancet was seated next to the young teacher Samuel at the door of the middle-aged sachem's wetu. This surprised me for Eliot normally wouldn't allow powwows anywhere near his converts, especially one as prized as Samuel who had been raised and schooled by the English Corporation For the Indians.

"I greeted Wannalancet and sat down on the other side of him. One of his squaws immediately brought me a bowl of hot fish and squash soup thickened with corn meal. As I ate the plump pieces of salmon and eel and picked the bones out of the broth so I could sip it,

I listened to Eliot speak. His sermon was about Jesus and how he told his disciples that he would make them 'fishers of men.'

"'What a strange thing', I thought, 'Would this god Jesus snare them in nets or spear them? Why would a man want to be like a fish?' Eliot called Jesus the Great Fisherman and I pictured a giant like Glooscap standing over us, his spear raised to pierce us. But the others were smiling, their eyes on the Englishman as he spoke our language with a strange accent. Every once in a while he would say something they didn't understand and his interpreter, Job, would point it out to him, but Eliot was more fluent in our language than we were in his. Those of us who had contact with the English knew some words and names by this time, enough to communicate with the help of hand language who we and they were and where we came from and what we or they wanted.

"The English trained their ministers to us from an early age, sending many to school in their town of Cambridge for a year or two, some longer. These they placed in the various praying villages to teach the Bible to the people. The names of these were: Samuel, John Thomas, Jethro, Simon, Joseph and Sampson, Solomon, James, Anthony and John Speen, John Moqua, Daniel, Samoset, Jude, Ephraim, William Ahaughton, Tuppukkowillin and his brother James, who was a printer. Many of these were the sons of sachems and their fathers ruled the praying villages where the sons taught.

"I saw them as apprentices to the magician Eliot and I had brought with me my apprentice-to-be, SpiderWoman's boy SunCatcher. This boy I would send to their school so he could learn their language, then read me their magic book. But Eliot was not to know the true reason for the boy's schooling so I pretended that his parents had sent me to introduce him to Eliot so when he was older he could go to their school and then preach to the families in quansik living on the land grant near pookookapaug pond that Noas and Nokin had granted. This delighted Eliot, who was very curious about the baby with the English-colored skin and dark blond hair.

"Before I could speak to Wannalancet in private and explain the real reason for bringing the boy, he declared he would also convert. He told Eliot he was used to traveling up the river in an old canoe but now he would get into a new canoe, meaning the new religion.

"His words almost got him killed for his people were not there to convert and become like the English. They had gone to the falls to fish and it was only a (planned) coincidence that Eliot was there. They would never leave their lands and go live in praying villages, they told Wannalancet.

"I did not stay to see how it turned out but later I learned Wannalancet had only added their god to his other spirit helpers. He was still one of us and wanted no further contact with the English.

"By this time there were many praying villages and I had visited most of them out of curiosity. I usually disguised myself as a traveler for powwows caught inside their villages could be taken by the constables before Wattascompanum at Hassinnimeset for punishment. Wattascompanum was my uncle, one of Naddawahunt's brothers. Before his conversion he had been a sachem of our people. Now he was chief sachem of all the "Christian" tribes.

"These tribes were located near Plimouth - Pattent at Maktapog; on Martha's Vineyard; at Natick; in Punkapog; in Hassannimesut; in Ogquoonikongquamesut; Manchage; Chabanakongkomum; Maanexit; Quantisset; Wabquissit; Pakachoog; Waeuntug and Weshakim. Most of the villages had ten to thirty families and were located on good, fertile land. They laid their villages out like English towns with gardens, fields, orchards and pastures and kept the sabbath. Besides powwows, strong bottled spirits were prohibited in their villages. They gave one-tenth of their harvest every year to the English as tribute, but they called it 'tithes.' Although they adopted English government and dress they usually lived in wetus for the English houses were hard to make and keep warm in winter and also couldn't be moved if they got infested with fleas. Most of the sachems in these villages had been given fine English coats like the one Eliot gave to Wannalancet upon his conversion.

"These coats were desired by my people who saw them as symbols of authority. Especially the ones with brass or silver buttons and braiding.

"The coats themselves were itchy and hard to get the stink out of but they did keep both arms warm while riding and any man wearing one was immediately given a little respect by the English. The other English clothes we cared little for. We'd wear a hat or shirt, again as a symbol of importance, but the shoes, pants and high stockings were not practical. We preferred bare legs or fringed leggings. There were other curiosities such as gloves, which our people thought were English skin the first time they saw the English peel them off their hands. There were cloaks, which were warm but they choked at the neck so we preferred to wrap a woolen blanket around us so our arms could be free. The royal females such as the sachems Weetamoo and Awashonks took to wearing English dress and spent many hours each day fixing their hair and costumes.

"Most of our women cared little for the English women's dresses and petticoats. They would laugh at the thing called a corset that the English women wore under their clothes. This was a stiff band of cloth that the women laced tight under their dresses so their breasts were squashed flat against their chests and their waists drawn in. It took their breath away and made them unable to bend or twist and our women wanted no part of such nonsense. If a trader gave them one, they would play a game, tossing it around the camp. Our women did like the blankets and the jewelry and occasionally would wear an English hat but they felt the other clothes were scratchy, too hard to keep clean, and too restricting, especially if they had papooses to nurse.

"But in the praying villages the people copied the English except for the shoes. None of us liked their shoes or boots for our feet were used to the hard earth and soft moccasins and couldn't adjust to the stiff, thick leather shoes. If we tried to wear them our feet developed painful sores at the toes and heels and if they got wet our feet would turn raw with rubbing against the stiff insides.

"All the praying villages were alike in many ways. I will tell you a little about each one I saw before the war.

"Their main village was Natick. I told you about how it was when it was first built. By the spring before the war Waban was the sachem there and John and Anthony Speen were teachers. Anthony had worked for Pometacomet as secretary prior to joining his brother in Natick. The English sacred ceremonies called sacraments were performed here, including baptisms and communions.

"I was told by Mattoonas that communion was when they ate their god's flesh and drank his blood. He said the blood tasted like wine and the flesh like English wheat bread. This was a great mystery to us. I thought it was the reason two of their men in Natick and others in the other praying villages died of a disease the English called "the stone" that made them vomit black bile.

"Other deacons or leading men were Ephraim, Nattous and

Piam Booham (Pambussa). The marshall general of the constables was Captain Josiah Pennakannit, who was the sachem at Nashoba on nagog pond.

"Nashobah had ten families. During the great earthquake Mother Earth broke open near the pond and we could hear the stone people humming or roaring near the cracks and caves. Some of the people said the hills were hollow and that the wind rushing through them made the noises but the praying tribe there paid no attention to it. They were more afraid of the Mohawks, for my uncle, Naddawahunt's son John Tahattawans, the previous sachem of Nashoba, had been killed by them while fishing for eels in the weirs nearby. This village was located in the middle of the new English settlements of Chelmsford, Lancaster, Groton and Concord so its people had much contact with the English. They also had planted apple orchards and had learned how to make hard cider, which was responsible for problems between them and the English and Eliot.

"The sachems saw the praying villages as a way to protect their people from other tribes, for the English would defend them if attacked. But once they granted the land and brought their people there they had to live differently. This was hard for many to do, as the people at Nashobah learned.

"There was a village near Plimouth at Maktapog that was led by Richard Bourne and Jude. Thomas Mayhew had other churches on Martha's Vineyard. At Punkipog, near the spring in the red earth and the blue hill and not far from the English village of Dedham, was another village. The sachem Ahaugton had moved here from the lower falls on the Neponist river. His son, William Ahawton was the teacher. Waban presided over councils at this village. This village was prosperous with many cows and pigs for they made shingles and clapboards from the cedars in their swamp and sold them to the English in the surrounding towns for their buildings.

"Another village was Panatuket on the upper Merrimack river falls. This was named after the waterfall nearby whose waters made the noise "panna tucket" as they fell on the rocks. Sam Shoshanim was the sachem of the Penagwogs living near the praying village. Old Jethro's son, also called Jethro, was sent to begin a village here just two winters before the war. Most of the people, including Old Jethro, did not want the new religion but when many died in the Mohawk war Eliot said it was a judgement from God so some got scared and converted.

"West of Natick was the tiny village of Magunkukquok in the place of great trees near Monoco hill. This wasn't much of a village and only eleven families lived there. Pumham's son Pomham was sachem and Simon and Job were the teachers. Simon suffered from "the stone" and had a yellowish color to him almost like the color of the plague.

"At Quaboag pond a village named Weshakim was starting but all it had was a few families. Eliot used a high rock there to stand on when he visited and the christian families treated it like it had much manitoo.

"On the Nipmuck river near Mendon was the little village of Waeuntug. James Tuppokkowillin (James the Printer) and Samoset traveled from Hassanamesitt to this place to preach and lead psalms and prayer.

"On a hill in Wabbaquasett was a small village called Quantisset. Daniel of Natick was the minister there. Also in Wabbaquassit was the village by that name on the Mohegan river. Sampson, brother to Joseph, who was at Chabungagunamung, was the teacher there. The area was very fertile and grew much corn. This caused problems between its residents and Uncas, who claimed the tribute they gave to the English rightfully belonged to him since he felt they were in Mohegan territory. Eliot managed to prevent a war by telling Uncas' man in the village that he was not interested in politics, that he was only there to bring people to God.

"Closer to Quaboag was Hassunnimesut, the place of small stones on the Nipmuck river. Wattascompanum was the chief sachem and James the Printer's brothers Anuweekin and Tuppukkowillin were the teachers. Hyems had moved there and was the constable. He was now called Black James. Piam Bow (Booham), the father of the two teachers, came from Natick and founded a second church nearby at Quanatusset. Monatunkanet, Petahee and Piam took care of it along with Anuwekin and his brother. Simon, Job and Pomham also kept in close contact with the new village.

"At the sacred lake of Chabanakongkomum a village was started by Robin Petavit, who died of "the stone." Joseph and Sampson were his sons. Joseph stayed in Chabanakongkomum and Sampson went to Wabquissit. This was a rather small village with only nine families but it had plenty of fertile upland meadows for their corn and animals.

"Not far from it was Maanexit on the Mohegan river. John Moqua had been sent there to be pastor. For many moon after Eliot preached about 'lifting up one's head and opening the doors and gates to let the King of Glory in' the people in Maanexit went about with their eyes on the sky. We all got a good laugh about that.

"Near to this was Manchage on Manchage pond. It was a new settlement without a real grant. Wabesktamin was the teacher there to twelve families. And not far from Mount Wachusett was the village of Pakachoog. This was located on a fertile hill that had a year-round spring of water, much like the springs at Quaboag old fort and south near my mother's village.

"John Horowanninit and Solomon Woonaskochu were sachems at Pakachoog and James Speen was the teacher. Matoonas was constable here also.

"But the village our war captains hated the most was Ogquonikongquamesut. This praying village was right up against the English village of Marlborough and the English meetinghouse was actually on praying village land. Their sachem, my uncle John Owannamug, died five winters before the war so Solomon ruled them as teacher. The village had wonderful fertile crop lands and pastures and abundant orchards. The cider made from the apples caused much drunkenness and the teacher before Solomon was kicked out by Eliot for drinking cider all the time. There were ten families there.

"Besides Eliot and Gookin we sometimes saw George Denison at the praying villages. He brought supplies to them and would help with sabbath services. Later, during the war, he became an English war captain against our people.

"I have told you about these villages so you can see how much the English had infiltrated our territory. Wherever they had a village, nearby was a praying village. In between villages they put praying villages and so on, all in order to destroy our people. They did not want us living in the way of our people. They wanted to bring us all in close to them so they could take the land we left behind. They wanted to keep close watch on us and, by having the villages on the main trails and between main villages, they were able to know what we were doing all the time from their spies- the Christian tribes.

"We didn't fully understand it then. All we knew was that something felt wrong, out of harmony with the great circle. We never thought of the Christian villagers as traitors but Pometacomet knew what they could be like from Sassamon's treachery.

"When the war against the English came, he raided Hassaminnisut and marched the people out, forcing them to join his army. He knew if he left them there they would join the English and fight against us.

"During the war, the English stashed the other "Christian Indians" away on Deer Island so they could use them as spies and scouts. Most of the traitors in our ranks who went to the English and gave away our plans during the war were from the praying villages Pometacomet raided.

"I tried to tell Pometacomet that they were only like us only on the outside, that their insides had been sucked out and replaced with new 'English' ones by magic. I told him the blood and water they took at communion made new insides which sometimes melted into a hard lump called 'the stone' that would kill them. This I had seen in a vision after visiting with Simon."

Chapter 28

(A re-telling of John Sassamon's murder and the eve of the war, 1674-5)

John Tattawaban rises and takes the talking stick:

"By this time I was growing aware of a new tribe in our midst: those of our people who were now Christians. They did not have visions such as our shamans had because they professed loyalty to the white sachems John Eliot, Daniel Gookin, Thomas Mayhew, and their converted preachers such as Gibbs in Nantucket and John Sassamon, who had begun to preach to Uncas' people in Mohegan. They no longer listened to their own sachems. We were now like a herd of deer that had been split, first by ourselves and then by the English.

"My father was one of Eliot's converts. He was old now and no longer traded. My friends, including Konkowasco, were now also getting on in years. This was a strange thing to think about, for we still felt young inside, but our bodies were not as strong or as fast as in previous winters and our thoughts traveled a different road.

"Shatookquis (Firehawk) was already considered old, but not when one thought that he came from a family whose members often lived close to 100 winters. His father had been over 80 winters old when he went to Creator's garden. Ousemequin also had lived that long. If the lung disease didn't get one, a man in our society could easily live 80 winters - and take part in the hunt for most of them. I don't know if you children will also live as long as we did - and still do." (*he laughs a little*) "You are taking on more of the white man's ways and eating and drinking more of his foods, especially his firewater. But these things are not as deadly as losing one's place in the Great One. My people in quansik used to be like a note held on a flute: we vibrated together through the air, our sound going on forever, always a part of the everything. Now, I don't know. I think there are too many different notes and it is hard for our people to hear each other over the white man's loud sounds.

"The English always seemed to be one step ahead of our people. When Philip appeared to be gaining control by selling lands to obtain coin and goods to buy guns with, the English began claiming that the sachems selling lands really didn't own them because they had been previously sold to English. In such a way the English were getting lands without even paying for them. This made Philip and the sachems who were his allies very angry. This was stealing, but we all knew that the English could change how something sounded with their snake tongues. They had one set of words for our people and another for theirs. The same event would be called one thing to them and another to us. I often had to deal with this as a trader. I would go to Boston with pelts or corn and they would make me feel like I was begging. Yet they would turn around and trade much coin for them and then laugh and say behind my back that I had traded for too little. Other traders were fed firewater and then robbed. The English courts would drag the matter on and on and then say they couldn't find the ones who had robbed us. Yet if one of our people walked through an English cornfield and picked up an ear of corn that had fallen, he would be beaten in public like a dog. And if a white killed another white and one of our braves were nearby (such as Matoonas' son) the English didn't hesitate to blame it on him and hang him. For other so-called offenses they thought nothing of selling my people into slavery. We treated our prey better than they treated us!

"So as a trader I walked a dangerous path. I had to deal with the English in their villages and settlements, with my people in their villages and with the new tribe in the praying villages. But I didn't let it bother me, for I, too, was in on Philip's plan. I saw guns in the hands of my people with every pelt or barrel of fish I traded.

"I spent much time in the large villages of Boston, Salem, Plymouth and Nantucket, which used to be called canopache- the place of peace. These were the places where their ships came in full of goods from England, which would be sold or traded for fish and furs and items made by the English on Turtle Island.

"Like Philip, I had come to realize that all English were not the same. The ones in Boston treated us a little differently than those in Plymouth or in the river towns of Hartford and Springfield. But these differences could change in the blink of an eye if they declared war on us. I knew from trading and listening that all the English cared about was acquiring more and more. They would never have enough land to make them happy; they would never have enough pelts to satisfy them or enough metal or food. They were like the animal called the pig- always rooting around, looking for more.

"With their latest tactic of saying we had already given them the land they wanted, I could see that they were tired of paying for our land. I saw the shadow of warriors standing on the edge of the territory they were about to obtain by conquest and so I traded even harder than I had ever traded in the past.

"My routes now always ended in Narrragansett territory, for they were the ones buying the guns from the Dutch through the Mohawks.

"My last trading trip began in Salem in the time of the *papasquoho* (December) moon. I brought in two sleds laden high with thick inland beaver pelts, fox furs, raccoon furs, a bear fur and a wolf skin. The sled also had deer, elk and moose hides, baskets, clay pots, dried herbs, baskets of colored corn in the husk, squashes, nuts and apples from the trees Aquittamaug and his people had planted in Wabbaquasett many winters past.

"I had been gathering my supply of goods since harvest, working my way north from Quinebaug to the Pennacook territory. I had several braves with me to make sure we weren't robbed en route to Salem.

"Our journey had been rough, for Creator had sent us much snow. As we pulled the sleds over deep snow, the thongs on our snowshoes often broke from the strain of pulling the heavy sleds. Even our dogs had trouble and we finally left them in a village in Hassanamesit (Grafton). While we were there, we saw James the Printer and he told us he had run away from his English teacher. James had been the man's apprentice for 16 winters and apparently the man thought he owned him forever because he had taught him the trade. He told me a reward was being offered for him, but I assured him I would not tell any he was there.

"We went from there to tantiesques where we obtained fine baskets and mats, then on to asquoach where we obtained corn and squashes. Our next trip was quabogud and there we saw some of Philip's councillors meeting with Konkowasco, telling him of Philip's plans to wage war on the English as soon as he had enough guns and gunpowder.

"We remained awhile in quabogud, for a large nikkomo ceremony was being held and people from Quaboag and Nashaway were there.

"Because I was just a trader I was not allowed to sit in on the councils held in the long house, but I learned afterwards that my friend Konkowasco, who spoke of peace, was outnumbered by those who wanted to join Philip. Most outspoken of these were Matoonas and Monoco.

"Shatookquis' brothers, David and Andrew, were now living in the praying village nearby so we knew they would be against war with the English. There were many praying villages in this territory now, as Konkowasco told you. Konkowasco said many of his people felt that the only way they would be safe from their enemies was to become like the English so the English would protect them. Yet I wondered how safe they would be from their own people when war came. Would they be considered English and therefore enemies?

"Everywhere I went, I heard talk of Philip's plans. Unfortunately, so did others such as John Sassamon and Benjamin Church, who had recently settled near Awashonks in Sogkonate. My father, Waban, who was by now totally bewitched into following Eliot's god, also heard these things. I wore two faces during this time: in the presence of Christians I pretended a love for their god but to my people I showed my true feelings.

"It was while I was staying with my father that I heard of the murder of John Sassamon at assowompsett pond. I knew immediately he had been murdered for going to the English to report Philip's plot. My father knew too, and told me he had also gone to the English to warn them. I asked him not to get involved for there were things he knew little of. I told him that where I had traveled most people did not think the way he and his Christian people thought. This was all I would say and my father and I argued, for he said I should go to the English and tell them everything I knew.

"I then left his village and traveled to the large coastal English settlements. While in Plymouth, I heard that three braves had been arrested by the English for the murder of Sassamon. These were Philip's councillor Tobias, Tobias' son Wampapaquan and Mattashannamy. Wampapaquan was a Pequan and related to many in quansik. The people began to say that the English had gone too far this time. The arrest of our people for the murder of a Wampanoag, especially one married to a Pequot, was not within the authority of the English. This was a matter to be handled by our people. The only person with a right to vengeance in this was Sassamon's brother and he should not have called on the English to enter a family feud.

"Despite my advice, my father did go to the English and told them the inland tribes they called the Nipmucks were conspiring with Philip so English soldiers were sent to the praying villages to find out what they could. Thinking to scare the English away, a group of Nonotuck squaws told the English living near the river that there were over 80 warriors marching through the valley. Around this time Pumham also became a traitor and told the English about the Narragansetts' involvement with Philip. Fearing immediate war, Tuspaquin and his son then sold a large tract of land at assowamset neck to the English. The father sold the lands for English protection; the son for money to buy more guns.

"The English then visited Meika and reminded the Narragansetts of what they did to the Pequots. That would be their fate, they told him, if his people joined any plot with Philip. They said the Narragansetts would be attacked by the soldiers on the quonicticut and by soldiers from the coast and that all their villages would be burned to the ground. Meika then sent word to Philip that the Narragansetts would not take part in his plans.

"This happened in the time of the *sesquannakeewush* (the new year - June) moon. Then Tobias and Mattashinnamy were executed by the English for Sassamon's murder.

"I was at monthop when this happened and I don't know what was more frightening, the anger of Philip's warriors or the signs we saw in the sky. That night we saw comets in the shape of blazing arrows shoot across the sky. The following nights we saw strange shapes in the lights that flickered to the north (aurora borealis). We heard the thunder of invisible horsemen and the sound of bullets whistling through the air. These were powerful portents but our shamans disagreed on what they meant. Weetamoo's husband Petonowowett, who was a powwow, said Creator was waging war on the English from the skies, sending fire arrows and bullets raining down on them. Some of Philip's councillors traveled to Pennacook to ask Passaconnaway's son Wannalancet what the great turtle said about these things and he said he had been told in a dream that the side that fired first would be the side that lost the war.

"By the time they returned, Philip's braves had led raids on local farms- they were shooting cattle, stealing corn from the fields and burning barns. Some became so bold that they even entered the houses and stole goods from the English.

"Philip was summoned to Plymouth but he sent word to them that he was a king to his people and would only treat with the English king of equal rank - King Charles II.

"Philip's sister-in-law Weetamoo led a war dance at monthop, which was interrupted by the Englishman Benjamin Church, who lived on sakonnet peninsula.

"Philip's men then visited Awashonks and Tolony and held a war dance in her village. Her sons Peter and William, who had both attended Harvard but returned because the English way of eating and living had made them sick, led the dance as captains of the Sogkonetts. While the dance was going on, Little Eyes brought Benjamin Church into camp. Little Eyes said he had been captured as he pulled his boat ashore. Church pleaded with Awashonks to remain neutral but she laughed in his face and told him that the next sabbath would not be peaceful for those in Swansea.

"Next, Weetamoo visited Philip at monthop and pledged her loyalty to his cause. Church visited her afterwards, trying to persuade her to remain neutral. Weetamoo dismissed him as a man trying to protect his own interests - the peninsula. Tired of his meddling, the Sakonnets attacked him at Punkatesse and drove him out of the area.

"Then, Philip sent the old men, women and children to Ninigret in Niantic for safekeeping. By this time he had almost 2,000 warriors pledged to his cause and Canochet had between 3-5,000 more.

"That summer I made my last trade. I traded my goods for a gun and joined Philip's army."

Chapter 29
(A re-telling of the beginning of King Philip's War, 1675)

Firehawk returns to the longhouse, refreshed from a long nap. His son had given him carrion-flower tea for his aching back. This root was so sacred that only high midiwiwan healers could carry it in a special bear-paw pouch.

"The winter before our war with the English began was one of the longest and coldest winters I could remember. In the time of the *wapicummilcum* (February) moon Philip sent Akompian, Nimrod and Tokannamamy to our villages to ask us to join in the Wampanoag-Narragansett plot.

" I was the sachem of lower quansik while my cousin Muttaump and my brothers Andrew and Nassawanno were sachems of the northern villages. A cousin, David Munnilaw, lived in quabogud and I lived in tantiesques. When the councillors arrived, they sent word to the surrounding sachems to come and listen to Pometacomet's men.

"To the north and east of us were Apequinash of quanansit, which was on the north-south path; Monoco of nashua; Shoshanim, also called Uskattuheun, of weshakim; Matoonas of packachog; John of natick; Simon Pottoquan of quinsigamond and Quanohit, James Quanopohit and Kutquen of hassanamesit. To the west was my brother Nassowanno and his son Lawrence and the very elderly Wahginnacut and Wequaquan of the Agawams, who sent a councillors to listen and speak for them.

"There were other sachems or elders such as Noas, now in hassanamisco, Old Jethro in natick; Caleb of tanumasket and Gunrashit of hassaminisco, but we did not invite them, for they were Christians, in league with the English. We didn't want them running to the English the way Waban had done about Sassamon.

"Now that we had English living near us we had to be careful with this gathering for if they suspected us we knew they would send their soldiers into quansik and make us sign an oath of loyalty. Despite these precautions, Thomas Quanapohit went to them and they sent soldiers to us and the Narragansetts.

"By this time, I was 72 winters. I could still hunt and keep up with the others, but I found that I could not go as long as they without rest. Like many of your people before the English and their diseases and unhealthy firewater and food, I expected to live to see the sunrise another 20 winters. Creator has granted me this and more, granting me also good health for most of my 94 winters. But now I am ready to walk the path in the sky and so I must speak to you while I still have breath to do so.

"I had sat in many councils, but never in one so fierce. James Quanapohit, Monoco, Matoonas and I were the oldest sachems there. We had fought in battles in Pequot or Mohawk but the younger braves had yet to prove their warrior skills and were ready to fight the English.

"Like this ceremony of remembering, that council went on for many, many days. Konkowasco told us of his vision of the red wolf and of Passaconnaway's words, but most who listened did not hear. I knew my son and respected his argument for peace at all costs until he had learned the secrets of their power, but the others didn't want to wait.

"Pometacomet's spies had learned that the English now had 73 militia companies, all armed with pikes and flintlocks topped with French bayonets. We were told that our warriors should buy bayonets, for they changed the gun into a spear after the musket balls ran out or if the gunpowder got wet. They were going to meet with the Mohawks to see if they could obtain some of these for the warriors, they said.

"The sachems of quansik and the other nippameag sachems present were swayed by the words of Pometacomet's councillors and by Matoonas' anger over his son's murder. Konkowasco told them that our people would not take part in the plot and I thought for a blink of an eye that the others were going to raise their tomahawks against him. He was accused of being a Christian and it was only through the intervention of my brothers and I that the fire in their eyes dulled to a red glow. He was told if he would not lead his people in battle, he did not deserve to be recognized as a sachem of the

Quansik. The others immediately began talking about having Mutaump lead the people around Quabaug. My heart was filled with sadness that night as I watched the braves smoke the war pipe, for I knew the consequences of war with the English, as had Ousemequin and my father. I knew Muttaump would never have dared defy *their* wishes to remain neutral.

"It was then that I realized my village would be in danger. After they left, Konkowasco and I held a council with our elders and we decided what we would do if the guns sounded in lower quansik.

"There were many warriors passing through tantiesques and Quaboag that winter and spring, and with each sighting on the east-west path or the path leading into Wabbaquasett, I felt the moccasins of worry walking on my breast. We also had English soldiers passing through as they traveled from manexit to quintisset, from one praying village to another, to obtain a pledge of loyalty from them. They came to tantiesques and we told them we knew nothing of any plans and that our tribes were neutral. 'Leave us alone,' Konkowasco told the English soldiers on their horses, 'Leave us alone. Let us live in peace. We have no war with you.'

"They were very threatening but when they saw he meant it, they turned their horses and galloped off - right through our fields of growing corn.

"My people wept when they saw the damage, but the squaws dug up more corn seed and replanted, so we would sow three harvests that year: early, middle and late.

"Again the English came into tantiesques and Konkowasco signed a paper telling them we would not fight them. This we hoped would keep them away for good, but the ink was hardly dry when we heard that the day we had feared had finally come.

"I was in quabogud hunting with Andrew and David when we heard the dull plonk of the booming rocks and then heard shouts as a taggamut was sighted running up the path.

"He was carrying a message sent from Pometacomet to the taggamets, who were carrying it to every village in his federation. The English had fired on some of his warriors in swansea. His warriors killed eight English and put their heads on poles at the kickamuit river. They were scalped and their fingers and feet cut off so their spirits could not walk or fight in the afterlife.

"Immediately Muttaump, who was war captain of quansik,

held war dances and the sounds of the drums and shouts of dancing warriors was heard in the warm night air throughout all of upper quansik.

"I returned to tantiesques after listening to the taggamut. The fighting began before Pometacomet was ready. He had just lost the support of the Narragansetts and he didn't have enough guns or powder for an all-out attack. His braves had instigated the attack, taggmaut said, for they were full of rage over the execution of Tobias and Mattaschumanamoo a few weeks before. They dared the English to shoot at them, taunted them, went on their farms and stole from them. They were led by the braves who had shot cattle and burned barns when the two were hanged. They knew that Wannalancet had seen in a vision that whoever fired first would lose so they taunted but hadn't fired the first shot.

"Our people then began moving to an island in a swamp on a small river near siog pond. We broke our wetus down and carried the mats to the edge of the swamp. There, they were placed on dugout canoes and dragged through the swamps then ferried across the river. We harvested all of the little green ears of corn we could find but had to leave the rest, hoping to be able to return and harvest it later. We dug up what remained of the past year's dried corn and hauled our grinding stones and samp mills by canoe to the little island in the middle of the swamp.

"In this patch of forest and rock in the middle of the swamp were many old people and mothers with tiny infants from asquoach and quobogud.

"We heard no more of war for the next half a moon. Every few sleeps we sent a party out to tantiesques to tend the cornfields. It would take them half the day to cross the boggy meadow and return. We sent the few adult braves we had with our women to guard them, and the boys and old men like myself stayed behind to fish in siog pond, whose village had been abandoned when the Narragansetts took over the area. Its people had gone to live with the Wabbaquasetts, for they had more braves to offer protection against Mohegan raids.

"The able-bodied men took turns keeping watch from the tops of the trees. The women and girls found copious supplies of berries on the island and with the fish in plentiful supply, we felt we would be able to live there until the English were driven out by the people. Because we had chosen neutrality, we felt our people would be spared no matter which side won.

"But this was not to be.

"First my half-brother Uppatachuk, or Sam, as many called him, and Muttaump came to see us to tell us Uncas and his eldest son, Oneko were in Boston to ally the Mohegans to the English. My cousin Muttaump and Sam said they were en route to Wabbaquasett to recruit warriors, for the Wabbaquasetts bordered Mohegan territory.

"They returned a few sleeps later with the Wabbaquasett sachems Keehood and Allumps' son Wollomachin (or Willymachin), plus almost 200 warriors. One of the warriors had been with Pometacomet's men in swansea and had a bundle of booty from a house he had sacked. Konkowasco told the group they could only stay that night. He said they would be fed and given shelter, but he didn't want to endanger our people's neutrality by turning the island into a war camp.

"But the afternoon the Wabbaqusetts arrived, our lookouts on the path between tantiesques and our island spotted several Englishmen on horseback. They ran away from them, fearing that they would be killed, but an Okommakamesit brave with the Englishmen called out that they came in peace and so one of my braves stopped. He recognized the Englishman in front as John Curtis, a trader from quinsigamond who had been to tantiesques often. He wanted to know where the village had moved to but our braves didn't tell him. But Curtis was a good scout and tracker and he saw the new path made by our moccasins when we moved and those from when we went back to check on our crops. Two braves ran into the woods and arrived in the meadow just a short time before the English party found us. Muttaump insisted we send Wabbaquasett warriors over in our four canoes to drive the English away. I didn't like the idea but I also didn't want them to see Pometacomet's warrior, so 40 warriors met the three Englishmen and their three Natick and Massachusetts scouts at the big oak in front of the river.

"The Englishmen wanted the sachems to come across but our warriors said no: the English must come to us. Then the warriors returned in the canoes, leaving the party to founder in the swamp.

"We watched with amusement as the horses sank up to their thighs in the thick mud and had to be pulled free by the English. Then we watched with more amusement as the men slipped and fell trying to find the way across the swamp to our 'island'.

"Many of the warriors lost interest and returned to their gambling as Grandfather Sun followed the path to the west. None really thought they would get through, but suddenly we heard the shouts of the warriors near the edge of the island and every man grabbed his rifle. The Englishman in charge, Curtis, charged up the bank and right into our midst, his horse rearing and stomping. There was much noise and confusion. We shouted to the different warriors and braves and the three Marlboro scouts shouted for us to put our guns down. Curtis was also shouting that he came from the great sachem of the English.

"When it quieted down, those who knew the Englishman's tongue refused to speak it with Curtis. The people wanted no more of anything English, except English guns.

"Finally, Muttaump, Uppatachuck, Keehood, Willymachin and Konkowasco told Curtis we would speak to him in my wetu. He brought the Natick George Memcho in with him as an interpreter and we asked him why he was in quansik. Konkowasco told him we had already signed an agreement, so why this visit by armed Englishmen?

"He said he had just finished escorting Uncas back to Mohegan, and upon return to quinsigamond, had heard his house was broken into. He was searching for the thieves, he said, but we knew he was spying for the English soldiers.

"The other two guides with Curtis - Robin Petuheuit's sons Sampson and Joseph- talked with the warriors outside the wetu while waiting for Curtis. They said the English were sending out armies to find Pometacomet, whom they called King Philip. They said since our warriors had not taken part in the battles so far, we should surrender, but we had done nothing wrong so didn't understand why we should have to throw ourselves on the mercy of the English.

"We brought Curtis in to the wetu four times. His story remained unchanged. He had traveled through hassanimisco, manchaug, chabanagunkamong, mayenecket, over the quinebaug river and to senecksig in Wabbaquasett. He then went to tantiesques and noticed the village was deserted. He noticed the newly-made path from the leadmine, followed it a distance and met our lookouts.

"We told him his path seemed strange for a man hunting for a thief from quinsigamond and he said the English authorities were looking for assurances of fidelity and so he combined two missions into one.

"Since we knew this was the real reason for his visit, we finally let him go.

"Pometacomet's warrior in our midst said the great sachem was planning on heading our way, so we told Curtis to go to Boston and get some kind of proof that the English were our friends and wouldn't hurt us. We figured this would keep them away from quansik for a while. We invited them to spend the night, again looking for a delay, as the later they left for Boston, the later they would return. But Curtis and his men refused and recrossed the swamp that night. This time they found the one dry path through it, thanks to George Memcho, who had observed our lookouts coming over to the island in the moonlight.

"At first daylight most of warriors left with Willymachin and Keehood to go north to menemesit. Muttaump stayed behind with a handful of warriors so he could talk to Curtis when he returned. He said it was important not to raise their suspicions.

"No sooner had they left then a messenger arrived from Matoonas. He had attacked the English settlement called Mendon and was raiding the towns in Nashaway.

"I posted warriors at every possible fording place and along the dry path and we began a long summer of watching and waiting. Every trip to the corn fields now became fraught with danger and we began losing crops to woodchucks, deer and raccoons. While our animal brothers were feasting on corn, my people were living on berries.

There is a long pause as the old sachem fights back the tears and lump in his throat.

"Creator plays strange tricks on his creatures some times."

Firehawk sits down, his body bent double with the pain of remembering.

Chapter 30

(A re-telling of the attack on Quaboag Plantation and other battles, 1675)

John Tahattawaban stands up. His body is tense, his posture straight. As he tells of his days as a warrior, he takes on a warrior's spirit and attitude.

"I was with Matoonas and Uppatechuck when we attacked Mendon. We held a sweat, then a war dance long into the night, dancing and pretending to kill English with our clubs, hatchets, bows and guns. In blood-lust trances, we acted out clubbing, ripping scalps off, and chopping heads and hands off the writhing people we saw in the embers of the flames.

"At dawn the next day, each warrior painted his face and body for the war. I sat in my wetu and took out my little doeskin bundles of red ochre from the mud around quaboag pond; black powder from the rocks at tantiesques, yellow ochre from the earth and white chalk from the rocks in Nashaway. These I mixed with a little bear grease on a large flat rock in front of the fire.

"The night before, I had received a dream after passing out from dancing and singing. In it, Creator showed me what I would be in the war. Waban means the wind, and I would have the spirit of the four winds helping my four limbs. I painted a red streak across the middle of my face and another down the middle, from forehead to chin. These were the four limbs. Then I painted my right eye and forehead area white; the right chin area red, the left chin are black and the left eye and forehead area grey-black. I kept my name of Windwalker, but for the war, I changed it to Circle of wind - Whirlwind.

"I repeated the pattern on my chest then tied an extra thong around my waist to hang my club and tomahawk pipe on. My knife was hanging in a thick leather scabbard across my chest. On a thong running across the other way, I had a leather pouch with rifle shot, a soft buckskin pouch of powder and strips of the soft inner bark of the basswood tree for patch and a small pouch of tobacco. I tied an extra knife blade to the end of my rifle. It wasn't as long as the English rifle knives called bayonets, but it made the gun a lethal weapon even when not firing.

"I did not carry anything extra. The women following us would transport other things, freeing us to concentrate on fighting and killing. I greased my body liberally so I could squirm free if grabbed by the enemy.

"Before we left, the shamans smudged us with sweetgrass smoke and chanted prayers to the Great Spirit to bring us victory in battle. Many of us had horses and mine was a reddish-brown mare with white spots on her sides. I had repeated my pattern on her face so she, too, would have the strength and invisibility of the four winds.

"With Matoonas and Monoco leading, we rode past the pond, then fast up the hill through the wood full of the trees the English called candlewood. We crossed the muddy brook then split up, dismounted and left our horses with two young braves as we crept through the hay and surrounded the English working in their fields.

"I caught a glimpse of Matoonas' dark, wrinkled face and his wide grin as he raised his hand and gave the signal to attack. The Englishmen were unarmed and killing them was like killing helpless children. They ran towards their houses, shouting to the women and children. One young man bravely met us with his scythe raised high. He managed to graze the arm of one of our warriors before a hatchet split his skull in two. When it was over, the only bullets shot were those of victory, for the men had given us no opposition.

"The warriors wanted to destroy the whole town, but other Englishmen were now gathering, each with a gun, so we shot fire arrows into the thatch rooftops of their barns and houses and then rode off, whooping in victory over the five Englishmen we had killed.

"At our war camp, we roasted the cows we had stolen and whooped five times over and over, revelling in our victory. We shouted that before we were done, all their fields would be watered with their own blood. 'Mother Earth will drink every drop of English blood!' we yelled as we poured cow blood onto her. We told each other that if all the towns fell so easily, the English would all be destroyed before the moon of the falling leaves.

"We raided a few of the scattered farms for food and corn on our return to menemesit. There we celebrated the arrival of the Wabbaqausett warriors. When Willymachin told us of Curtis, we sent extra men to guard the paths in quansik. But the news of the Mohegan alliance made our leaders decide to lay low until they could contact Pometacomet and see what his plans were. From the Wabbaquasett warrior who had been with him we knew he was hiding in the swamps of Pocasset but didn't know if he wanted help or was planning on coming inland.

"Then two things happened. Curtis reappeared almost immediately in Quaboag and Keehood told him that he and another sachem would go to Boston in two weeks to speak to their governor. This was merely a stall tactic and it wasn't long before Curtis again showed up in our territory, at menemesit. The sachems told him that Black James, Constable of Chabungagungamong, had told them the English would kill all who did not worship their god. Curtis said that wasn't true, but by then we knew it was true and some of our people went to the praying villages to seek refuge. While Curtis was at the island the second time, Konkowasco was in manchaug to see if the neutral people could receive sanctuary in their praying village.

"This time the leaders were fed up with the English poking their noses into quansik, spying and delivering orders from their English king. Our warriors met them on the banks of the menemesit river and refused them entrance into the war camp. Matoonas met with his war captains and sachems and they came up with a plan. He sent the message that our people would meet with Curtis and the man with him, Hutchinson, the next morning at 8 o'clock near the English village they called Quaboag Plantation (Brookfield).

"Instead of meeting in the open, we followed the brook, heading into the valley until we came to a place where the path was swamp on one side and steep, rocky hill on the other.

"Our scout reported that he overheard the three Massachusetts with Hutchinson tell him we were planning an ambush. This raised our ire towards these turncoats and we vowed to kill them first. But Hutchinson didn't listen to them, as English never listened to my people. He marched his men into the swamp, along the narrow path, and when the last horse was in our trap, we closed off their escape and ambushed, running down the steep, brush-covered hill on the side and from behind dead trees in the swamp. Mother Earth drank well that day, for before we were done, eight English lay dead, their ochre-colored uniforms turning brown from blood so they looked like they were made from earth .

"George Memecho was captured, but the other two scouts helped the English escape through the woods to their village. A brief council was called about Memecho and it was decided not to kill him, but to keep him so we could pry information about the English from him. His hands were tied with thongs and a rope put around his neck so he could be pulled behind one of the horses.

"Muttaump and Matoonas led the chase and we arrived at the small village in time to chase Curtis and another Englishman, who were galloping out to seek help from the English in Marlboro, back into the village.

"There, all of the people were in one house, like chickens in a pen. In a fever from the battle, our warriors ransacked the other houses along the straight road, looting and destroying whatever they pleased. They found barrels of hard cider and began slaking their thirst from the *matterrllawawkeeswush* (ripe beans- August moon) heat.

"As they drank, they shot volleys of balls off, shouting and taunting the scared English in their square house.

"After hours of this, we saw a side door open and a young man of about fourteen winters ran out, trying to make it to another house. I was with the warriors who caught him. He struggled and screamed as we tied him down over a tree stump and chopped off his head. If they wanted to act like chickens, they would die like them, we said.

"Then some of the warriors who had drank a little too much firewater decided to kick his head around in front of those in the house, shouting and taunting, hoping to scare them all to death. We had no respect for these people. They were poorly armed and they screamed when captured and killed. They were weak. They were disgusting.

"After a while the warriors tired of their game and put the head on a pole in the middle of the town, just as Matoonas' son's head had been put on a pole. Matoonas was full of revenge. His attack on Mendon only made him want more and more. He hated every single English, no matter how little or old. He said he hoped he did not die until he saw them all killed or driven away from Turtle Island forever.

Most of us shared his sentiments, though some were not so vengeful. Myself, I would have been satisfied to see them all flee, never to return, but I had chosen the way of the warrior and so I did what the others did. But I didn't drink the firewater, for I had seen too many people go crazy from it.

"We were in the barn next to the house by now, so we could fire freely and not worry about getting shot. We decided to give them a taste of ther own medicine and burn all of them inside like they had done to the Pequots. We attached strips of flax to our arrows, lit them and sent them into the thatch of the roof and through the windows. We heard lots of shouts and saw thick smoke, but they beat out the flames and cut a hole in the roof and the smoke escaped. Next we piled hay next to the house and set it on fire, but they dashed out and beat it out with their coats. If the warriors had not drunken so much cider and firewater, they would have been able to stop them, but many were no good by this time. We tried again, this time with warriors covering the door from the meetinghouse next door, but they didn't run out, instead they broke down a part of the wall next to the fire and extinguished it from there.

"By then it was dark and our warriors were passing out from the firewater. The leaders took away what they could of it and posted guards for the night. But the guards were more interested in sneaking over to a bottle or barrel than in keeping watch and Curtis managed to sneak out of the house. This we didn't know until the next day when we saw him bringing troops in.

"In the morning, some of the warriors began constructing two wheelbarrows, using barrels for front wheels and wheels off the farm wagons for back ones. They placed poles from the fences end to end, overlapped and tied with hempen rope so the wheelbarrows were very long. They ran planks across them and then we began heaping them high with flax, hay and candlewood.

"The day was very humid and hot and it took us longer to do simple things. Sweat ran like blood down our bodies as we worked. When we were ready, we held the ends and rolled them out, positioning them next to the house.

"Just as we lit them, the white man's god intervened. There was a great clap of thunder and lightning and rain poured down, soaking everything.

"As our warriors waited inside the barn for the rain to lessen, the mugginess of the day overwhelmed them and they began drinking the cider once again.

"Our lookouts also let the heat overcome them and so they missed the approach of the troops with Curtis. We barely escaped as the English troops galloped right into the middle of the town and stopped in front of the boy's head on the pole. Almost on cue, the rain stopped and the sun came out.

"There were too many, we decided, and our warriors were in no shape to do battle, so we snuck around, setting fire to everything we could, then jumped on our horses and galloped out, towards menemesit. Our only casualty was the Wabbaquasett warrior Poquatow, who fell captive when his horse was shot out from under him.

"We quickly lost the English pursuing us and then stopped in a swamp near quaboag pond to let our horses drink. While there, Caleb of Tatumasket and another warrior spotted Wampanoag warriors and Pometacomet. They brought them to us and then Muttaump sent word to menemesit for the other sachems to join us at quaboag old fort, where Pometacomet's people were waiting.

"The coolness of the fort's wooded setting was refreshing, but the air was still heavy and warm. There were about 40 warriors with Pometacomet, plus his wife, son and several other squaws and children. John Apequinash and Quanansit joined Muttaump and we repeated the story of our attack on Quaboag Plantation to them.

"Pometacomet had his own exciting battle story and we listened as he told how his people were chased over annowon (Rehobeth) plain. He said if the English had pursued them, they would have all been captured or killed, for they had almost run out of powder. Once into quansik territory, Wetamoo and her people plus most of the Wampaonags went south into Narragansett while Pometacomet, his family and the forty warriors, including ten wounded, came to Quaboag.

"The wounded men gave their guns to the others, so all his men had a musket, but not much powder to go with it. Pometacomet said he planned to go to the Mohawks and ask for their help. They always had access to plenty of gunpowder, he said. He had basketfulls of unstrung wampum and he measured out a small basket of it for Apequinash, Quanansit and Muttaump as a reward for their victories. This they could use to buy more guns and powder with, he said.

"At daybreak we left the fort and traveled to menemesit. We

broke camp and moved everyone northwest to the Nonotuck village on the bluff overlooking the quanicticut. From there, Pometacomet planned to go west to schagticook to meet with the Mohawks.

"The English soldiers and Mohegans under Uncas' son, Josias, were all over Quaboag. We had left some of our old people at menemesit. Konkowasco was to send a few braves up to help them travel to his island. But as they neared Quaboag, the English soldiers spotted them. They captured an old man and tried to make him talk, but he refused. The Dutch soldier who was wearing Pometacomet's hat from the swansea fight threw the old man down on the ground and drew his sword. The grandfather threw his hands in front of his face and yelled, 'Don't kill me - I am neutral!' but the Dutch white man brought his sword down. It sliced the old man's hand off and split his skull half-open. Then he cut again, this time slicing off the grandfather's head.

"When news of this reached the old man's son, who was living with the Okommakamesits (Marlboros), he led a party to the English village nearby and killed seven of their men. Naddawahunt's son David was captured and condemmed to death by hanging, but the English took him aside and told him if he said the village had been raided by the Christian Marlboros who lived near their village, they would let him go. This didn't make sense to David, but he didn't like the Christians, so he gladly gave them the names of the eleven he knew at the village and he was released. He then learned that they wanted the land the Christian village stood on, so this was how they got rid of their neighbors.

"The English raided the village and bound the eleven together at the neck, then marched them off towards Boston. This should have been a warning to the others in praying villages, but they were so bewitched, they continued to love the English and their god and more joined them as scouts against their own bloodkin.

"The English also raided and burned other villages in the area and Wannalancet moved his people from naamkeke near pawtucket falls into the woods to avoid them, but not before several were captured. He would not raise his war club with us, though, for he had seen visions and had promised his father not to war with the Englishman. As soon as it was safe to do so, he began moving his people further north to the Pennacooks, out of the way of the fighting.

"Around this time we heard that the Mohawks had told the

English soldier Talcott that they would not join their cause for they hated Uncas and the Mohegans and would not fight alongside them. They said they were not our enemies and so would remain neutral.

"This was good news in a way, for a war against the Mohawks and English would have been short and bloody with our people dying like flies in an early winter.

"While we were at the army camp, the village nearby received an unwelcome visit by the English soldiers. Earlier that year when the English demanded the guns from Pometacomet's and Awashonks' people, the English in Springfield and Hatfield had also demanded the guns in the Pocumtuck villages, but after the sachems met in council with the governors and assured them they were friends of the English, they gave them back.

"But now the soldiers came again and this time they were warlike and demanded that the guns be loaded onto their cart right then and there. The old sachem who had spoken words of peace told them he needed time to gather all the guns and to return in a few days.

"This was Umpanchella. He had listened to Konkowasco tell of his visions and knew a war with the English would never lead to victory. He called a council and argued with Pometacomet and Muttaump over warring on the English villages in Pocumtuck. Unlike Konkowasco, who decided to withdraw and give up his sachemship, Umpanchella tried to get his people to send Pometacomet and the Quaboags away. But this was too much for the warriors, who had set their moccasins on the war path.

"They grabbed Umpanchella and threw him into the large fire, shoving him back as he tried to run out. His cries made many of the young warriors laugh, such was the state of their minds. Warriors on the path of blood become like our brothers the wolves. They forget how to be human. They live to stalk and kill and howl in victory. Warriors who had little babies of their own in camp thought nothing of grabbing an English baby by its heels and dashing its brains out on the side of an English house. Our enemies ceased to be people: they were prey to be killed. Even our women forgot they were human at times and did savage things to the enemy. They knew that the enemy would do the same thing to them if they caught them first. This is why we have sweats and ceremonies after wars. We have to rid ourselves of our animal skins and become human again.

"After killing the sachem, the war chiefs held a council and it was decided that the villagers should go north to pocumtakuke (Deerfield) to join the main army gathering there.

"We missed the English soldiers by a matter of hours, for they, too, had held a war council in the night and had attacked the village at dawn. They followed our trail and we took refuge in the swamp at the base of wequomps mountain.

"Many of the villagers died in the swamp and our progress was slowed as we retreived each body so it could be buried properly when the fighting was over. We barely made it to the woods near pocumtakuke, where we joined Monoco, Sam and the Nashaway warriors. The women, old people and children were sent further north into Squakeag to safety and we began plotting our next raid in the shadow of the English garrison.

"Perhaps because we had been traveling all night, we did not see the English soldier until he saw us. He ran back to the garrison, shouting, but our bullets split his back open like a ripe berry. We found his horse in the woods and were about to launch an all-out attack on the garrison when a fresh supply of English soldiers rode into the garrison on the other side. We raided the surrounding countryside, burning houses and barns. It made us laugh to watch the white people screaming and running towards the garrison, but we didn't kill any as our powder supply was low. From there, we traveled north and met up with more warriors outside the English village of Deerfield. This time we had ammunition and from our horses we chased after the people running through the high hay and corn and the mothers carrying children as they ran from the houses. We killed eight English before they reached the safety of their pallisade.

"Mocking the English 'justice' we beheaded the people and stuck their heads on poles in the meadow. In the heat the smell of blood was so thick that the flies came from all over and the heads swarmed with armies of our winged brothers.

"We climbed the hills around the village and through the smoke from their houses and barns, we watched their movements inside the pallisade.

"Before we could attack again, a messenger arrived from Pometacomet's troops to to our south so we left off our attack and rode hard to the south, narrowly avoiding detection by the English war captain Mosley and his men.

"Towards dusk we were met by Pometacomet's men, who were

in the woods watching a team of oxen pulling a loaded cart on the narrow, rutted path towards Deerfield. There were 36 Englishmen on horseback with them. They struck camp in the woods as we waited for more warriors to join us.

"We were going to rush in and attack them there, but Muttaump said a better plan was to wait until they got to the ford in the river. We could hide on either side of the ravine and ambush them, cutting off their retreat. If we attacked them in the woods, some might get away and sound the alarm. If we just waited, we could have total victory and not be chased away. Then we could get their guns and the goods in the cart.

"By moonlight we crossed the plateau, followed the river, cut through the high grass, carefully covering our trail, and waited at the fording place on the path.

"As Grandfather Sun began to spread his golden blanket of light over the high grass, we readied for battle. Each ate a handful of nohikik mixed with water from the brook, checked his gun, patches, powder or supply of arrows. Although the musket was favored by most, some of the older warriors preferred the bow. But they tipped their arrows with metal if they could. A big advantage of the gun was that we didn't have to retreive our arrows during battle. If we had both when we ran out of arrows, we could switch to musket fire. But one shot from a musket was more accurate and deadly than six volleys of arrows.

"Under the hazy first rays of the sun we waited, tensing when our spies returned from where they were watching the English camp to tell us the wagon and a handful of men were on their way. They were leaving the rest of the men and the horses behind. This was not good news, for it increased the likelihood of escape to the English in Hadley or Deerfield. Monoco sent a party to the camp to attack and take the horses when they heard the first gunfire from the ravine.

"As the birds began singing in the treetops, we heard the sounds of wooden wheels creaking then saw the English come out of the forest and towards the brook. We all lay as silent as the dead, waiting for our prey to fall into the trap.

"The English stopped often and looked around. If they had brought a Mohegan or other scout with them, they would have known it was too quiet near the river, but they had no scout, just the war captain called Beers. We saw the tops of their heads over the tall grass and the horns of the oxen moving up and down, side to side. The whip cracked regularly as they goaded the oxen towards the bank of the stream. The oxen stopped as the path fell away and it took coaxing for them to cross the shallow stream.

"We waited until they were halfway across the stream then Monoco gave the hand signal and we burst forth, whooping and screaming, our guns firing, our arrows flying. The surprised English tried to run, slipping on the rocks and the wet bank, but we met them at the top, our tomahawks raised, our guns leveled. The captain named Beers broke loose and led a party to a hill, gaining upper ground. But they were outnumbered and it wasn't long before every man lay dead, his blood wetting Mother Earth's dry skin.

"Our warriors from the English camp joined us, herding some horses before them. It was a glorious victory. Although several had gotten away, they managed to capture some and their horses. Sam decided to keep the captives alive so we could find out what the English army was planning and how they planned their battles.

"In the cart, we found a keg of rum and our warriors began drinking it and dancing. They whooped and shouted happily as they went around the battlefield, chopping heads off and sticking them on poles. Monoco and Sam took a couple of men who were not quite dead and hooked a chain under their jaws, hanging them from tree boughs near the path as a warning to other English. Their screams tingled in our veins and down into our loins. I can remember feeling ashamed the first time in battle when I got sexually aroused, but the older warriors laughed and said it was Creator's way of reminding us that from death came life. Sometimes when we took a female captive this feeling made us feel like raping her, but such a thing would have brought great dishonor on the warrior who did it, so instead, if a warrior captured a female, he could either claim her as his wife or give or sell her to someone who wanted her. Often familes who had lost daughters would ask to adopt young female captives. Male captives who had shown a great deal of courage might be adopted into the tribe if they could run the gauntlet and prove they were up to our standards for warriors. But this war was different. We were not interested in captives: we wanted to kill every last English person we could - unless they could be used for information or ransom money.

"Because of the firewater, our warriors didn't chase the ones who got away and so we knew we couldn't attack the villages by surprise.

"As night fell we roasted the oxen, gorging ourselves as we danced and reenacted the battle. When the sun began to paint the sky beyond the treetops the color of the inside of the blue clam shell, we fell into deep sleep in the woods.

"By the time I awoke at midday, our warriors had taken the ammunition and supplies from the cart and were loading them on horseback to take to the main camp near Deerfield. One of our spies had returned with the news that their war captain Treat was riding up the quonicticut with about 100 soldiers. We sent word to the other war captains and held our position, knowing the English would ride here after learning of the battle from those who escaped.

"The next day they rode into sight and we debated whether to ambush them like we had the others, but Treat had Mohegans with him who told him how to avoid ambush, so he sent only a handful of soldiers onto the battlefield to bury their dead. We had a handful of warriors to their many, so we decided to try to pick them off one at a time from the woods. As they started to take the bodies down from the trees, we fired at them, keeping up the harassment until they gave up and rode towards Deerfield. We would have openly chased them if we had had more soldiers. Instead, we followed silently, secretly in the woods.

"That night, as we slept on the hill overlooking Deerfield, Treat and his soldiers led all the villagers out, down the path to Hadley. They managed to escape because our warriors were again drunk on firewater and the night watchmen were lying against trees in drunken stupors. That morning many warriors realized that their firewater was as lethal as their bullets.

"We spent the rest of the day burning their houses and barns and then herded the livestock towards our large camp further north. We were able to take many metal articles with us for use as shields and to melt into musket balls. But to our disappointment we found their powder house empty - if indeed it had ever had any powder in it at all.

"We rode to Pocumtuck to tell them how the English had escaped. But all was not lost for they left their corn and our growing army would need every kernel in the long winter months ahead.

"For the next week we had spies watching the garrison at Northampton. Every day our numbers grew. Pometacomet had the support and following of the Nashaways, Quaboags, the Pocumtucks, Nonotucks and Squakeags.

"Under Monoco a party of warriors snuck into the fort and attacked a group of about 20 English as they were going from one house to another. Our warriors managed to get inside and get out without harm. We attacked and set fire to the north fort after looting it for food and valuables. Then we sent a stampede of hogs and cows out the gate, right into the arms of our people. We also captured an English boy of about fourteen winters and tied him to a tree in camp.

"Unlike the men captured at Quaboag, this one was not kept alive for information. He was taken solely for torture and death. For two days and nights our warriors taunted him and tortured him with fire, steel, snakes and whatever came to mind. He withstood much but finally gave in and began screaming, sobbing and begging for mercy. This made us laugh and lose our respect for the weak English and so our captains decided to roast him alive at dawn the following day, like the pigs and cows. However, during the night a brave from podunk, Toto, set him free. We learned of his treachery later, for that morning none took responsibility for freeing the young Englishman.

"We didn't have time to seriously look for the traitor as our lookouts sounded the alarm and we had to quickly break camp and abandon our site amongst the pines on the hill. From there we went back to Deerfield and joined the main party of warriors outside the village.

"After we saw reinforcements arrive, our spies climbed the walls of the garrison outside Deerfield and reported that the English planned to go to the corn fields outside Hadley and bring the cut corn back to the garrison.

"Immediately the war captains got together and planned an ambush along the route from Deerfield to Hadley. It was decided to place it south of Deerfield. We traveled by night to avoid the patrols led by their war captain Mosely, crossed a brook and hid in the swamp.

"We watched as the soldiers and a group of farmers with carts approached. From where I was in the high grass I could hear the creaking grow louder and louder. I could smell the oxen and hear their tails swishing the flies. Through the stalks of hay I caught glimpses of the soldiers on horseback and glimpses of white shirts and dark pants as the farmers walked alongside the carts. I counted the guns. Each soldier was holding a flintlock, but the farmers - and this I could hardly believe- had put their guns on the empty carts. They were gathering the wild grapes along the path, talking and laughing as if they were on a picnic. I felt myself tense with the excitement of this discovery. Now all we had to worry about was the soldiers.

"Closer, closer, into our trap. The voices were dangerously near now and I knew if we didn't attack soon they would discover us while searching for grapes.

"The war call was sounded and we all jumped up and began shooting at the soldiers first, then at the farmers as they ran through the brook to get their guns.

"The battle was over almost as fast as it began and the brook, its shores and the high grass were strewn with dead Englishmen. As we moved in to decapitate them we heard Mosely's men and when I looked up, they were charging straight into our midst, flintlocks booming, swords and bayonets glinting in the midday sun.

"I scrambled up the sides of the brook and retreated to the high grass, standing up to fire then ducking back down into the hay. Mosely had a good 70 soldiers with him- all well-armed. But we had more and we were giving them a fight, picking off horses and men. Monoco set up another ambush, then stood on top of a hill, shouting in English, 'Come, Mosely, you seek indians, you want indians, here is indians enough for you!' But before Mosely and his men could charge into the ambush, their war captain Treat arrived with 100 English and 60 Mohegans.

"Now we had trouble, for the Mohegan traitors knew where to seek us out and how to chase us into the woods, unlike the English who stayed in a clump and fired together, exposed like a herd of cattle.

"The fighting continued as Grandfther Sun moved to the land of the west. When we lost the light we retreated back into the long shadows falling across the fields and into the dark of the woods. We had many dead with us, rescued from the battlefield in the thick of the fight. These we brought to a place of pine trees, burying them beneath the branches of this sacred tree, for nothing was more respected than a warrior who died in battle. We chanted over the bodies, smudging the area, each giving his respect as our brothers began their walk to the land of the southwest, to Cautanowwit's garden.

There, they would live as members of the elite, sachems of the fields of glory. We included their flintlocks, knives, hatchets or bows with them if we had been able to obtain them when we retrieved our brothers. We mourned not only the loss of our brave warriors, but the loss of their weapons, for every flintlock was worth its weight in the white man's most precious substance- gold.

"We rode most of the night, then set camp and held a victory dance as we ate and sang. Some were able to capture English guns or souvenirs such as hats or the soldier's pale leather or woolen coats and they wore them proudly over their war-painted bodies to show how they had couped the enemy.

"The next day we moved on, towards quanawatchoog (longhill) fort: (Springfield) for our leaders wanted to persuade the English-loving Agawams at the fort to come over to our side. The Agawams said the English had demanded their guns but they had refused. Then the English demanded hostages. While they were stalling them, we arrived.

"Over the next two weeks there was much coming and going of Ousemequin's yongest son, Sunconewhew (who had married a Nonotuck maiden), Wequaqon, Wahginnicut and their Agawams as they parlayed with Shatookquis, Sagamore John, Pometacomet, Monoco, Muttaump and Sam. Wequagan's son Squompe (Noas) was there but he was a member of a praying village so we refused to talk to him. The Agawams finally decided to join forces with us when they saw the troops leaving for Hadley and we planned to attack the English village of Springfield after taking the fort. Forty Agawams led our main party - 300 warriors - to the fort in the middle of the night. We planned our attack strategy well but did not know the Podunk trader Toto had told his English employer of our plan.

"Early the next day we saw two men riding towards our fort. We managed to shoot them both near the river. One died on the spot and we gained a fine horse. The other rode, bleeding heavily, into the garrison, our troops at his heels. We advanced on the garrison from all sides, but instead of confronting a panicked population, there was stillness and quiet. House after house was empty, its inhabitants gone. Our warriors searched for powder, bullets or guns but found little. One took a pewter platter and tied its handles to thongs so he could wear it across his chest like the armor Standish wore. We set fire to the empty houses and advanced under cover of smoke. Then bullets came from every direction as we realized they had laid a three-sided ambush for us.

"We rushed the houses and many fell, including the warrior with the chest plate. As we carried him off the battlefield, we ripped it off and threw it at the English in contempt. The warrior should have known better than to rely on English material for protection. The only English thing that had any value to us was the flintlock. Everything else was just like their words of friendship - empty. Before we left we burned a room full of books, including their sacred Bible.

"We tried setting fire to the houses where the guns were, but the Englishmen fought hard. We killed a few at the window where Toto was fighting with the English. It was then we knew who had told the English of our plans and who had released the young Englishman a moon before. It seemed the English's best weapon had been one of our own people - and the Mohegans.

"We continued the assault well into the day but finally had to retreat east of the river when two companies of English and Mohegan soldiers arrived, all well-armed, on the west side of the river. For the second time we suffered losses and this time our dead outnumbered the English dead. An old woman (wenise) was captured in the tall grass and Mosely set his dogs on her, watching and laughing while they ripped her apart. When we learned this, a new, deeper, rage filled our hearts. If they wanted to kill like animals, they would be killed like the beasts they were!

"We took a break from battle then so we could send warriors to the cornfields to guard the squaws as they brought English corn into our winter camps. While our days were full of the heat of muskets and blood, our nights were growing colder and frost would soon destroy all corn that remained in the field. Already some of it was black and we knew our armies would need much corn to get them through the winter. Much of the corn in quansik had been destroyed by Appleton and the other English war captains. We had little fish for we had been too busy warring that summer to catch and dry stores of it for winter.

"During this time we learned that the Mohegans near punham (Warwick) had captured some of Pometacomet's old men, old women and children as they were making their way towards the big Narragansett fort in the swamp.

"Before the first hard frost we attacked once more - this time at Hatfield, which was the English headquarters for trade in the Pocumtuck territory. Pometacomet had 800 warriors with him to fight Mosely and Poole's armies on one side of the quonicticut and Appleton's on the other at Hadley.

"Pometacomet's advisors suggested we try to lure the English out by setting night fires in the woods around the fort, but there were Mohegans in with the soldiers and they alerted them to our plans. So only ten English came out, accompanied by three Mohegans. We killed them easily but no more were sent forth, so at dawn the next day we attacked the fort. I was one of those who advised against this direct assault, for the English were most vulnerable outside their forts, where we could surprise them. Inside, they had the advantage. But Pometacomet and the other captains were itching for battle and said they wanted to burn the fort like the English had burned the Pequot's fort. They wanted to smell English flesh burning and hear English screams.

"But again, the English reinforcements arrived and we found ourselves in the middle of fire from both sides of the river. Many warriors fell that day and towards dark we gathered our fallen brothers and retreated into the woods.

"After this battle, Pometacomet went to see his wife and eight-year old son in the huge fort the Narragansetts had constructed in a swamp. The Pocumtucks, Nonotucks, Squakeags and Agawams retired to a fort to the north of Deerfield and I went with the Quaboags and Nashaways to mememesit and nichewaug to stay in our newly-made winter camps there.

"As the snows began to fall, we repaired our guns, made musket balls of melted booty and some made metal-tipped and horn-tipped arrows. With every pass of my knife and hatchet blade over the grindstone, I thought of English skin being sliced open. Many war councils were held that winter to discuss how we would attack in the spring, but we didn't know that with every day we waited the English army grew stronger and wiser, for the Mohegans were teaching them how to fight our way.

"I traveled to Natick during the *quinnekewush* (December) moon to see my family. It was a risky journey, but I was able to bring them back with me to menemesit so the long winter nights in my wetu were not so lonely. During the winter my oldest son underwent his manhood ceremony. Afterwards he became a warrior. This was unusual, for normally we waited four winters between the manhood ceremony and the warrior ceremony, but in those times we needed every warrior we could get, so my son at the age of 14 winters joined our army.

"I helped in his training as a warrior. He learned how to memorize the pattern of sticks the war captain placed on the ground, how to then take his place as a stick in the formation, and who to watch for his directions. Much of the winter was spent in such training, for we planned many attacks as soon as the snows melted."

John Tattawaban pauses, wiping the tears from his face.

"These are not tears for my dead son, for he died an honorable death as a warrior. These tears, my children, are for the loss of our lands and our freedom. These tears are for you."

Chapter 31
(A re-telling of the battles along the Ct. River 1675-1676 and of the massacre of the Narragansetts)

Tom Pequin next takes the talking stick.

"That winter was like no winter I have ever seen. Bands of warriors were constantly moving from one camp to another, spreading messages, plotting, trading for corn.

"Corn was like the white man's gold that winter. With our corn fields burned, we were forced to steal the English corn, if we could keep them from taking it first.

"After the attack on Hatfield, we went to the cornfields north of the river near Northampton. We surprised eight men gathering corn and chased them into the stockade then burned their houses and barns. We then traveled to the meadows opposite the mill at the red rocks and, as the sun beat down straight overhead, we killed a man cutting wood. The following day we killed two men and a boy at the same place. We tried to burn the grist mill but that dog Appleton arrived and outnumbered us so we retreated.

"In Springfield we burned the gristmill so the English couldn't grind the corn they had gathered. Our spies told us Pynchon was going to lead a wagon party to the gristmill to the west where the two rivers joined in Woronoke, so we rode there and laid our ambush. There was a stout fort at the site. We were able to ambush them and kill three but the rest ran to the safety of the well-pallisaded fort. Some of us wanted to set fire to the log fort, others said no. Later we learned the fort had an underground cellar so we wouldn't have killed the people inside anyway.

"I went to Hassanamesit to see my wife and children and while there some people who had been camped near Mendon came running into camp, escaping from Henchman and his dogs. They said Henchmen's men had surprised them and got right up to the door of their wetu. They had killed two soldiers and then escaped.

"Aware of the constant patrols of English soldiers in the area, I brought my wife and children down to Konkowasco's camp and learned that Pometacomet was nearby, en route to Narragansett with some Wampanoags and inland warriors. I caught up with them near the cat rocks and accompanied them to Canochet's village in Narragansett.

"Canochet had just returned from Boston. The English had taken him there to demand that he turn over all Wampanoags living in asylum in Narragansett. He was glad to see us and furious with the English, even though he was wearing their present to him - a dark wool coat trimmed with silver. He said they wouldn't listen when he said the Narragansetts were neutral. On the canoe trip back from Boston, Roger Williams had warned him not to break the treaty with the English or he'd be sorry.

"The next day Pometacomet and Akompian sat in with Canochet and his advisors. We warriors related our many victories along the quonicticut and Canochet liked what he heard. He decided not to send the wounded W ampanoag warriors or any of Pometacomet's people to the English and instead sent a letter telling the English the Narragansetts would not send a Wampanoag nor even the paring of a Wampanoag's nail to them.

"Following this, the English declared war on the Narragansetts and Canochet, Pumham and Magnus held a huge war dance at the large fort under construction in the cedar swamp between the uspuaquag and schickasheen rivers. Most of the Narragansett and Niantic braves throughout their territories danced at that war fire, their hatred of the white man burning as brightly as the flames they thrust their spears into.

"Flushed with the excitement of the war dance, one war party attacked a house, burned it and brought back the cattle and the owner, a man called Tift."

"To avoid execution, T ift told us many things: that a lar ge army of English and Mohegans with a large supply of food, powder, lead and flints was being formed from several shore villages and that they were under the direction of the war captain Treat.

"The Narragansett warriors kept Tift with them to use as a spy or to ransom for money, for the Dutch and French on the other side of the quonicticut wanted money or furs instead of wampum as payment for guns.

"Canochet's village received a visit from Roger Williams soon after Tift's capture. Even though war had been declared, there were some Englishmen the sachems allowed to travel freely because they had shown loyalty to us in the past and were now of use as liaisons. Williams was one of these. He said the people in his state of Rhode Island were angry over Boston's actions, for it was a violation of their treaty. They had no jurisdiction over the Narragansett territory, he said, and added that he and his people were protesting the action to the United Colonies commission. He assured Canochet that he and his people were not at war with the Narragansetts.

"But no sooner had he left then our spies told us the colony they called Connecticut was raising a large army to our west and Church, Appleton, Mosely and other war captains were raising a large army to the east.

"Now the weather was bitter cold and the swamps around the fort were frozen over. The snow had begun early that winter, which was one reason the northern campaign had been halted. Without leaves to hide our prints we could not ambush and we learned that the English were not easy to kill once safely inside their forts. As we were learning about the armies the English were gathering, another snowstorm came, laying a thick blanket on top of the hardened snow beneath. Hunting was hard to do in deep snow and our brothers of the woods had retreated into snug dens to avoid the extreme cold. We spent long days inside our wetus or the longhouses, huddled near the small fires, our bearskin robes pulled tight against the frigid wind that cut through us like knives.

"Also cutting through our middles were the pains of hunger. Our harvests had been meager and our corn pits were frozen over. Many tried to fish on the frozen rivers or ponds near the fort but the cold was so great they could not stand to be out in it for long. The grease we spread over our skin to keep us warm turned white and flaked off, it was so cold.

"Hunger does strange things to a person's mind and some of the warriors began to talk of making peace with the English to end the suffering.

"The old people, women and children suffered the worst that winter. When food was prepared they let the warriors eat first, for we needed our strength, and they ate the crumbs remaining. Many old people just stayed in bed and stopped eating, quietly singing their death songs in the dark wetus.

"I often thought of my wife and children during the long hours of night. I wondered if they were starving at the winter camps in menemesick, for the Narragansetts had more food than our people had gathered from the English fields, yet they were hungry. This was one reason Pometacomet had come here - to ask for dried corn. But he soon saw that the Narragansetts were also starving, so he instead asked if they could spare some seed corn for the spring.

"A strategy was being worked out amongst the leaders. Come spring, war parties would attack the towns in the east, luring the English troops away from our fishing grounds and corn fields in Quansik, Pocumtuck and Squakeag. With the troops in the east we could plant our crops and harvest enough corn and dry enough fish to feed all our armies next winter. It was a good plan, but it did not fill our empty stomachs that winter.

"To take our minds off our hunger we told stories of our feats in battle, we listened to the old stories of the Narragansetts and we cleaned our guns and sharpened our knives and tomahawks. With my steel-bladed knife I carved designs in my war club, using the chipping technique the Penobscot traders in Kennebec showed me. As I worked, I put magic into the designs. Each arrow on its sumac-berry-stained red handle would kill an Englishman come spring. For each arrow I added a feather, joining all in a vine that wound round and round. The vine was my people and Mother Earth. I sang a power song as I worked, the same song I would sing before joining my brothers in battle.

"It was strange to see Pumham, Pometacomet and Canochet drawing in the dirt floor of Canochet's longhouse as they planned their spring campaign. These leaders had been bitter enemies only a short while ago, Pumham fighting both the Narragansetts and Wampanoags for showamut and Canochet's father Canonicus fighting the Wampanoags over sowams and over lower quansik. While they had been fighting like chickens over a peeling in the chicken yard the real enemy, the English, like a weasel, had stolen much behind their backs. Now they were all fighting this common enemy. Yet we knew in our hearts that once the English were driven from Turtle Island, the fighting over scraps of land would resume - that is, after the Mohegans and other traitors who had helped the English had been dealt with.

"The leaders debated whether the Mohawks fell into this category, for they had not actually helped the English but they had not actually helped Pometacomet the way the other tribes had. Pometacomet decided to try to go west and talk with them as soon as the weather allowed travel. He said he would go north, to quaboag and menemesit, then cross the quonicticut and meet with the Mohawks outside schaghticoke, near the great trading post the Dutch called Albany. If nothing else, he knew they would take any beaver or other furs he brought and trade them for guns, powder and shot at the fort. For their help, they would receive a share of the furs, but Pometacomet was hoping that since they had to have heard of our autumn victories by this time, they would want to join our cause. If the Mohawks joined us, all white men, from weshakum (the great sea) to the great lakes in the west and up into the great bay to our north would be exterminated, driven away in their huge boats or killed where they stood, their unnatural square houses burned to the ground. Pometacomet would go into our peoples' stories as the leader who had brought all the nations together for the great cause of driving out the white serpents.

"Such were the words spoken around the council fires in the time of the *quinnekeewush* (December) moon that winter."

Tom Pequin falls silent. For a long time he stares ahead, his eyes filling with tears that break and run over his deep wrinkles and sunken cheeks. He begins to sing his warrior song softly, his lips tight with the pain of remembering. His old, bony hand trembles as he wipes his leathery face and continues,

"The weather was so cold we never expected an attack. Even with snowshoes the drifts were so deep and the air so freezing, travel was out of the question for any sane person. But the English were not sane. Neither was the warrior we called Peter Freeman, who had been sent out of the fort in disgrace for raping the squaw of his host. Such a thing was never done, yet before the snowstorm he had followed her outside the fort when she searched for wood and had thrown her into a snowbank, using her against her wishes. Why he didn't kill her to keep her silent, I don' t know, but he didn't and she ran back into the fort, yelling and crying.

"At first we thought the English were attacking and we all ran out, grabbing our guns and scrambling into position. The best shooters were in the towers or the outer walls and those like myself who were neither good not bad were positioned along the inner wall. When the swamp was not frozen over, there was only one approach to the fort over a log, which was in the crossfire of the towers. But because of the severe winter, one end of the pallisade was not finished, its trees frozen into the ground and not upright. At this spot were our best shooters, for if the English found our weakness here, they could cross the frozen swamp and gain entry into the fort out of reach of the warriors' guns in the towers.

"As we watched for English soldiers, word spread of her reason for yelling and we straggled back into the middle of the fort. We sent out a party and soon Peter Freeman was captured and brought under guard into Canochet's longhouse. His host, Bear Who Sleeps in the Sun, confronted him, and, as was our custom, had the right to kill him or set him free. Sun Bear was furious and said he should die a long, slow death, so he was stripped and taken out of the fort, led beyond the river and left there to freeze to death. He was left lying on the snow as food for the wolves. He was told no one would give him a proper burial so his spirit would forever stay in that place, moaning in distress.

"This was a severe punishment. Even if we fell into the hands of our enemies, if we behaved bravely and did not cry out, they would bury us properly. But rape was worse than murder, for we treated our women like we treated Mother Earth. All female things brought forth life and if we made our women angry, Mother Earth could turn against us and refuse to grow our crops.

"After taking Freeman out to his death place, we held a ceremony in which Sun Bear's wife was given gifts and the shamans sang songs to Mother Earth to forgive the evil of that one man. We ate well that night, feasting and drinking and offering gifts of beans or corn to Mother Earth and all the females in our midst. Even the old people and children all ate well and we fell asleep with full bellies and happy hearts as we heard the women, including Sun Bear's squaw, laughing. And while we slept, Grandfather Snow sent a huge snowstorm to bury Freeman's frozen body. Or so we thought.

"We learned later that the English army had been marching through Narragansett and had come upon Freeman soon after our warriors left him there to die. The English, who were lost, took him in, gave him clothes and food and he told them everything - where they were, where our fort was and what our weaknesses were."

Tom Pequin shakes his head slowly as he says,

"Such powerful magic these English had! When they needed something, they got it, usually from us. After the war there were many who said the English had won because their god was so powerful. They became Christians and went to live amongst the whites, dressing like them and forgetting their real ways. My cousin Ono Pequin often tried to convert me. He said their god was all love and forgiveness and that we were destroyed because we were bad and did not believe in their god. As for me, I agreed their god was powerful, but I did not agree that he was good and full of love. For what kind of god would save a man like Peter Freeman? What kind of god would forgive and even reward such an act? No, I call their god a powerful Hobbomock. I spit on their god!"

As his spittle sizzles on the hot rocks at the edge of in the fire, Tom continues,

"Following the ceremony, our fishermen were blessed and many big pike and bass were caught the next day, pulled out of the ice of the usuapaug. We had more than we could eat so the women buried some of the fish in the snow and then set up drying racks near fires in the middle of the fort to make dried fish for war parties once the snow began to melt.

"The somberness we had felt just a week before had passed and now the sound of the women's happy singing took the place of the old people's death songs. We played snowsnake, lacrosse, kicking stick and the stone game, with the young braves gambling for musket shot or powder. One or two even gambled their most prized posession - their gun - but such gambling was frowned upon by our war captains, since a warrior's battle position was linked to his weapon.

"Little did we know that a huge army of English soldiers was marching through the deep snow, pressing deeper into Narragansett, guided by that traitor Peter Freeman.

"I had spent a cold, sleepless night as a watchman in one of crude lean-tos outside the fort and as the dawn rose, grey and lifeless against the dark treeline, I was looking forward to going inside and sleeping on a warm platform under the furs, cuddled next to the thick, furry deerhides covering the inside walls of the bark-lined wetus.

"The wind was blowing snow around and flapping the mat door of the lean-to behind me as I quickly slipped out to urinate in the snow.

"To my right I saw other warriors coming out of the little lean-tos and then I saw Peter Freeman's face in the dead underbrush at the edge of the swamp. I let out a shout, for I felt it was his spirit come to seek revenge, but no sooner had the cry escaped my lips then I saw a tall Englishman in a buff-colored jacket leading the biggest army of soldiers I had ever seen across the frozen swamp.

"Those of us posted outside began firing at them, leading them towards the fallen log where our snipers, including the man Tift, could pick them off one by one. We seemed to be succeeding as our shooters in the towers picked off their war captains and many of the soldiers. The English began to retreat into the woods, our bullets chasing them and striking those who lagged behind.

"Those of us on the outside made our way into the fort and took up positions on the outer wall and waited for the next attack. As we waited the overcast day turned darker and the snow began to fall again.

"Again they tried to force their way into the entrance, but then Freeman yelled to the men to follow him and he led them right to our weak spot. We scrambled to get there before they did, but many got in and the fighting was hand-to-hand in the narrow space between the outer and inner walls. We were forced back into the center of the fort and took shelter behind baskets of corn inside the wetus as we fired at the advancing soldiers.

"Then I smelled smoke and our greatest fear was realized: they had set fire to our fort! Memories of how they had burned the Pequots alive in their fort not far from here made all of us run to the exit, trying to get out through the thick smoke.

"I covered the retreat of the screaming children, women and old people as best I could until I could no longer stand the odor of burning bark, reeds, corn, leather and human flesh.

"Outside the fort I sank into a pocket of snow up to my knees. I fell into the snow, getting the powder wet in my gun. An English soldier saw me and raised his flintlock, but before he could fire one of my brothers rushed him from behind, splitting his head in two with his tomahawk. As the soldier fell, his blood stained the snow near my head a bright red. I jumped up and headed for the cover of the dead trees in the nearby swamp. There, in the bitter cold and growing darkness, I saw the villagers huddling together, trying to survive the freezing cold.

"As dark came we watched our fort burning, the shapes of the English soldiers silhouetted against the flames. Our warriors sought out the people in hiding and gathered them all together inside a hastily-made cave shelter in the middle of the swamp. Many had burns on their hands from trying to beat out the flames. Some had no eyebrows and burns on their faces. Some were so burned we knew they wouldn't survive the night, but we brought them all to the snow and brush cave and then went back.

"By this time it was the middle of the night and Grandmother Moon was showing us the way over the deep snow. We got to the fort and found it deserted. An old man who had pretended to be dead said they had come into the fort, stuck their bayonets into everything then taken some of the saplings from the burned wetus, made litters of their guns and the saplings lashed together and carried their many wounded out, in the direction from which they had come. He said the younger English soldiers wanted to follow us into the swamp but the older ones said no because their powder was low and they had found none in our fort, for they didn't know that we each carried our own supply on our backs.

"Then a strange thing happened. The wind, which had been bitter cold, shifted and turned warm, almost as if Cautanowwit were sending it from the southwest. By dawn the snow was melting, making our travel a little easier. We brought the people back out of the swamp and took our dead to a ravine, where they were burned in a common grave, each with his or her personal items.

"Children, I will never forget that site. The ravine was piled high with charred bodies. Some had no hair or skin left, only white bone. They had been roasted the way we roast our meat and it made us cry to see such a thing. In my host's wetu ruin we found two families burned together in a lump - the grandparents on the outside shielding the squaws and children in the middle. They had all melted together, the grease on their bodies frying them alive. As we lifted the bundle, a little boy's moccasin fell off and I recognized it. It had belonged to the boy who was the same age as my youngest son. I wept for him - for them - and feared for my family to the north.

"Messengers arrived then from Magnus' fort saying the English had also burned it and planned to burn Pumham's.

"Pometacomet decided to take his warriors north, to tell Quaboag what had happened, and to try to get the Mohawks to join us. Pometacomet and Canochet tried to appease Ninigret and Pessacus, who had sent a message that some sachems wanted to talk about a peace treaty. Pometacomet told them to stall so they sent representatives who pretended to be interested in the English words while the corn supplies in Narragansett were being dug up from under the leaves in the pits and moved further into the swamp, to a new village under construction.

"The Niantics' ambassador to the English was sent back but a few days later the English captured one of our women and sent her to us with the message that they would talk peace if all the Wampanaogs in Narragansett were surrendered to them.

"Canochet sent a messenger back thanking the English for their offer, but told him to say, 'It was not we who made war on the English but the English who made war upon us without notice.'

"There was much dissention now in Narragansett, with the older sachems wanting peace and the younger ones like Canochet, Panoquin and Quinnapin determined to fight to the death rather than become slaves of the English. For we knew this was the fate we would meet if captured.

"As Canochet's warriors were planning to go on raids to get English cattle, Pometacomet and my war party went north to Quaboag, our horses making good progress in the slushy snow. Everything we had smelled of smoke. Even my skin smelled of it and it wasn't until after the war when I was adopted by the Oneida that I lost the odor - but not he memories it held. Even now when I smell something that got too close to the fire, I hear the screams and see the charred bodies of the Narragansetts. Not even the fierce Mohawks or Tarrantines would have done such a cruel, murderous thing.

"Those of us who returned to quansik that winter were changed men. Our hearts had melted into hard masses of black hate and we knew we would never surrender to, or be friends of, the English again."

Chapter 32
(A re-telling of life in the war camps and Mary Rowlandson's capture, 1675-6)

A middle-aged woman stands up. Unlike the others she is not elderly. Her face is still round and not sunken from loss of teeth. Around her neck is a shell necklace and small cowrie shells are sewn onto her thick winter deerhide mantle. Hanging from copper wires in her earlobes are small silver coins. All these things are signs of her status as a weathly woman, as the tamasham of the trader who lives outside the village.

As she begins to speak, her eyes take on a faraway expression, as if she were looking through a cave opening on an ancient land.

"You know me as Painted Canoe's tammasham BasketMaker. But when I was a girl in quansik, I was called Water Flowers, for I loved to gaze at the tall yellow and blue iris that grew on the banks of our streams and rivers.

"I was not yet a woman when the drums of war were heard throughout the valley. Like most of the girls, I looked after my younger brothers and sisters while my mother worked in the fields or did chores requiring her complete concentration.

"The winter the Narragansett fort was burned I went with my family to the petowamacha hills to stay with Squakeag relatives on my mother's side. As food became scarce, we traveled to wachusett to stay with other relatives.

"I remember feeling very uprooted during those long dark days. The adult women were kept busy nursing those with a chest sickness, what the English call a cold. Many old people and little children died that winter from this cold. Even the English were suffering from it, I heard, so we knew Creator had not sent it to us alone. My little brother was very sick with it and I remember spending many hours sitting next to him where he lay on the sleeping platform in the crowded wetu. I tried to get him to play the counting stick game with the other children. We would hum as we threw the flat, painted sticks into the air to get points for the lightning (zigzags) or rain (spots) on the faces when they landed. Other times, we took bowls of water and made cattail reed ducks, floating them near him. We girls played with corn-husk dolls but my little brother just laid there, coughing, his eyes burning. He slept a lot and often had sweat all over his body as if he had just come from a sweat lodge.

"While we were in wachusett, a white woman was brought in with other captives from Lancaster. This woman had been shot in the side while running with her little girl to the garrison at Lancaster. The bullet went through the mother and into the daughter's stomach and she died a few days later. The white mother wouldn't stop crying and rocking her child, but when she fell asleep the dead girl, who was about the age of my little brother, was taken from her in the middle of the night and buried on the top of the hill. I did not like the English, this is true, but I felt sorry for the girl and cried for her as if she had been my sister. I wondered what it would have been like to play counting sticks with her and if she liked to run and play in the fields and woods the way we did. Her face was all sunken in for she had suffered for many days before dying, but there was a beauty in its paleness, a haunting beauty that I saw in my dreams for a long time afterwards.

"One of the warriors who had lived with the English before the war carved the girl's face on a stone. He did this because he said they often put carved stones over their graves. On one side he carved the little girls' face and on the other a bow and arrow to show how she had died in battle with our warriors.

"After her daughter's death the woman was taken away but later she returned and lived with Weetamoo, who had ransomed her from Quinnapian (John Magnus). At first all she did was cry but later she began to help the other women by sewing little shirts from the trade cloth in camp for their children. Mrs. Rowlandson showed our women how the shirts were made and they tried to make some for their own children, for the shirts helped keep the chest cold away, she said. She had another daughter and son as captives at menemesit and she often pleaded with Weetamoo to let her join them or for them to come and stay with her in wachusett. But Quinnapin didn't own them so he couldn' t arrange for them to come to wachusett.

"But what I remember most about that winter was the gnawing pain in my stomach. We got so meat hungry that we even killed and ate some of the horses and boiled their hooves, scooping out and eating the jelly inside. Only older horses or ones that were a little lame we killed for our warriors needed them. Even the horses were lean, for they had to forage in the pine woods where the trees had blocked the heavy buildup of snow. The warriors often snuck into English barns and stole hay or oats for the horses, but if they were discovered they would usually panic and burn down the barn and all its hay as they escaped.

"We had very little energy that winter and when we had to go through the deep snow to find wood we would return dizzy and lightheaded. While Pometacomet was with us one of our hunters killed a bear and we were all invited to the feast. But with so many of us, there was very little bear meat for each. The grease was added to our thin soup pots, though, so we at least had the feeling we were eating meat.

"Not once did any of us complain. Every day my mother brought us to the stream outside the camp and we washed our faces and hands in the bitter cold water while saying a prayer of thanksgiving to Creator. Even though we had little, we knew it could be worse, we could have nothing, so we were thankful for a handful of cornmeal, dried beans, our peas or the English green peas.

"There were many warriors in and out of the camp during that winter. Sometimes they would ride in whooping and shouting from victory, other times they would be quiet and withdrawn.

"I don't think I ever loved *sequan* the way I did that year, for we were able to get away from the smokey, stuffy wetus and drink fresh, cold water from the streams and dig up roots or eat new shoots off the cattails to ward off our hunger. The birds and game came back with the spring and so did the fish. My brother had recovered and I took him and my little sister to the fishing places where my mother was helping dry the naumkeag. You should have heard the prayers of thanksgiving at the *namassack keewuch* ceremony that year! You would have thought we never had fish before the way we cherished each morsel, sucking all the bones dry.

"Around this time some Englishmen came into our village and a short while later the English woman was sent back to her people. I was happy for her, for I knew how it felt to be separated from one's family because my father and older brother had been gone all winter, first in one war camp and then in another. Once they had come back with a war party and brought us gifts they had taken from the English houses. My brother gave me a doll made from cloth and he gave my little brother a wooden top and my little sister a bullroarer. I played with the doll many moons- until my family crossed the quonicticut. I darkened her face with red ochre from the pond at weshakim shortly after my brother gave it to me, for I couldn't bear looking at its white face: it reminded me of the dead girl buried in the middle of the night in wachusett. I burned the English dress on it and made her a buckskin dress and moccasins, sewing little seed beads into the outfit in a flower design.

"The spring and early summer that year were almost normal for us children. We did our chores under bright blue skies and played in golden meadows and fields. But then came the day we had to pack up everything and begin the long, hard march that took us forever away from our lands.

"My little brother and sister died from smallpox the first winter after we crossed the housatonic. After they died, I put away my doll and my memories of quansik and later became the wife of Painted Canoe.

"Sometimes in my dreams my soul flies back to quansik and sits amongst the irises on the shore of a stream, looking out over the yellow meadow. In my dreams I watch the birds flying overhead and the colorful butterflies on the purple loosestrife that grew so thick along the shores of the quaboag. I can still smell the wet earth in the streambed and the wet reeds and leaves as I hear the water singing the song of my people. The white man might live there now, but Mother Earth still sings in our language and the birds and wind over quansik speak the tongue of my people."

She sighs deeply, then says,

"It hurts to remember any more. I am of the Oneida now and my home is here. I thank Creator for my good husband and children and pray that the English will leave us in peace now that they have all of our lands on the other side of the quonicticut."

Chapter 33
(A re-telling of the war campaigns, 1676)

John Tahattawaban again stands up. He, like the others, had become very sad as BasketMaker talked about their homeland.

"The Narragansetts stalled the English, pretending they wanted peace, while they regrouped. About a moon after the massacre in the fort, some Narragansett braves appeared in quansik carrying the heads of two Englishmen.

"I was with a war party that had just gotten back from ransacking and burning an English farm and, as always after these raids, we were passing the hard cider jug around and telling the crowd around us of our raid.

"Some of us wanted to accept the Narragansett warriors, but others from quansik who had a grudge against Hyems and Allumps' Narragansetts tribute demands were unfriendly. David, who was now sachem in quabogud, stood up and challenged the Narragansetts saying that anyone could bring a few English heads. He said they needed more proof of their loyalty to our cause and sent them away. The next day more Narragansetts showed up, each with a head. The day after that more came into camp with more heads and hands, so the warriors relented and accepted the Narragansetts as allies. Our camp swelled dramatically as the Narragansett warriors and their families streamed in. They said their territory to the south was now overrun with English troops who were burning and destroying everything they could find. The English had taken all the Narragansett food stores they could dig up and had captured large numbers of old people, women and children. The warriors were angry. They had not started this war, they said, but now that the English were pursuing it so fiercely that they were determined to fight to the death.

"The leaders in upper quansik - Sam, Monoco, Matoonas,

Muttaump and James the Printer - found their troops doubling from 250 warriors to 500 almost overnight. Because our food supplies were so low, they sent the Narragansetts to the other camps - to wachusett where the Nashaways were under John and Quinnapin and to the main camp near Northfield and peskeomscot where the Nonotucks, Pocumtucks, Agawams and Squakeags were.

"I was with the group that escorted a large number of Narragansetts to the place of the split rocks (peskeomscot) and while we were there we learned that Pometacomet was across the river in schaghticoke, negotiating with the Dutch through the Mohawks for gunpowder, guns and lead shot. Some French-speaking braves were with Pometacomet to help with the French negotiations. Then we heard distressing news, that Pometacomet was ill. This could only mean one thing - he was being attacked by an enemy's spirit magic, so word was sent down the camps to find a Narragansett shaman to send to him, for we knew they had the most powerful medicine next to Wannalancet, who would not get involved in the war in any way. He had taken his people north of the river, away from any contact with the English or the tribes bordering his lands.

"After our Narragansett brothers joined us we became very desperate for food so every day war parties were sent out to raid the nearby farms or villages. Most of these raids occurred in Nashaway territory, for they had the most people and they were in the best position since the English towns to the east had been abandoned. We'd ususally ride near a town or farm, dismount and tether our horses some distance away in the woods then creep up quietly, splitting up into small groups as we advanced on the buildings simultaneously. If met by gunfire, we would immediately pull back and then direct our forces towards the building from which it came. Usually the only sounds were heard were from starving livestock, which we quickly rounded up and rode back to camp with. If the animals were too far gone, we would butcher them on the spot and take the meat home. We butchered the pigs in the woods away from the houses, for they were not easy to herd and made a lot of noise. Their squeals reminded us of whines from scared English cowards and we held them in contempt. But we did like their meat and fat.

"We had no respect for the cows, for they were but slaves to the English, bred and fed for their larders. They seemed to lack the life Creator had given the wild animals and under normal conditions we would not have bothered with them, but starvation does strange things to one's feelings and that winter we ate anything we could find. I think that if the winter had gone on and on we would have eaten human flesh, but we were saved from that by the abundance of English livestock in the countryside.

"We began taking more English captives that winter to trade for the Narragansett prisoners. Netus led the first hostage raid in Sudbury, which we burned after taking a whole family captive. Next, Quinnapin led a raid against Lancaster. I was with the war party that night and remember creeping on my belly in snow towards the house at the top of the hill. There were five houses and a meetinghouse in the center of the town but most of the people were in the house on the hill near the pond. We were going to attack at dawn but learned that the Christian traitor Job Kattenait was on his way to Cambridge to warn Gookin of our plans so we attacked that night.

"We first positioned some warriors on top of the barn roof, for the barn stood on a hill overlooking the garrison house. Then we set fire to the surrounding house and our warriors on the roof of the barn shot those running towards the garrison. From the roof our warriors could see into the garrison house, which was now full of panicking people with lit lanterns. The main party, which I was in, rushed the garrison entrance and several English men ran outside to drive us away. They immediately saw how large our party was and tried to get back inside, but we knocked three down with our tomahawks and clubs. The fourth, a young man of about 14 winters, fell to his knees and begged for mercy, clinging to my leg as I raised my tomahawk and split his head in two. His begging bothered me more than the killing for it was so loathsome.

"By then the English were firing at us from the windows so we retreated out of firing range.

"The sun came up and melted some of the snow on the tree limbs. In the daylight we discovered that the loop holes of the garrison were covered with fire wood and we repeated our strategy from Quaboag Plantation, setting fire to a cart of flax, hemp and hay after positioning it near the dry firewood.

"One of the English men dashed out with a bucket of water and immediately quenched it but as soon as he went back inside, we refired it. The thatch roof and wooden sides of the garrison smouldered, sending thick billows of black smoke into the cold air, then we heard a roar as it went up in flames. The sight of the English screaming and running around brought bitter satisfaction to the Narragansett warriors. 'Burn, English, Burn!' they yelled, 'Burn as you burned us!' The air was full of smoke and screams and our wild whoops of joy. We were intoxicated with this. Each whiff of smoke in our flared nostrils was like a whiff of a powerful drug, every scream made our flesh tingle like a lover's tongue. The English boy's blood on my leg and foot burned like fire and made me feel alive.

"Through clouds of smoke we saw the people bolt out the door and try to run to the next garrison, which they didn't know was also burning. The warrior on my right aimed for a young man but a woman carrying a child ran out and the bullet got her instead. She fell, still clutching the little girl, and he grabbed them both to claim as hostages. At the same time I saw a woman and young man in the doorway fall as bullets rained into the garrison.

"We took many captives and put them under guard in a house at the top of the hill then went over to the river, which was flooded from the recent thaw, and spent the rest of the day tearing up the bridge planks so the English troops sent by Gookin couldn't get to the garrison.

"The night came quickly and we ate the cattle, roasting it in the flames of the houses. At every house we thronged, drinking, dancing, whooping, celebrating our major victory long into the night. This garrison would be like the one in Quaboag now - deserted, empty, its lands free of English.

"At dawn we broke up into smaller parties, some to bring food to menemesit and the villages near the quanicticot and others to go to wachusett and quaboag. The captives were brought out of the house and claimed by their owners. The wounded woman with the wounded child was to be killed, but she cried so hard when her son, a young man of about 16 winters, and her other daughter were separated from her, that the warrior who owned her allowed her to come along with them. She was tied and led on foot behind the horse of her owner, who carried the little girl for a distance. The girl moaned constantly from the pain of the bullet wound in her hand and side and the Narragansett warrior He Who Leaps Over Fire, finally put the faint woman on his horse and let her hold her dying child. The hostages were brought to wachusett, where the little girl died, then marched on to menemesit and the other camps. The woman was separated from her other children but Weetamoo had taken pity on her and she was bought by Quinnapin when we returned with her to wachusett.

"The whole incident with the mother and daughter was strange, for we never took wounded prisoners, especially wounded children. But the Narragansetts were desperate for prisoners to ransom their families with, so the Narragansett warriors who captured them had orders not to kill any women or children. Some of our warriors delighted in the mother and daughter's suffering but most of us were angry with the Narragansetts for letting them suffer. We would not let an animal suffer so, we said, we would put it out of its misery, but he owned them so we could not kill them. BasketMaker spoke truly when she said the little girl was a pitiful sight. I, a warrior who would not hesitate to grab a small child or baby by its feet and dash its head against something hard, could not bear to hear the little girl's pitiful moans as her insides filled with the green death and her little hand turned black. The situation reminded me of the time I had been hunting and came upon a wounded doe in a clearing bravely protecting her dying fawn from the wolves that had wounded them both. I knew they were doomed and said a prayer to the deer spirit as I let my arrows fly, killing the mother then the fawn. All of the wolves scattered except the leader, a big, grey fellow with yellow eyes. He turned and looked at me as if he were angry that I had spoiled his sport. I knew then what made men different from wolves or cougars. We are weak when it comes to suffering and I think that is why we sometimes torture our enemies. We are testing ourselves more than we are testing their courage. It is more honorable to give in under prolonged torture than it is to give in when torturing. That is why it usually takes the order of a person of higher rank to stop the torture.

"This is why we allow our women to buy our captives, for we do not condemn them when they show kindness. We know inside that without our women we would be all hard and cruel. We would be wolves and never know the joy of laughter or friendship. We know our women are more spiritual yet we also know they can be fiercer than the mightiest warrior when it comes to defending our young. As you know from learning about a mother bear and her cubs, this is the way of nature. This is why Creator made both male and female. What we call weak in a man is strong in a woman.

"On the same day as our raid on Lancaster, Monoco led a raid on a farm in Concord. Two boys were killed as they threshed grain in a barn and their sister was taken captive. She was not docile like most of the English women. She stole a horse during the middle of the night and escaped. We teased the warrior she had stolen the horse from, because she had also stolen his saddle - right out from under his head! That Englishwoman I would have liked to meet!

"A short while later Monoco and James the Printer led a war party against Medfield. I was with the war party that night as we crept through the thick underbrush between the houses and hid in the outhouses and under the sides of the barns until first light. We waited until they woke up and started out to the outhouses before we opened fire, our bullets spilling blood and urine into the snow. We set fire to the houses and shot the people as they ran from their burning houses towards the garrison. We then crossed the bridge, burning it after us so the English couldn't follow. Before we lit it, James the Printer wrote a note that said, 'Know by this paper, that these indians thou hast provoked to wrath and anger will war this 21 years if you will. There are many indians yet. We come 300 at this time. You must consider the indians lose nothing but their life. You must lose your fair houses and cattle.' He put it on the bridge post and signed it with a mixture of blood and ink. Having lived amongst the English he knew how much they valued their posessions and how they would cry over the loss of everything. The note told them we had nothing to lose, our lives not worth living if we had to be English slaves.

"James was one of the Christian indians who had refused to go to the English camp on Deer Island in the *quinnekewush* (December) moon after Pometacomet had liberated many people from the praying village at Hassamineset. He learned that many people on Deer Island were starving and cold and were in threat of being murdered by the English. Only two men - Gookin and Eliot - seemed to care about keeping them alive and those two men almost lost their lives arguing with the other white men over the matter. The island was not a good place to be and certainly not the safe place the English claimed it would be. There were no wetus and little wood, no food and much sickness. So James had joined our cause and never looked back, all his English schooling and training shed as if it were a skin he had grown out of.

"We then roasted a large ox on the hill overlooking the burning town. We tore off great chunks of its flesh and held them up, taunting the miserable little English in their smoldering ruins. Afterwards we had to move out, for we learned that English troops, including James Quantapohit and Job Kattanit, were marching towards Medfield.

"A handful of sleeps later we attacked Weymouth during the night. We didn't linger to celebrate our victory, though, for the town was only a couple hours' walk from Boston. What thrill we felt in attacking so close to their main settlement! The danger we were exposing ourselves to took much courage.

"We then went to wachusett, where we learned that a large English war party was coming up from quonicticut towards quansik and that it was going to join with the soldiers persuing us, so we helped the old and sick people and the women and small children in wachusett break camp and move west, to the swamps west of quaboag. One party went east, to Groton, to get cows and pigs for food and the other to lead the English troops out of quaboag as we took the people further west, towards the river. I was with those who stayed behind to lead the English troops away so our people could make it across the river.

"After two days the troops, including that man Mosely and his dogs, caught on to our ruse and headed for baquag (Millers) river. We didn't follow because we knew our people would be far enough ahead where they could cross the river safely. Instead, we joined the wachusett troops and attacked Groton, using the same strategy as at Medfield, hiding in the outhouses. However, we were thwarted as four men with two carts came through the meadows at dawn and discovered us. They ran back and warned the others so all we were able to do was shoot one and capture another before they got to the garrison. We set fire to the barns and houses and retreated to plan an ambush. A few sleeps later we returned, set our troops up below the crest of a hill and a handful of warriors lured the English troops towards us. As soon as they got to the top of the hill we let out a loud whoop and opened fire. While the English were falling like flies, a couple parties circled around behind them and got into the town, burning and ransacking with abandon, the settlers all holed up inside the garrison.

"A few sleeps after that we watched as the town was abandoned and carts full of goods and people left under guard by a company of English soldiers. Our powder was low so we did not attack, but instead took shots at individuals as they retreated.

"That night we held a huge feast and fire in the middle of the abandoned town. Again we had driven them away. Again we had reclaimed our land! We thought it was easy to drive off the English. Our victories had been quick and cost us few warriors. We were full of contempt for their weakness and their clumsy way of fighting. We felt nothing could stop us now- we had the lands from Medfield all the way to the river in our grasp: the English had flown. Next we would go after some of their major garrisons. But first we needed powder so I went with a small party to Squakeag to see if Pometacomet had brought any back from schagticoke.

"I found Pometacomet at Northfield. A large ceremony was going on to formalize the alliances of the Wampanoags, Narragansetts and inland tribes. Belts of wampum had been presented to the grand sachems a week before I arrived, but the warriors were still talking about how impressive the leaders had been, seated in the longhouse, all clothed in their finest regalia. Canochet, Aguntus Pumham, Quinnipin, Pessacus, Sanchonakhu, Weetamoo and Annawon and all the Agawam, Nonotuck, Pocumtuck, Squakeag sachems and Quansik sachems who weren't at wachusett had attended. Not since Nanepashemet had such a gathering taken place this side of the quonicticut. We were creating a new league of nations. Pometacomet was a prophet leading us to peace so we could drive out the common enemy.

"I was told Pometacomet had given a speech that went something like, 'My brothers from the great sea to the great river, from the bay to the high mountains, today we unite into one family, one people. Today there is no Wampanoag or Pokanoket, no Massachusett or Narragansett. Today there is only one tribe - the tribe of Mother Earth's children. Today we share the pipe as one blood, one flesh. Today we eat and sing and dance as the true people of Turtle Island, the people who will drive out the white maggots that have been eating away at our land, at our culture, at our beliefs.

"'Yesterday we did not know that the ships that flew across the ocean carried the eggs of our destruction in their bellies, but today we know and today we will rid ourselves of the vermin that have infested our land. Today we will drive them away and restore our forests to their natural state. No longer will our trees be like English cattle- something to tame, to use for their own needs. No longer will our waters be dirtied with English soap and the stench of their clothes and their animals. Today we will reclaim what they took by cunning and force.

"'The English brought sickness and a new god. But they also brought steel knives and guns. Today we will turn their own weapons on them. Today, English guns will kill English people. Creator wants it to be so. We your sachems want it to be so. Today we are all one and they are all one. Today we pledge to fight and die together as one nation. Let the drums proclaim it, let the skies thunder it, let our waters sing it! Today, my people, today, we have just been born and we are hungry for English blood!'

"When I arrived a war party was just returning from Northampton. The raid had been unsuccessful, for they attacked the garrison expecting to meet with little resistance but found Treat and 200 Connecticut English and Mohegans in the garrison. They did claim a small victory, for they killed four men and one woman and burned all the houses and barns outside the stockade.

"The war captains went into conference in the longhouse and I was invited to sit in. They had to get the English away from the Deerfield area soon so we could fish the falls in the area and dig up our seed corn from the pits and tree trunks where it was stored and then plant our crops in the fertile fields. We could not spend another winter like the last. Warriors cannot march forever on empty stomachs.

"A plan was agreed upon. We would lead constant raids on the eastern settlements to draw the troops away from the quanicticot. There would be many raids, quick, like lightning strikes. We would raid and then withdraw to strike the next day somewhere else. The English would have to send all their troops east, away from our crops and families in the west.

"It was a great plan and the next morning I rode with Canochet's men to wachusett to tell the war captains there about our sequan campaign strategy.

"When we arrived at wachusett the captains were not there-they had taken matters into their own hands and were out raiding the countryside to the east for food and powder.

"We finally met up with the largest party north of the Eel river. We found them exhalting over their victory agains the Clark Garrison on the river near Plymouth. The war capatin, Totoson, was dancing around the fire, retelling how they had waited for them to leave the garrison to attend church. The rattles in the long rattlesnake skin hanging down his dark, stocky back shook as he raised his gun and war club, whooping over the death of eleven of the enemy. They were in high spirits for they had gotten 30 pounds of gunpowder and eight guns before burning the house down. This was a great prize!

"Totoson, who was a powerful powwow, told us he had seen the powder in a vision and had decided to use their god against them, attacking when they went off to church. He gloated over how helpless their god had been. If he were as great as they said, he would have saved them, Totoson said, the hard cider loosening his tongue. This powwow could send his snake spirit in his sleep to kill a man and had chanted the spell to make himself invulnerable to bullets.

"A few sleeps later our spies told us the settlers at Plymouth and in the montop bay had abandoned their towns and fled to larger settlements. Overjoyed at the victory, we rode to the bay to see for ourselves. In the territory the English called Rhode Island we came upon an Englishman who had refused to abandon his farm. He didn't run from us but instead knelt down and began reading loudly from the Bible.

"A Wampanoag warrior dismounted and walked up to him, threatening so he would run, but he said his god would protect him. This made us all laugh and the warrior split his head open with his tomahawk then we used an English knife and split his belly open, stuffing the useless Bible into his bleeding guts. Tatoson said this would tell them how much their god was protecting them. We put our faith in our weapons! Little did we know how deadly their book could be to us in the end.

"That spring I took part in many of the eastern raids. First came Warwick then Marlboro. Marlboro was a main garrison for their troops and had four fortified houses. We were setting up a fine ambush (again on the sabbath) around their meetinghouse when the old preacher discovered us and so only one person was killed. We burned eleven barns, thirteen houses and got some cows, but it was considered a poor victory. Marlboro was crucial to the English troop movements so we planned another attack later in the spring.

"To the west our brothers were also attacking that sabbath, for it was what they called Easter, the holiest sabbath of the year and they all attended church that day. This we learned from the former Christians in our ranks. It was their most vulnerable day and we took advantage of it.

"The day before Easter, near seekonk, Canochet and our party encountered their war captains Pierce and Amos with fifty soldiers from Plymouth and scictuate and Christian indian traitors. We laid a fine ambush and the next morning I and a few others appeared in front of the soldiers, limping as we lured them after us across the pawtucket river. As they crossed, our warriors on the western bank who had been lying in wait, sprang up and took them by surprise on the riverbank. We closed around behind them in the river then led the stragglers into a swamp where we tortured and killed them. Of the large company, only eight English soldiers and a few traitors escaped. We celebrated long into their holy night. One of the former praying indians said sarcastically that they died on the same day as their lord. He said 'Let's see if they rise in three days!' and we planned a surprise for them if they did, burning seekonk two days later. The whole circular village was burned to the ground and no soldiers rose from the dead to defend it.

"We returned to wachusett, high from the victories, but were met with anger from the old sachems who said they were sick of war and hunger and wanted peace.

"While we had been feasting on slaughtered cattle and drinking cider our old people were eating rotten ground nuts and the little shoots of trees to survive. Our reception was not what we expected, but we didn't let it dampen our spirits and we began planning our next round of attacks.

"It had been easy so far. We had lost very few warriors and had gained so much.

"At that point we had no respect at all for the English soldiers. They would not hide behind trees and protect themselves but instead stood in lines firing their guns while fully exposed. We laughed and laughed at how foolish they were. Did they think they were invisible in their ochre-colored uniforms? Killing them was almost too easy. At this rate, we felt they would be jumping on ships back to England by the time our corn was planted. We could not understand the wisdom of the old sachems' fears.

"We had forgotten that the deadliest enemy is often one's own brother."

Chapter 34
(A re-telling of old stories and of new ones in the winter war camp,1676)

Many Winters Bear stands up slowly, shaking off the years as he remembers:

"There are the old stories and there are the new stories. In time to come, in the time of the seventh fire, these stories will be the old stories. But they will be told by the English, through English eyes. This is why you must know the truth as we saw it.

"I was at the treaty-making feast that spring. During our encampment that winter I had heard the other story-tellers talk about their histories.

"The Wampanoag story-tellers talked about Weetucks, or Maushop, who like the Abnaki god-hero Glooscup, was a giant. He came to their people from the north on an ice floe and protected them from a huge, people-eating bird. In Mashpee territory there were many things left by Maushop such as piles of stones in the ocean dropped from his apron when he was bothered by a bird about his ears and the stone on the shore of saconet which had been Maushop's wife Squant until she was abandoned when he left the Wampanoags forever.

"Their Keeper of the Stories said Squant wore her long hair over her eyes, for once, while she was alseep, an enemy crept up and cut her eye holes square. The Wampanoag women felt sorry for her because her husband had been so cruel to her so every year at the time of their cranberry festival, they sent a maiden into the swamps to leave a basket of cranberries for her.

"Maushop liked to smoke the hellebore or white poke and the island of nantucket was made from his pipe ashes. The giant would stand on the great rocks and catch whales with his bare hands. One day he turned his sons into killer whales and his daughter into the large striped sea bass. He told his sons to always be kind to their fish sister. Whenever a whale was sent to the people on shore, the Wampanoags would give thanks to Maushop, then, in memory of Squant and Maushop's daughter, let their women eat first. They loved the whale meat so much they would eat it raw, ripping huge chunks from the carcass with their bare teeth.

"The Narragansetts also told many stories about a god-hero Trickster. Trickster was a god-rabbit who made much mischief for our people.

"They said one time in the days of the ancient ones four braves went to Trickster to seek favors from him. The first one asked to become a great hunter, and so became one. The second asked to be a great lover, and this was granted. The third asked to become a great medicineman so he could help his people, and this was granted. The last asked to be immortal so he would never die. Immediately Trickster turned him into a stone, for the stone people never die. Such was one of Rabbit's tricks.

"Another time Trickster was walking along a pond shore. There were flocks of geese, swans and ducks on the water and he was hungry but had nothing to catch them with. So he sat down, hung his medicine bag in a tree and began singing. He called to the birds to come and sing with him and when they gathered around he told them they had to sing the magic song while dancing around him in a circle with their eyes closed tight. He said if they opened them, their eyes would be forever red and sore. So the birds sang with him. Then he grabbed a swan and it screamed, but he said, 'That's right, my brothers, sing louder!' One by one the birds were killed but then the bird we call the hell-diver opened his eys. He yelled out and all the others followed him to the water, but Rabbit caught up with him and turned his eyes red. He said, 'From now on all the other birds will laugh at you for your red eyes.'

"Another time Trickster had killed a bear. While he was feasting on it, he heard two saplings scraping together so he climbed one to separate them and stop the noise. His foot got stuck and before he could get free the other animals found the bear. They said, 'Let's eat while Trickster is caught' and so began gorging themselves on the fat of the bear. Beaver was the first and he ate so much that even to this day his fur is greasy. One by one the others ate then at last came little rabbit. There was hardly any fat left and that is why when you cut a rabbit open you find only a little fat at the neck and in the groin. By the time Trickster got free all that was left was the skull. He changed himself into an ant and ate the brains but when he changed back his head got stuck in the skull so he couldn't see. He wandered around the forest, banging into first one tree then another, until he got to the river. There, as he was swimming across, he heard the people on shore shouting, 'A bear! A bear!' He was so frightened he kept paddling until at last he knocked the skull on a rock in the water, freeing his head. The people laughed when they saw the bear was actually Trickster and he ran away.

"Another time there were two blind men that were sent to live on the opposite shore of their people's village to protect them from the enemies attacking the village. They were given food and goods and a rope was tied to lead them from their wetus to the water's edge.

"At this time, Trickster had taken the shape of brother raccoon. As he swam along the shore he discovered the rope, and following it, saw the old men sleeping in their wetu. He went back to the water and untied the rope, tying it to a bush away from the water. When the first old man rose, he followed the rope but when he tried to dip water, all he got in his bucket was sand. He went back to his friend and said, 'The lake has dried up!' Laughing at his trick Trickster retied the rope to its original pole and then watched as the other came down and found water in his bucket. He went back and the two men argued for awhile. Then they made a meal of eight pieces of meat. Trickster snuck in while they were each eating one and grabbed four pieces of meat from the stew pot. When one reached in for another piece, he discovered only two left. He accused the other of gobbling up most of the meat and they argued some more. Trickster was enjoying his trick so much he was rolling around laughing. He then jumped up and tapped each one in the face with his hand-paw. They began fighting with each other and Trickster slipped in and grabbed the last two pieces of meat. As he was leaving, he laughed out loud and they stopped their fighting. He said, 'I have played a nice trick on you. Maybe now on you will not be so quick to find fault with your brother!'

"There were many, many tales of this trickster, including the one in which he was killed.

"Trickster's powwow had combed the brains out of a people to the north so they would be slaves to Trickster. But they cried out and

Gluskap walked through a blizzard to find them. When Gluskap killed the great hare, all the people he had enslaved ran free and became rabbits. What happened to Trickster after he died is now part of the secret teachings of the Midewiwin medicine lodge, to which Konkowasco belongs.

"All these funny tales were good for taking our minds off the pains in our bellies and for making the long days of darkness pass. But I told a tale that was better than all these - and one I could prove.

"In Quansik the first man was born.

"This is true, my children. In a huge boulder amidst a group of boulders on the hill in wombemesscok there is the womb of man. In a boulder there is a small cave shaped like a baby curled inside its mother's womb. It has the life cord going from its belly up the rock and a few shallow steps leading down, where man first climbed down onto Mother Earth. The womb-cave is exactly the size of a young man. Our storytellers and shamans knew this spot and when we climbed in we could hear the heartbeat of the rock.

"The rock people are the oldest of our ancestors. They are older than Grandmother Earth, Grandfather Skan (sky) and Grandfather Sun. They are the bones beneath the flesh of Mother Earth and respond when we call upon them. They formed in the heat of the fire spirit and carry it with them as well as the spirit of destruction. The most powerful of them are the ones that are clear or white and sparkle in the sunlight, absorbing the energy of the sun while reflecting its blue or the more powerful energy of the moon. These were much valued as arrowheads in my younger days, before the gun, for they would listen to their maker and he could warm them in his hands before shooting and they would strike their target right where the hunter wanted. They lie in lines along Mother Earth's skin. Our best shamans like Konkowasco know where this power travels on the earth's surface and will perform their most sacred rituals on these lines. If you don't believe me, then sometime lay face down on the earth and hear the rock people hum.

"The Iroquois know about the rock people's power and that spring while I was at the treaty-signing, I heard this story from the Mohawks who accompanied the Dutch traders Jacob and Jarrad to Agawam with four bushels of gunpowder.

"They said there was once a time when there were no stories on Turtle Island.

"One day in a Seneca village a fatherless boy went out to hunt on his own for the first time He shot a small bird the first day and the next day he returned to the woods and shot two birds. This went on for nine days. Each day his string of birds got larger and larger.

"On the tenth day he noticed a large, flat-topped rock like our booming rocks in the middle of a field and he went and sat on top of it while fixing his arrows and eating a little nohikik.

"Then he heard a voice. It said, 'Give me your birds and I will tell you a story'

"'What is a story?' he asked.

"The stone said, 'Give me your birds and I will tell you.'

"So the boy put his birds on top of the rock and sat in the grass, listening as the rock told an ancient story about the beginning of the world.

"He was told if he came again the next day and brought birds, the stone would tell him another story. But he was not to tell anyone else.

"This went on for many days and the boy's mother got suspicious because he brought so few birds home. She asked another boy to go with him to find out what was going on, but, he, too, wanted to hear the stories and neither brought home many birds. So she asked two of the adult braves to follow them and they heard the stories. Then the story stone told them to bring the whole village and the next day they brought a feast and put it on the rock then sat in the grass and listened.

"For four days this went on. The story stone said, 'Some will remember some of the words, some none of them and some will remember all of them.'

"The ones who remembered all became our first Keeper of the Stories.

"After four days the stone told the people he had told all the stories and would speak no more. He said for them to treat their storytellers the same way they had treated him, to honor them and bring them food and gifts for the stories.

"From that time on, we, the Keeper of the Stories, have passed on the old and new stories to our people.

"In our own stories from quansik one of the first humans was called Flint and was made from stone. And we have another story about the woman who turned to stone. These will be for another day."

Many Winters Bear takes a drink of hot sassafrass tea then continues,

"At the time of the treaty-making, guns were also brought to the council fire from some French traders, Mohawks and Agawams. Our shamans had observed the stars and the sunrises and sunsets and they told us that at the time of the year that the English called Easter there would be much medicine in the sky. Even though the snow was still on the ground and the rivers had patches of ice in them, they said we should go forth. The English would die on the same day their god rose, they said.

"Many raids were planned for that day. The Agawams, led by Wequash, Weawose, Whowssamoh, Pawwawwoise, Mawcahwat, Sanchamoise, Wesoncketkhem and the half-Mohegan, half-Narragansett hunter Menowniet led a war party down the quonicticut, through the pine meadow cuskhonkamag (Windsor Locks) to massaco (Simsbury). The large town,which sat on both sides of the tunxis (Farmington) river, was deserted. We found only one man and killed him, then plundered and burned the forty houses there. The snow was melting more each day and swelling the river so we were only able to destroy half the town that time. But we waited in a cave overlooking the town for many sleeps, waiting for a chance to cross.

"The same day - which was so overcast everything was in half-darkness - a war party attacked a group of women, children and English soldiers as they traveled by horse-drawn carts to church in the ascushnet (Longmeadow). They laid an ambush at pecowsic brook and were able to kill the men and women in the last cart crossing the brook. Two women and children were captured but the following day Pynchon, who knew our ways, tracked the war party to the swamp nearby and regained the women, one of whom was dying from her wounds.

"As we regrouped at our main camps, celebrating our victories, we recieved word of the victories in the east, but the Mohawks picked this time to camp near us to our west.

"Pessacus and Pumham led a raid, driving them back across the river, but they captured one who told them the English were trying to get the Mohawks involved. At the bidding of the English, the long island (Manhatten) Governor Andros had approached their leaders, asking them if they would be willing to attack the Connecticut valley tribes. The Mohawks had refused, saying they were neutral, but now they were worried that their presence in Agawam at the time of the Longmeadow attack would implicate them and destroy their claim to neutrality.

"A war with the Mohawks was averted through much diplomacy and assurances that the English would never know Mohawks had been present at acushnet. Our leaders told the Mohawks that the women who were captured could not tell the difference between a Mohawk and any other warrior. To the English we were all one, they told them. We were all one inferior race of savages that they called Indians. The Mohawk captive was sent back to Mohawk territory with this message and a request for gun powder.

"The following week after the *namassauck keeswuch* (April) moon, I went with the warriors on other raids. We found English farmers and soldiers in the meadows at hockanum and killed one while he was inspecting a fence. We got two soldiers as they ran up the slopes of hockanum (Mt. Holyoke) and we captured another man. In all, it wasn't much of a battle, but it gave us the results we wanted as the English council ordered Savage and his troops east to help them fight off the war parties there. With Savage went Mosely, Whipple and three other captains and their men. This left only one captain - Turner - at Hadley with about 150 soldiers. There were no Mohegans in Turner's company, and since we had over five times as many warriors throughout the valley, we were no longer afraid to go out and do our fishing and planting.

"However, our happiness was but a sunny meadow soon to be cast into shadow by large clouds.

"First, we received word that the Narragansett war leader-sachem Canochet had been captured and executed by Oneko. Our spies said they had seen his head on a pole in Hartford.

"The English had learned of his resting place from a fat indian near his camp. The soldiers surprised Canochet's guards, who ran towards his camp, shouting for him to run. It was bitterly damp, but Canochet threw off the blanket and his silver-trimmed coat, along with his belt of wampum so he could blend into the colors of the underbrush. He probably could have escaped from the English captains Denison and Avery, but Oneko's army of Niantics, Pequots and Mohegans knew how we fight and caught up with him as he tried to cross the river. Although he held his gun high, it got wet and the priming pan wouldn't fire, so Canochet was captured by the Mohegan Pequot Monopoide. 43 warriors with him were also killed that day.

"The English took Canochet to Stonington and told him they would spare his life if he would persuade the Narragansetts to make peace with the English. Our spy said he heard the English say Canochet's reply was a firm 'No!' And he told them his death would not end the war.

"They tortured and beat him but he would not give in so finally they sentenced him to die, but he refused to be executed by a warrior of lesser rank so Oneko was chosen for the task. When Canochet heard of his death sentence he replied, 'I like it well that I should die before my heart is soft or I have spoken words unworthy of myself!'

"At anguilla he was executed. First the Peqouts mutilated him, then the Mohegans cut off his head and quartered his body. The Niantics burned his body in a fire and sent the head to Hartford to show their loyalty.

"Canochet's death was the first thread to snap in our finely woven plans. It set off many arguments between the older sachems, especially the Narragansett and Quansik sachems, who all wanted an immediate end to the war. But the younger sachems and warriors were still playing in the sunny meadow, still high from their victories, so to them the old men's voices were the almost silent hum of the rock people.

"After the Hadley raid, most of the warriors went to wachusett to help keep the pressure on the eastern settlements so they would stay away from our fields to the west.

"The mood in wachusett was mixed. The Narragansett warriors were full of black hate and rage over Canochet's execution and wanted all the English to the south driven out, but Pometacomet arrived from the west and held a long war council, reminding them that the eastern settlements were our priority, for we had to have corn for next winter if the war should go on that long.

"Sam, Quanohit, Kutquen and Gunrashit thought the English were looking for a way to end the war when the Christian Natick Tom Nepanet arrived at wachusett with a letter from Gookin that dangled peace if they would return a large number of their captives.

"They sent word to bring the captives to wachusett and then had Peter Jethro write a reply that said they sent it by one man but if the English liked it to send more than one to back to negotiate with them.

"To rub salt into their wounds and to let them know our superiority, it began, 'We know your heart great sorrowful with crying for your lost many, many hundred men, all your house and all your land, and women, child, and cattle, and all your thing that you have lost on on your back side stand.'

"Then they sent messages to the relatives of the captives. To Rowlandson they said his wife and child were well but one child had died. They told him his sister and her three children were also well. They told John Kettell his wife and child were well and instructed Mr. Rowlandson's sister to ask for three pounds of tobacco for there was hardly any to be found, our fields destroyed before harvest last summer. The women signed the letter as well as Sam Uskattngun, Gunrashit and two other sagamores.

"Mrs. Rowlandson was with Pometacomet and Quinnapin near Northfield when the letter arrived. They were met at the ford of the baquag (Miller's river) by a squaw who told them they had to go to wachusett because a letter had come about the captives. Pometacomet had grown fond of the quiet Englishwoman, who was now with her older daughter, and he took her hand and said to her, 'In two weeks you shall be mistress again.'

"Then he brought them to wachusett where the Christian Indian Peter Conway and Nepanet acted for the English. They called her into the lodge and asked her what her husband would pay for her release and she told them twenty pounds sterling. They asked the others also and then left for Boston to see if the English would agree to the terms.

"Pometacomet did not stay in wachusett after bringing Rowaldson there. He went with his warriors and raided Billerica, then joined with Tuspaquin's men to attack and destroy Bridgewater. Other attacks followed in quick succession as they finished what they had begun in Chelmsford, Marlboro, Weymouth, Hingham and Wrentham. In Wrentham there were two houses full of English people with smallpox and the warriors argued long and hard over whether to burn them as they had the other houses. But our warriors were so afraid of the disease that none would go towards the houses to stack flax, hay and wood against them for firing, so they were left alone. Many felt they would die anyway or be left with the ugly pits all over their faces that the disease left. Our raids succeeded in reclaiming the lands their villages of Groton, Billerica, Lancaster and Marlboro sat on. All were now abandoned except for the garrison at Marlboro.

"But the main attack that sequan was on Sudbury. This town was known as the place of the five paths. All the troops had to pass through Sudbury to get to Quaboag or Marlboro, so it was the main target. If we could reclaim Sudbury, we would have control over the whole inland area and then could drive them downriver and out to sea or towards the shores and into the sea. We would keep advancing until they ran out of land under their feet and had to leave.

"There were over 500 warriors with Pometacomet and the other war captains-sachems. Under cover of a crescent *sequonaonkeewush* (April) moon, our warriors approached the town. At the signal - a triple owl hoot passed from party to party - we attacked, burning the outlying houses. We attacked the garrison house on the other side of the river but knew our best victories came from ambushes, so we left off and waited for the reinforcements to arrive.

"The first to arrive were the Quaboag men - Coswell and 18 others. They rode hard and didn't slow down so we couldn't get into position to ambush. We killed the four at the rear, but the others got inside the garrision safely. Concord sent eleven soldiers and we were able to lure them into the meadows where we ambushed them, killing all but one. The river between the town and the garrison was flooding its banks, but we crossed it and waited as Watertown's men, under Mason, approached the east bank. They drove us out of the village and across the bridge to the side where the garrison was. We hastily tried an ambush by firing guns on the other side of the hill but they didn't take the bait and escaped into the garrison. On the first day of the attack a captain Wadsworth had escaped with about 70 soldiers to Marlboro and we knew they would return with more men, so we laid an ambush. We used the limping warrior decoy and got them to the crest of the wooded hill. There we waited until dark then set fire to it. We waited upwind and grabbed them as they ran, choking and coughing from the smoke into our arms. Some escaped to the stone mill nearby and we caught one old man in the swamps. A former Christian Indian grabbed him and shouted over the crackling, roaring fire, 'Come, Lord Jesus, save this poor Englishman if thou canst, whom I am about to kill.' With a swift blow from his tomahawk the man's brains spilled out and we laughed at their god's impotence.

"While we were busy with this, more troops arrived at the garrison. Huntington had been on his way with his English and Mohegan soldiers to build a fort on the cabassauk (Merrimac) at our fishing grounds. Their arrival at the fort turned the tables of the battle in favor of the English so we finished looting the houses then set fire to them as we withdrew with their fat cattle.

"We camped outside the Marlboro garrison that night and woke them up at sunrise with 74 gunshots - one for each Englishman we had killed at Sudbury. Then we burned the remaining buildings, rounded up stray cattle and headed back to wachusett.

"On our way back we learned that English farmers working fields on the shawmut to sakonnet (Boston to Providence) road had spotted two Wampanoags. They had chased them into a swamp and murdered them. This made Pometacomet very angry and he swore revenge.

"Another thing made him angry when we returned to wachusett. He learned Sam and the other quansik sachems had ransomed Rowaldson and the others at the gathering place - a high boulder east of Wachusett pond.

"He was very angry that Sam and Monoco had not waited and included him in their negotiations. He was told they had asked the English to leave their people alone during planting so they could negotiate peace. And that when one stole food from one of the English negotiators' saddlebags the sachems apologized, blaming it on 'the bad indians.' But what angered him the most was that they had agreed to send all the captives back to the English in hopes of obtaining a peace treaty.

"The wrath of Pometacomet was fierce. I think he would have killed them all if he had been a lesser sort of sachem. He called them old men and spat on the ground in front of the old quansik sachems, breaking an arrow in two and throwing it down at their feet. By such action he dissolved their partnership. He told them they were seeing things upside down, that the captives were worth more as captives than as treaty gifts. He blamed James the Printer for starting talk of surrender and said he should have killed all Christian Indians like he had originally planned to do that winter.

"His anger covered a deeper emotion, for he was crushed that the inland tribes had betrayed him and the cause. I think Pometacomet's heart began to die that day on the rock high above wachusett.

"He took the Narragansett and Wampanoag warriors and headed south, into Narragansett territory, leaving our area unprotected since most of our troops were in the east with Muttaump and Tuspaquin.

"I stayed on in wachusett where my family was but I knew in my soul that the clouds were moving over our meadow and it was just a matter of time before the thunderbird would fly over, clap his wings and send the storms upon us."

Chapter 35

(A re-telling of the Turners Falls Massacre, 1676)

BasketMaker stands up, her eyes glistening with the pain of remembering.

"At the end of the starving winter, my family returned to peskeomscut, for the fishing was good at that spot and the villagers needed many women and girls to help plant the huge corn fields they were putting in.

"There were three villages on the river there, one very high at the head of the great falls, the other lower, on the other side, and the third a distance below on an island in the river

"That spring we often saw warriors riding in through the rain, they and their horses covered in mud. I think there has never been such a rainy sequan. Many times we would plant only to go back a few days later and see the seed floating on the ground or eaten by the crows. Our mats in the wetus turned moldy and had to be thrown away. The corn in our storage pits also became wet and moldy from the flooding when the heavy snowfall suddenly melted in namassack keeswuch (March-April). Some of the people ate it anyway and became very sick. Some had gotten used to the English wheat and rye flour our warriors brought back when raiding the towns but when the rye turned moldy it could kill the person eating it. They would thrash around and dance in the spirit world before dying. Our shamans made the people throw it into the river and told us Creator gave us maize to eat, not wheat, rye or barley. They said the English foods were meant for the horses and English cows, not for us.

"Although I was young, I worked in the fields that spring. We were all so weak from starvation that it took three times as many squaws to do what one healthy, well-fed squaw could normally do. Often I had to sit down in the wet grass to keep from falling down as my head was filled with a lightness.

"I remember many sachems coming through our villages - Pumham, Pessacus and the valley sachems. There were many long councils of war in the longhouses, many serious faces. One of the sachems I remember was a Tarrantine named Megumenay. He came down with Squanto from the coast to the north. He was a very sad sachem. His squaw often told the story of how the English traders had overturned the canoe carrying her and her newborn baby into the sea. She said the English had heard all Tarrantine babies knew how to swim at birth and wanted to see if it were true. The wooden cradle-board full of moss had floated. Swimming frantically, she had managed to grab it as it bobbed away, but a few days later the baby died, its lungs full of sea water. I remember her large, sad eyes as she told the story to any who would listen. She did little work in the camp. Mostly she just sat staring into space, chanting a lullaby softly while rocking back and forth, her arms wrapped around her chest. My mother said it was the dead baby sickness. She said squaws sometimes got it if they didn't have any other papooses. She tried to help Weame by bringing babies to her but she would forget they were there and either almost smother them from holding them too tight or would let them fuss, blind to their discomfort, so the women stopped bringing their babies to her. The squaws said amongst themselves that she should get pregnant again, but I think she and her husband were too sad to make babies. Mostly he went out on war parties and left her alone.

"We worked all day in the fields, which were far away, then walked back to the villages. My family lived in the largest at the upper level of the falls and when we got home in the evening my mother and I would have to haul water from the river to start the next day's meal. If my brothers had caught fish or small game we threw it in the pot. Usually there were some fish left over from the day's drying so we had watery fish stew. But sometimes our warriors returned from a raid with cattle or hogs and we feasted. We were developing a liking for the beef meat, which was sweeter and juicier than venison but we especially loved the pig meat.

"The squaws would split the pigs open carefully, pealing back the thick skin and scraping off all the rich, white fat. Sometimes we were given a scrap of it to suck on and I can remember how good it tasted. They would take the skin and singe the hair off it then slice it into strips and fry it on hot rocks. This, too was a treat for the children. And the meat - it was nothing like the smoked or salted pork we get now. Maybe I remember the meat as tasting better because we were so hungry, I don't know.

"My oldest brother worked with a man repairing guns so the warriors would always sit around and talk to him as he worked at their forge. In a three-sided longhouse they heated a bed of hot coals, fanning it with a huge bellows. Then they took tongs and buried metal into the coals. This they would take out when it was as bright as the sun and with a large hammer on a metal thing called an anvil, they would pound the metal into the shape desired. They would put it back into the fire over and over and sometiemes dip it in water to cool it down. They also made musket shot by melting metal and pouring it into iron molds. When they took the molds apart, there would be a row of little black balls. They melted whatever metal they could find. Many gave them their English silver brooches and chains so my people could have bullets.

"When the warriors came into camp, they told of battles. I remember them saying the house of the English Governor Bradford was burned and his wife and children captured. An Englishman was killed at that place and another in their village called Haverill. But then the English had a victory when they came upon a group of warriors hunting a bear near Mendon. The warriors didn't see them until it was too late and we lost 16 men.

"Other war parties told of the attacks in the east such as the ones led by Tuspaquin. The raid on Plymouth was not carried out because he had received a vision of a bear on its hind legs before the battle. This was not a favorable omen. If it had been a deer, he would have led the raid, but since it was a bear, they passed. Which was a good thing, for it rained so hard their fires wouldn't have burnt anything, anyway. Bridgewater was a different story, though. They had been able to burn many houses but the English had been warned by a traitor so they found no dead bodies in the ashes afterwards. Then came raids on Halifax. The warriors said all the English to our east had fled their villages and gone to the large settlements where there were garrisons and large numbers of soldiers. But the Narragansetts in the south were not so lucky. The English there, accompanied by Mohegans, were tracking them down and killing them or taking them prisoner. We learned also that the ministers

Gookin and Eliot had turned against our people now and were training scouts from Deer Island. These men who had told us they came to love us and bring us the love of their god were now forming companies to kill us. When he heard this one of the warriors in camp scratched a cross on his war club - a cross made of arrows. He said he was saving two arrows for the two ministers and that his war cross would be more powerful than their Christ cross.

"We also learned that the Mohawks were threatening to make war on Pometacomet and his army and this worried us for we were close to their large village near schagticoke. We had warriors on the other side of the river on constant watch for any approaching Mohawk war parties.

"We learned of the raid on Middleboro as we feasted on cattle from Hatfield. Our warriors had watched as the English brought 70 cows and some horses to the meadows to graze near Hatfield and then had ridden down and stole them all - without chase. They brought most of them to the English pens in Deerfield and then herded some up to our villages so we could have meat.

"While we danced, sang and feasted on beef the young Englishman they had captured a moon before slipped away. When the warriors discovered it, they decided to let him go for they were sick of looking at his face. They said, 'Let him go and tell them how well we like their English cows!'

"I was to see the man again a few sleeps later after the warriors had gone."

A tear breaks over BasketMaker's lower lid and runs down her face. Her hands shake as she smoothes the length of hemp she is twining.

"One thing about beef was that if you ate a lot of it you became sleepy and cow-like. After two days of eating our fill of the lean cattle, fish and milk, we slept deeply and even the thunderstorm and heavy rains did not keep us awake that night.

"The smoke flap blew open so rain fell on my face. This and a loud thunderclap brought me instantly awake. As I opened my eyes, the wetu lit up from lightning. Then I heard another noise. Inside the wetu we were all awake now. We huddled together as we heard warriors outside. They returned a little while later, replaced our smoke flap and told us it was a herd of moose fording the river, frightened from the storm. This made sense for even our dogs were frightened and were inside the wetus, huddled together with us.

"We watched their torches fade away as they went to the other village, then settled back down to full-belly sleeps.

"I quickly fell back asleep but another loud clap of thunder and burst of light awakened me with a start. I heard my mother scream and then heard the thunder again and saw another flash of light inside the wetu. My little brother, who was sleeping next to me, screamed and I felt his body jerk then felt hot blood squirting all over me. The dogs and rest of us inside the wetu were all scrambling now, desperate to get away from the thundersticks poking into the door flaps. People were screaming 'Mohawks!' outside and I felt my insides grow ice cold with fear. Then we heard one of the English soldiers grunt and the thunderstick at the western door fell. I grabbed my little sisters' hands and began running through the dark, screaming and ducking whenever a gun went off. All was confusion and noise. A dog squealed as it was hit by a bullet near me and then I remember being at the edge of the cliff above the river. People were jumping into the roiling water and swimming towards canoes."

"I don't remember jumping, but suddenly I was in the river's fast current, struggling to rescue my little sisters and get them into a canoe. I grabbed one and was headed towards the other when a I saw a bullet slam through her and then hit the paddle of the canoe that had been making its way towards her. As she went under, more bullets made the canoe twist and then turn over and we all swam furiously towards shore, fighting the current taking us towards the falls.

"Lightning kept hitting the water, dancing over everything, crashing trees down. On the shore I thought I saw the thunderspirit dancing, his feathered cape and staff moving cruelly up and down as he danced our deaths. I managed to claw my way onto a rock, dragging my half-drowned sister with me. We saw the English soldiers coming down the cliff, shooting at everything, and I hid her inside a small cave made by the rocks and hid myself in another.

"From where I hid I could see the thunderspirit dancing, grinning at me, his evil figure coming closer and closer in the driving rain. Then I saw Englishmen climbing over the rocks, their steel swords glinting like lightning bolts in the living dark."

BasketMaker's voice turns very quiet, very flat.

"Then I saw a sword come down and heard my little sister scream. In the dark her little head toppled down the rocks. As a flash of lightning illuminated the night I saw her head fall into the river, her eyes wide in terror and her mouth cut off in a scream that would never end.

"I jumped out after it, I don't know why, but I knew if I stayed in the rocks I would also be killed like her, so I jumped into the river again and dodged bullets and rocks as I joined the large number of people swimming towards the falls. I was swept over, flung into the air, then fell, expecting to die as the others had on the rocks at the bottom. I don't know how, but I landed in deep water and after falling down and down, I began to rise, my lungs full of pain. My head burst above the water just as I had to exhale and gulp. One second more and I would have drowned.

"I swam to the lower village in the river and found that the warriors had gone to the aid of my village, as had the ones in the village on the other side of the river. But it was too late. Even from the distance, I could see smoke and the glow of fire and knew the whole village had been torched.

"Our men tracked these English, lead by a man called Turner, through the woods, over the banks, through the south meadow and to Hatfield. The English had left their horses and were hunted down like the animals they were, by our warriors on horseback. Our warriors killed 38 of them but we lost 300 people that night. I was one of only a handful that survived. My youngest sister and brother, both little more than babies, had been rescued from our burning wetu and all three of us went to live on the village on the island in the river. The food stores and canoes were moved to this fort and another layer of logs was added to its exterior to make it stronger.

"We stayed in this village until the end of the war when we joined a group headed west, to seek refuge in Mohawk territory.

"In one night I lost almost my whole family. In one winter I lost my childhood and my past.

"It was many years before I could cry about this. For a long time I was like one in a trance. I know I grew up, but until I met my husband and became his wife I was as cold inside as that river on that night so long ago."

Chapter 36
(A re-telling of the war in 1676 and of the old sachems' plea for peace)

Tom Pequin again speaks.

"I was in the east when pesskcomscett was attacked.

"Things weren't going as well as they had earlier that spring. We had just finished an unsuccessful raid on a garrison in what the English called South Scituate. We burned a mill on conngues-sakunkas (Herring) brook then followed the river to the blockhouse on the riverbank but we were were forced to turn back so we continued on to the garrison at the millpond. But there, too, the English were too strong and we had to retreat without a single trophy, gun or cow.

"It was raining, so we piled brush against trees for our shelter. Pometacomet was with the tribes fishing the shores of Narragansett and up the pawtucket river. We heard he and his men planned to attack Stonington and Norwich and then rejoin Tuspaquin. We stayed in the area waiting to hear if he had been able to obtain more gunpowder from the Dutch at Manhatten. Our powder was damp and our shot was low. This of course was our own fault for we sometimes went crazy firing our guns when we attacked the English, wasting many balls and powder. And then we would celebrate afterwards, firing a shot for each English killed. This would get out of hand when the cider took hold and we lost much shot and powder this way. We all collected small pebbles to use instead of musket balls but this could be dangerous, for if one got caught it could explode the flintlock barrel, as happened with Benjamin Tuspaquin, who lost half his jaw when his rifle exploded in his face.

"Despite the rain our spirits were high for we had found two bears mating and had managed to kill the male. The handful of squaws who accompanied our party had immediately begun cooking the meat but we were so hungry we ate handfuls of it raw, licking the blood off our arms as it trickled down, sucking our fingers clean. We were planning to wait in the east one more night and then head west to wachusett to bring some of the meat to the people there.

"Tuspaquin was in council inside a wetu with his war captains when we all sprung to our feet at the sound of a horse galloping hard towards our camp. But we lowered our guns when we recognized the rider as one of ours and not an Englishman or Mohegan.

"That was when I heard about the massacre of our women and children in peskomscett. Many of our warriors had sent their families there to keep them safe, away from the battles. The sound of our wailing filled the valley and was answered by the howls of our wolf brothers so that the whole night was one long blur of wail and howl. Although my family was in wachusett, I was as anxious as the others to ride forth at first light, for if the English had attacked one of our western camps, were they planning to attack the others?

"There were some angry words that night between warriors and Tuspaquin. Many Quansiks and Nashaways felt it was Pometacomet's fault for leaving the area and taking the Narragansetts and Wampanoag warriors with him. They said his strategy of putting all the forces in the east left our people vulnerable to such attack.

"When we rode west in the grey sliver of dawn, many never intended to return to fight with the eastern tribes. We vowed we would not leave our lands again. We would fight on our own soil, from our own villages.

"Wachusett was deserted, its people in hiding in the swamps, so we continued to quaboag pond, but the presence of many English soldiers there made us avoid the main trails. It took us much longer than ususal to arrive in the Northampton area for we had to go over the mountains and the travel was slippery and slow-going. Our horses had to pick their way down the steep, muddy slopes and several warriors received injuries from falls.

"Finally, we met the troops from pesskcomscett and rode to the site of the massacre to see if we could find any more survivors. I will never forget that scene - never! There were half-charred bodies sunk in mud under the black bones of the wetus. Down below it looked like the English had fished our people out of the river and left them to rot on the rocks in the river and on its steep, rocky banks. I remember bitterly thinking that while my people had been fishing that spring for salmon, alewives and shad, the English had done their own fishing. On the other side of the river the village wasn't so bad, but our gun repairer and his forge were completely destroyed.

"As we buried our dead we waited for powder and more troops to arrive so we could avenge this cowardly murder.

"To the south Pometacomet's men had a close call on the pawtuckett near seekonk but he managed to get away and send some powder to quansik. He sent word for us to attack to the east to draw the English away from our corn fields, but we were too full of revenge to listen.

"We observed troops coming up the valley to Northampton so immediately planned a raid at Hatfield, further north from them. Twelve houses and barns were burned and we got many sheep and cows. These we sent back to camp with the youngest warriors and then we rowed our canoes across the river to their stockade. We killed five before reaching the garrison but they were too well-fortified inside so we had to retreat.

"We knew news of the attack would reach Northampton so we laid an ambush for the troops along the road but the Mohegan scouts with the soldiers told them we would do this so the captain Newberry ferried his men across the river below Northampton and marched them up to Hadley where we met them trying to cross the river.

"Our guns were able to keep them on the other side for they didn't have enough boats for all their soldiers. They retreated from the banks but then we ran out of powder so we also had to retreat. Then I went with a group of warriors to Chabunagungamung where the powder and fish Pometacomet had sent were waiting for us.

"Again, travel was difficult and it took us longer than we expected to reach lower quansik. In the swamp near the ponds we met many fleeing warriors. They had been surprised at Chabunagungamung by Mohegans and English soldiers, they said. 19 warriors had been killed and 33 captured. The powder and fish had also been taken to the English fort at Quaboag Plantation. We laid low near it for a couple of days, planning an ambush, but the troops didn't leave the fort.

"During that time we climbed to the top of steerage rock at Asquoach and did not see any signs of troop movement to the west so we decided to travel back to Hadley and finish our raid to drive them out of the area and away from our crops and families.

"We heard that the Nashaways were losing heart in the war and their sachems were returning the captives to try to get the English to sign a truce. It seemed as if all the older sachems had lost their courage when Pometacomet left. They did not think that we could hold the inland territory by ourselves but those of us fighting the battles felt differently.

"But one thing that made even the warriors waver was the large number of Mohegans the English had helping them. We knew the trick Uncas was up to, for he would grab our lands as soon as the ink was dry on the treaty. We would all become his subjects and have to pay him tribute. The English thought he was helping them because he liked them, but we knew that as soon as they killed enough of us he would step in, take over all the tribes and then declare war on the English and drive them out. This was why some of our sachems didn't care who signed the treaty, for they said we would eventually win.

" They said they didn't care if their war captains in the end were Mohegans, but many of us hated Uncas and the Mohegans and vowed we would never fight with them. They were the reason our ambushes were failing and the English were now fighting behind trees and under cover. They knew our trails and our methods and, like the dogs the English used, they too, tracked us down. As much as I hated the English, I hated the Mohegans more. If they had joined Pometacomet instead of taking the English side we would not be here today in Oneida territory. We would have driven all the English out and then driven the Dutch out and maybe even the French, although I don't mind them as much as the others. The French are not so land-hungry and they don't treat us like we're heathens. It is true that their blackrobes try to cram the Bible down our throats, but they have treated us differently than the English have. The English came in, grabbed land and more land and then told us we must follow the English god and their English laws. But I ramble like an old man.

"After finding the troops at Quaboag, we returned to the river. There, we heard the English had trampled the corn fields of the Wabbaquasetts. It was the same group of soldiers that had gotten our gunpowder and killed the men at Chabunagungamung afterwards. Then we received news that weshakim had been attacked so we rode east to help them defend it, hoping to regain our powder and supplies in the process.

"By the time we got to weshakim ponds the English were gone. Sam was also gone, for he was at wachusett with the English arranging for the release of the English captives.

"But, unknown to him, his wife and children were amongst the 29 captured at weshakim. Muttaumps's wife was also captured. This was a bitter leaf to chew. As Sam was giving up the English wives and children, his own were being captured.

"We tried to find the English troops but the trail was cold so we returned to the river to attack Hadley. We arrived near the fort under cover of darkness and divided into two main groups, with my party hiding in the tall grass of the meadows around the fort. We sent the other to the south of the stockade and waited until morning.

"In the morning three soldiers opened the door at the south of the fort and went into the fields to spy on our warriors there. As soon as they got clear of the fort we all rose up and rushed forward, shooting and whooping. But the top of the fort was immediately full of soldiers firing at us. This was unexpected, for we thought there was only a small number of soldiers in the fort. In the confusion of smoke and dust we retreated up the valley.

"We sent out spies in all directions and soon learned that the men from the raid on Chabungagunamung had been moving west to Hadley while we were moving east to their north. Not only that, we learned that 500 soldiers from Concord had also gone to Hadley, which put the number of men inside the fort at about 1,000.

"This was not good. This meant the area was now being reclaimed by the English we had driven out last year. Our fields and our families were in great danger and so we decided to move half of them to wachusett and the other half to Narragansett.

"As we were breaking camps and finding safe places to store what we could not carry another group of soldiers arrived in Hadley, led by the captain Henchman.

"Reluctant to leave our crops, our shamans called upon Wannalancet and Konkowasco to join them to try to drive the English away, much like the shamans tried when the English first came to Turtle Island.

"They gathered in a swamp and held the same ceremony Passaconnaway had held in the time of our fathers.

"I can't begin to tell you the strange things we saw and heard that night. Spirits of ancestors sang and danced their war dance on

Mother Earth and in the sky. Every kind of animal spirit screamed and flew around and different colored lights danced everywhere and thunder rumbled. But the strangest, most wonderful sight was a bright white bow that appeared in the dark sky. This was an omen, we all felt. This was our bow, victorious over their guns, our way of life victorious over the English way of life. This was Kichtan defiantly holding his bow up in the sky for all English to see.

"Our shamans invoked the winds and thunder and torrential rain to wash the English away, down the river, but the next day they were still in the area. They were spotted at peskcomscutt taking their soldiers down from the poles we stuck them on, going about their business as if they had not seen or heard the spirits the night before. This made many of our people lose their heart for the war. The English were too stupid to be scared away. Like ants they just kept coming. We would kill them and they would keep coming.

"Two skirmishes occured in the next two days while we were gathering what we could from our unripe gardens. In one, the English killed the older brother of a Pocumtuck sachem and captured six squaws and children. In the other, five were killed and a boy and girl captured by the Mohegans.

"Our scouts found several small parties of Mohawks camping to the north and so we moved out, leaving our beautiful corn fields behind. This was the last time I saw those lands. Like the others here except Tahattawaban, who joined Pometacomet in Narragansett, I went to wachusett.

"While we were in wachusett the English sent word to the sachems that anyone who turned him or herself in within 14 sleeps would be pardoned if they had not killed any English. Sam, Muttaump, John, Shattoquis and Nassowanno sent a letter to Waban to take to the English. They asked them to take good care of Sam's and Muttaump's wives who had been captured at weshakim pond. They said they had spoken with the Nashobah sachems Tom and Peter Dubler and that all wanted to make peace. They said they had been destroyed by the English soldiers and asked for mercy, calling upon the English god.

"I remember the words well, for I hated them and the weakness they represented: 'We do earnestly entreat you, that it may be so by Jesus Christ. O! Let it be so! Amen, Amen!' The tone of the letter was set by the Dublers, both former Christian Indians. They told the sachems that the only way the English would pardon the sachems was if they converted and agreed to worship the English god. They loved converts, they said, and would do almost anything for them.

"But the Dublers didn't know how the English hearts had changed. Eliot and Gookin were no longer holding Bibles: they were holding guns. The letter was never answered nor was a subsequent one sent by Sam in which he reminded the English that he had given them their captives back. He asked the English why they wouldn't return his people.

"Waban sent a messenger to the sachems telling them that if they wanted to live they must flee, so with a heavy heart the camp at wachusett broke up. Some went north to the Tarrantines and others south. Some stayed, hiding in caves, fugitives in their own land.

"I was with those who went south to Konkowasco's island."

Chapter 37
(A re-telling of the death of Pometacomet and the end of the war, 1676)

John Tattawaban lowers the pipe and passes it to the person on his left. He stands again, his tongue sharp as an arrow tip as he speaks of his role as a warrior.

"When I threw my spear into the war fire, I vowed to fight until my death for the cause. When the inland tribes began to waver and return captives, I left them to be with Pometacomet. Many of my own people, the Massachusetts, were helping the English either as scouts or as spies. The Christian Indians also helped them, especially James Quanapohit and Job Kattanit who pretended to join Pometacomet only to sneak away and report his plans and troop strength to the English. Because I was so angry with my people and the inland tribes, I never returned to my homelands after the war.

"Now I will tell you how the rest of the war went with me.

"After our strange reception by the old sachems in wachusett, we went north to see if we could get the support of any of Wannalancet's people. They were not interested and ran from us, but we did get some of the tribes further north interested and so returned south to Pokanoket with more warriors.

"On our way back down the river, Wannalancet sent word for us to come to him and we did, hoping it meant he had changed his mind.

"We found him living in poor conditions, in a swamp. His people were hungry and unhappy but he refused to join our cause. He said he had seen how the war would end in a vision and wanted no part of it. Any person even suspected of helping would die or be sold into slavery, he said, and he urged us to lay down our arms and live with his people. Of course we wouldn't listen, but I think our visit was what led him to come out of hiding briefly and lead the exorcism ceremony Konkowasco and the other sachems took part in.

"We knew he was a man of great power and we asked him if he still had his father's familiar, a huge snapping turtle. He said he did and Akompion asked if it would tell us how our battles would go. Wannalancet was exasperated with us at this point but he brought it out, probably to convince us to stop. We sat in a tight circle on the dirt floor of the wetu, the turtle in the middle.

"The old turtle slowly unfurled its claw-tipped legs, then its head began to emerge, the yellow eyes looking straight at Akompion. Wannalancet asked it the question and the turtle opened its mouth as if to speak then pushed itself suddenly towards Akompion, snapping as if it would bite him. We all moved back against the reeds and saplings and Wannalancet blew tobacco smoke into the turtle's face, thanking it for helping its human brothers. The turtle withdrew into its shell and Wannalancet put it into its basket. He looked right at Akompion and said, 'You have had your answer from me and from my future-seeing spirit. If you leave this place and continue to make war on the English, you will find your head on a pole outside one of their villages. They will snap it off you like a turtle snapping the head off a duckling.'

"Some of our men listened to Wannalancet and refused to go on, but Akompion said he had promised to return to Pometacomet and so he could not stay. We gave Wannalancet some tobacco and one of the baskets of corn we were carrying. I remember seeing one young mother so thin her rib bones stuck out through her flesh. Her tiny baby was still nursing. Until the acorns ripened and she could get milk from them she was feeding the baby her own flesh. The other mothers had tried to talk her into taking it out into the woods and dashing its head on a rock but she wouldn't, so they both suffered. We told Wannalancet his people would be better fed if they went to wachusett but he wouldn't listen. He said the only way they could hope to survive the war was to stay hidden from both sides.

"Then we joined Tuspaquin near the fowling ponds in the place that used to be Ousemequin's summer village. We stayed only a short time in each camp for the English had spies everywhere. We learned of the attack at weshakim ponds and of peskomscett from Tuspaquin's men as we moved towards Narragansett, hoping to rendevous with Pometacomet. Wherever we went we looked for food, for crops to scavenge. But where the English had missed them our brothers and sisters on four legs had not. I felt that whatever spell the English were using, it was hurting Mother Earth and all her creatures as well as us. The few bears we had killed in our travels had been cubless, which we knew meant that they were starving, too. You see, the mother bear is very much like our own squaws. She won't get pregnant when times are bad. The squaw I saw in Wannalancet's camp was very rare. In our camps there were no births that summer.

"We were on the outskirts of the great plain near what the English called Rehoboth when we saw Pometacomet's men. As our two parties joined, I recognized a Christian Indian in the Wampanoag camp and told Pometacomet he was not to be trusted. I told him he was a friend of Ben Petonowit (Weetamoo's third husband) and had been sent there by Church to spy on us. He didn't believe me but the next day's event proved me correct.

"We planned a raid on some farms on the outskirts of swansea at wannamoiset for the following day and Pometacomet took 30 warriors with him to hide in the high grasses. The rest were to wait for the sound of gunfire and then come out of the woods.

"I was with those in the woods and as soon as I heard a gun go off, I rose with the others to rush out, but we were almost knocked down by Pometacomet's men rushing back into the woods. We ran down the ravine to where our horses were tied and rode hard until midday, when Pometacomet caught up with us and sent the message to stop at the next brook.

"There he told us what had happened. Tipped off by the traitor, an army of English soldiers were waiting for them. He said he had snuck up on a boy in the field farthest from the house, shot him with an arrow and was just finishing beheading him when he heard his men shouting and shooting. He stood up, saw the English soldiers chasing our warriors, and headed for the woods. They had Christian Indians with them and were trying to ambush the whole group. They barely got out alive.

"He held up the boy's head and said he never even had a chance to put it on a pole, but we would put it on a pole here and dance our victory dance around it. One of his men had captured a black man, a servant on the farm, and we took turns taunting him, spitting in his face and burning him with hot coals to see if his char-black skin made him immune to fire. He had no dignity and begged for mercy so we soon tired of our game. We were going to kill him since he was useless for ransom as a captive, but Pometacomet said he might be useful if he could be persuaded to get the other slaves to rise up against their English masters and kill them in their own beds. He ordered the man released and had food brought to him. That night I heard Pometacomet speaking very softly to the man, telling him we were fighting because we didn't want to become like his people, slaves to the English. It was hard to communicate though, for the slave didn't speak much English and our interpreters didn't speak his native language.

"We kept moving and at daybreak went west, to follow the pawtucket river up towards their main town of Boston. On our way one of Pometacomet's spies hailed us from the riverbank. He had bad news. The captain Talcott had taken his army (which we suspected was the same one we met at wannamoiset) north and had ambushed one of our safe camps, the one in the cedar swamp, hidden in a basin of hills at nachek. This was where we had sent some of the survivors of the Narragansett swamp massacre. At the camp were Magnus, Pessacus' agent Watawaikeson and Stonewall John and their families. The Pequots and Mohegans with Talcott laid an ambush around the camp and most of the people inside were killed. Some were captured and taken to Stonington. The spy, who had been riding non-stop from there with an appeal from Pessacus to have us join him in Narragansett, said he had witnessed the brave death of one of the Narragansett war captains.

"He said the captain bragged he had killed 19 Englishmen and a Mohegan so Talcott gave the Mohegans the right to execute him in revenge for the slaying of one of their warriors.

"Uncas' men made a circle around the warrior and ordered him to sing and dance. They cut off one of his fingers at its base by slicing the skin then breaking it off. The spy said he heard it snap from where he hid in a tree branch. But the Narragansett never stopped singing and dancing, even as they repeated this on the rest of his fingers and then his toes.

"They asked him how he liked the war now and he shouted back, 'I like it very well. I find it as sweet as the English do their sugar!' The spy said throughout all this the English captain never took his eyes off the bleeding, singing, dancing warrior. He said they were filled with a strange excitement, like that of a man lusting for a woman. The Narragansett was the bravest warrior he had ever seen. He said even when they broke his legs he never screamed. He just kept singing his death chant, in which he kept telling of the English and Mohegans he had killed until they finally ended his suffering by splitting his head in two with a war club.

"We sang a song to honor this brave warrior, our guns held high to Grandfather Sun as we let him know his spirit would go to the southwest escorted by our song.

"The following day another messenger arrived with more bad news. Awashonks and her Sakonnets had surrendered to Church at the farm near Falmouth. The spy said they were at this very minute feasting, fishing for eels, flatfish and clams, playing football and horseback racing on the coast on Buzzards Bay while Awashonks and Church were drinking wine to celebrate. And, as if this weren't a big enough blow, the messenger said Church was taking a group of Awashonk's warriors with him to fight against Pometacomet's men.

"It was at this time a messenger from wachusett told him of the letter Sam, John and the other sachems had sent to the English asking for a treaty.

"Pometacomet became very quiet for a day or two. He went off to fast with his closest advisor and friend, his father's brother Akompion. When he returned he called us together and said he had received a vision that showed him wolves submitting to their leader. He asked each of us to come before him and bare our chests to his pointed gun. He said he had to know we were all willing to give up our lives for him, for the only way we could win was if we were as strong as a wolf pack. A few warriors slipped away so they wouldn't have to do this but he said this was fine with him, he didn't want any warrior with him from now on who wasn't committed unto death to the cause. There would be no surrender, no peace treaties, he said. The way of the warrior in this war was to fight until he died, to die with gun, bow, tomahawk or knife in hand.

"He told us if any man valued his squaw or family more than he did this cause he should return and leave with them for when we drove the English out anyone who had not been committed wholly to Pometacomet would also be killed. This message was sent to all the sachems from the sea to the quonicticut and a few sleeps later we learned some of the inland tribes were moving west, towards the quonicticut.

"While his own people were deserting him, Pometacomet also lost the black slave. He escaped at night near Taunton and ruined our surprise attack on the town the next day. We found it well-defended by soldiers so were only able to burn two houses. 'So, the negro prefers life as a slave to the English to freedom with my people!' Pometacomet said bitterly when told the news of the man's escape. He vowed that he'd never clean an English barnyard or cut English wheat. He said the only thing he'd ever cut was English heads.

"Our next two raids were equally disappointing. We were driven off at Bridgewater after killing a few cows and the next day when we returned for their carcasses we were driven off even harder. We barely escaped the second time and were tracked through the swamps as we made our way towards the Taunton river skirting the assowompet ponds then on towards the swamp near Dartmouth. Through the night we traveled non-stop, carrying our many wounded warriors across the backs of our horses. Towards daylight we finally stopped to rest our horses and treat the wounds.

"We no sooner got the fires going and dozed off when we were awakened by shouts and found our guards racing towards camp, pursued by Sagkonnets. We had to leave our dead and dying warriors as we mounted our tired horses and rode away. Besides our wounded and dead, we also lost our blankets and kettles and most of our supplies as we fled deeper into the swamp. I don't know why the English stopped chasing us - maybe they stopped to interrogate our wounded-but if they had continued we would have all been captured for we and our horses were so exhausted we could not have gone much farther.

"We ate raw snakes, cattail roots, shoots and tops and the bark off the slippery elm and chestnut trees that day and boiled sassafrass root to try to get some strength back. I was one of those chosen to watch so I climbed a pine tree on the outskirts of the swamp and waited for any signs of the enemy. The day was hot and I almost fell asleep. The sudden caw of a crow brought me fully alert but all I saw was two birds chasing the crow, whose nest was high up in the branches of the pine.

"As I looked out over the swamp I watched the dragonflies flitting over the stagnant water, the bees humming in the flowers and the birds flying to and fro amongst the dead trees. I felt a pang in my middle like the worst hunger pang I had ever had. Only it wasn't coming from my stomach. It was coming from my heart. I found myself crying harder than I had ever cried in my life as I breathed in the full summer scents and felt Grandfather Sun hot on my arms. Just two summers ago I would have been lounging in front of my wetu or traveling through the villages trading. My life was gone. My wetu was gone, the villages I had visited - all gone. The laughter, the baby-making, the feasts of green corn and strawberries - all gone. Never had I known anything, other than the plague, to destroy so much in so little time. But even with the plague one could go to live in another village and live as he had before. Now the only place with feasting and laughing was in Sakonnet. Our people all lived like roaming animals now, always on the run, hiding from the enemies, and from their brothers as they led the English to their dens.

"I can tell you now about my sorrow that day, but at the time I never let anyone know of it.

"At nightfall we moved slowly through the swamp towards the Taunton river, making camp in one swamp after another. We chose swamps for two reasons - the dogs couldn't follow our scent in water, and the English got bogged down easily for they didn't know how to leap from log to log the way we did. With our bare feet we could feel stones or logs underneath and make our way but their heavy boots and shoes would slip or fill with mud and get stuck, slowing them down. We didn't have any dogs with us, they were all dead, killed and eaten during the winter. The English, however, had big, muscular dogs that loved our flesh. We thought they fed them our dead to give them the taste and we were afraid of their dogs more than we were of their guns.

"While in the swamps we were found by some of Awashonk's people. We raised our guns to kill them but they were holding their hands high to show us they were not armed. They had been cast out of Sakonnet for refusing to surrender, they said. They asked to join us and after much questioning, Pometacomet accepted them. They told him Pumham had been killed by the English in hand-to-hand combat and the survivors were nearby, in Middleboro with Pumham's son. They told us 15 warriors had been killed and 34 captured in the English ambush led by Mohegans.

"Pometacomet said we would meet with them but he first wanted to visit the safe camp where his wife and son were and so we made our way through the swamps to their hiding place in the great cedar swamp near acushnet.

"There, he learned that some of the inland sachems had fled north to the Tarrantines but others had surrendered. We were told John and 180 of his people had turned themselves in and that John bought his life by capturing and delivering Matoonas to the English. I think we all knew in our hearts that day that the end was near. Our army had broken apart. Our confederacy was no more. We were now but a small band in the middle of a great sea of enemies, both English and native.

"Pometacomet called a war council and told us we would have to retreat into Narragansett territory so he could begin talks with the Mohawks. He said we could no longer count on help from our own tribes. His downcast face and sad eyes sent arrows through my heart. Some of us said we would go to Boston and kill all of John's people but Pometacomet said no, the English would do it just fine, we would see.

"The women and children at the camp were very happy to see us. Pometacomet's sister said they kept hearing of battles and had been afraid he was dead. A feast of fish was prepared and we ate until we were full, then the men with families retired to their wetus and the rest of us slept under the stars around the fires. We had dug up a cache of fresh guns to replace ones we lost or damaged and we planned to take the women and children with us to Narragansett.

"The Sakonnets left to find and bring the Narragansetts to Pometacomet. But the next day one returned, his chest heaving from running. The English had found the Narragansetts and then discovered the Sakonnets, he said. Only he escaped. This news threw Pometacomet into a panic. He yelled at the warrior for coming back to the camp.

"He called everyone together and told them to break up camp, that they would move out at night, but before we could round up the women and children who were gathering berries we heard the English and their dogs. Pometacomet threw his wife and son on a horse and we rode out fast in the opposite direction. We found a patch of thick woods and waited for the others to catch up but they never came. I was one of the warriors who snuck back to bring them away but found no one there except an old woman who was drawing her last breath. She told me Tyask's wife, his son and 63 other women and children had been rounded up and taken captive. I found two other people dead near the gun pit - and the guns gone. We buried our dead in the pit and returned to Pometacomet and Tyask with the bad news.

"When we returned we found a party of Narragansetts in council with Pometacomet. They had escaped from Middleboro and were going to lead us to a safe place in Narragansett.

"Our main obstacle to Narragansett territory was the Taunton river. The English held all the good fording places so we went up and down searching for a place to cross. We finally felled a tree and began crossing, but the noise of the hatchets and the tree crashing over the river had alerted the English, who were on us like flies on dung. Pometacomet and the warriors took the women across the narrow trunk, guiding them through the branches above the strong river currents. We were all across except Akompion, who was leading Pometacomet's sister across, when the English broke through the underbrush on the bank and began firing. We shoved the women up the opposite bank and began firing back but Akompion was shot and fell into the river on the English side. Pometacomet's sister fell on the other and got caught in the tangle of branches beneath the log. By now the English were crossing so we couldn't hold our positions any longer and with a great agonizing look backward, Pometacomet had to leave his sister to the English, who were fishing her out of the river.

"We set fire to the end of the log before disappearing into the woods. We heard the English falling into the water as the smoke blinded them and they slipped. We waited and when we didn't see any English emerge on our bank we sent the people on, to nippeninecket pond. Pometacomet refused to leave the river, saying he was going to cross and free his sister as soon as the coast was clear. We argued with him, telling him our best course of action was to continue, but the loss of his uncle, who had been like his father, and of his sister, devastated Pometacomet.

"The next morning he set out to sneak across the log when the English caught sight of him. He jumped off the log and rode towards the rest of us to warn us the English were still after us. We hurriedly fled nippeninecket pond and rode towards the pond at winniconnet as we made our way to the great swamp north of Rehoboth. We were planning to get Weetamoo and her people near Taunton to go with with us.

"We had almost made the swamp when the English closed in. In a desperate battle our warriors faced their soldiers while forming a semicircle around our women and children at the edge of the swamp.

A band of Sakonnets snuck around behind and grabbed some of the women and children, including Wootonekannske and Pometacomet's son. Quinnapian's Narragansett women and children were also captured in like manner, but we were occupied with holding the English soldiers off so we didn't realize this until afterwards, when we followed the others into the swamp.

"Pometacomet was so overcome with grief he cut all his hair off but he knew if he showed weakness the others would want to surrender, so he left the camp, joining the warriors gathering firewood. He said he would not leave the area until he had recaptured the people the English had taken, especially his sister, his squaw and his son. We tried to talk him out of this plan. We said there would be time to return with fresh Narragansett warriors after the rest were safely in the south but he said it would be too late. He was afraid they would be put on a ship and sent away or be killed if he didn't regain them immediately.

"He spoke the truth but we were only interested in getting the others away so we disagreed. Pometacomet was so angry over this he shot a Wampanoag warrior. The slain warrior's brother rushed forward to fight Pometacomet but their fight was cut short by the sounds of the English. I was watching this with horror when a bullet whizzed by my ear and lodged in the dead wood of the cedar log bridge, sending a puff of smoke up right near my head. We ran back to the camp, got the people up and moved deeper into the swamp. It was the middle of the night by the time we finally settled onto a patch of rocks to sleep.

"At dawn the English found us again. We sent the women and children in the opposite direction and tried to ambush the English. We lost many warriors but Pometacomet, Tatosen and Tuspaquin escaped and helped us find our hiding people. Many of our children had been sent up trees like bear cubs and it took us some time to get them all gathered together again.

"By the time we finally secured a good camp site, we noticed the brother of the slain Wampanoag was missing.

"At dawn the next day Tatosen took some warriors with him to make contact with Weetamoo. We sent word to her that we needed powder desperately since much of ours had been lost or had gotten wet in the swamp. Tuspaquin also left to try to get more warriors or supplies from Pocasset.

"No word came back from Weetamoo. For many sleeps we waited in the swamp, aware of the breath of the English on our heels.

"Pometacomet knew something was wrong and sent me and several others to investigate. We found the dead body of our messenger to Weetamoo in the meadow beyond the swamp and returned to tell our leader. He said Weetamoo would be in grave danger if the English had forced the mesenger to talk so we set out for her camp in the swamp near the mouth of the Taunton river. As we approached, we heard the English so we slipped into the trees and watched.

"Leading the English to Weetamoo's camp was the brother of the Wampanoag Pometacomet had killed. Weetamoo's people were fleeing across the Taunton in make-shift rafts of saplings laced together with vines. Weetamoo jumped on a raft and was pushed out into the current. We watched in silent horror as we saw it begin to break apart mid-stream. The sachem couldn't swim well and she slipped off, her arms flailing at the bullets pinging the water all around like rain. Her head went under several times as the river carried her downstream.

"Then she entered a rocky patch of churning water and we saw her no more.

"We immediately returned to Pometacomet and learned that he had sent Tatosen and a war party out after we left to try to sneak into the English town and free Pometacomet's relatives and the others. We told him there were English everywhere and that it was not safe for any warrior to be outside the swamp. We said we had many close calls and only escaped detection because of the manitoo of the areas we traveled through. We told him he was not safe in that place because of the traitor that was with the English and the Sakonnets.

"He wouldn't to listen to us and we spent many days waiting for Tatosen to return. Pometacomet refused to leave the area until his squaw and son were delivered to him. Every man tried to talk Pometacomet out of this madness but he would not listen. We knew he would do to us what he had done to the Wampanoag so we kept silent. But our worries hung in the air like the thick scent of late autumn, like overripe plants rotting and dying.

"Later I learned Tatosen's band had been ambushed by Church and that his father, Sam Barrow, had tried to surrender. He had been told he would be given no quarter and no mercy because of his involvement in the Clark Garrison murders. He was executed on the spot by a Sakonnet after being allowed a final puff on his pipe. (Tatosen and his squaw and son had been taken in by the Agawams, not far from there, but they died from smallpox a few winters later).

"By now we were in a place of rocks in the swamp. We had a better view of things and the huge boulders could serve as a fortress against bullets. The weather had been very hot but the night had been cool so wisps of fog crept into the swamp, gathering together until they formed a wall of white.

"It was in such whiteness that we awoke to the sounds of the English and Sakonnets. They had crept up on us, led again by that traitor whose brother lay dead in this same swamp.

"Everything happened so fast. I remember fighting hand-to-hand with a Sakonnet warrior. I twisted away for a second and then brought my war club down with a hard smash on his head then I grabbed my gun and ran deeper into the swamp, not knowing if the figures in the mist were our men, the Sakonnets or the English. I listened hard, trying to find the direction where Annawon's yells of 'Iootash! Iootash!' (stand and fight) were coming from so I could join him.

"Then I heard the English yell 'We got him!' and knew they had our leader. My heart turned cold in my breast as I tried to get closer to shoot whoever was holding him. The fog cleared for a brief instant and I saw Pometacomet up against a rock, held there by the guns of the two Sakonnets Alderman and Caleb Cook. The fog closed again and I heard two gun shots and knew our leader was dead.

I yelled 'Iootash! Iootash!' now and the others found me and I led them further into the swamp. We wondered why the English didn't pursue us, so I and a few others crept back to see if they had gone.

"What I saw instead sickened my spirit with a sadness that lives to this day. Not only did a person of lesser rank kill our leader, that was insult enough, but they had beheaded him, drawn and quartered his body and left its quarters hanging on four trees in the swamp. The head and one hand were lying on the muddy ground. Alderman picked up the hand, wrapped it in English cloth and stuffed it in a bag. The head was lifted up and spat on by the Sakonnets and English soldiers. This was too much to bear. I tried to rush out and avenge Pometacomet but the others held me back.

"After we calmed down a little, we returned to camp and sent a messenger to Narragansett to ask Quinnapin what the Narragansetts would have us do, but our messenger returned with the news that Quinnapin, his brother and their group had been captured by Mohegans. The two sachems were to be executed in Newport, he said.

"Pometacomet's pniese Annawon was now our leader. He was a fine war captain but did not have the authority a sachem has. There were many arguments during that time with each warrior wanting to do something different. I wanted to go west, cross the housatonic and try to find refuge with the Mohawks but the men who had been with Pometacomet on his last trip into Mohawk territory said the Mohawks would just as soon kill us as look at us. Others said we should go north and seek refuge with the Tarrantines, but the path north was full of English. One warrior had a plan to go down river, get in boats and go north by sea but we said they had too many villages on the coast and someone was sure to spot us.

"Day after day the plans were discussed. Day after day the enemy was growing stronger in spirit.

"Our camp now was at the bottom of a steep rocky ledge. It had an overhang that kept our fire smoke from being seen.

"We had our guns lying on forked sticks to keep them off the damp ground and, as was our custom, I covered them with mats to keep the dew out of them. Our guns were all we had now. We had no villages, no wetus, no animals, nothing.

"At sunset after many sleeps, one of the squaws told Annawon she feared something had happened to her sister, for she had gone out earlier to forage for wood and berries and hadn't returned. I led a party out in search of her but after many hours in the dappled moonlight we found no trace.

"When we returned to camp we couldn't believe our eyes or ears. Annawon was seated at the fire with the English! He was asking for amnesty. He was offering them food.

"I felt violently ill and had to clench my teeth to keep from vomiting. Betrayed by Pometacomet's best-loved war captain! Here was a man who took the loyalty test to Pometacomet's cause now surrendering to the English. We heard Tuspaquin's name come up many times and knew that Annawon was making a deal such as John's so we left to find Tuspaquin and warn him.

"The moon was full, which helped us see our way, but it also hurt us for it made us more visible to the English and the traitor

Sakonnets. As we traveled around Pocasset the next few nights it was like walking in a ghost world. All that remained of villages were wetu skeletons and weed-choked cornfields. Yet the English villages, despite our burnings, seemed alive. I can't explain it, but I felt as if I was walking in the land of the dead, our dead, and often wondered if I had died and this moonlit land was my eternal home.

"Our travels brought us almost to the doorstep of the English. We found a small camp of Pocassets near Plymouth and while resting there heard that Tuspaquin's squaw and child had been captured by Annawon. Tuspaquin then surrendered to Church in exchange for a captaincy in the English army.

"We knew then beyond any hope our cause was dead. We had no leaders, we had no army.

"While I planned my escape to the west I heard that Tuspaquin had been executed after bragging that his powerful medicine made him immune to bullets. ' So much for the English promises,' I thought bitterly. So much for our medicine, too, for if the medicine of one of our strongest powwows was useless against the English, we were surely lost. I remembered then Wannalancet's words and Konkowasco's visions and I wept. We had lost the war before it even began and these men had known and had tried to warn us. If only we had listened.

"I remained in hiding near Plymouth for a while longer. The sachems continued to be captured and brought in tied like animals for slaughter. Squando and Wannalancet, Muttaump and Sam were ambushed as they were en route to the general court to surrender and ask for amnesty. Their guns were empty but they were fired upon then disarmed and brought in as war criminals. Monoco and Old Jethro were brought in, Old Jethro having been betrayed by his son Peter who showed the English his hiding place. These were executed and their peoples were all either executed (if they had killed English) or sold into slavery.

"By the end of the *pohquitaqunk keeswush* (September) moon, at a time when we would have been harvesting our crops and feasting and readying our weapons for deer hunting, I was creeping through the woods at night making my way far north to the Tarrantines.

"I was found by a war party in Pigwacket. I was half-dead from starvation and exhaustion for I had not dared to stop to hunt or fish. I was driven by one thought only: I wanted to get away and continue to fight. I would never surrender and die in a noose on their Boston common.

"I did fight for many more winters but one day I heard some of my people were here in Oneida and so I traveled west to be with them. That is how I came to be here.

"Now that I am close to dying I have hung up my gun and bow and now I try to find things to love and not hate. But it is not easy.

"Everytime I hear the words Mohegan or Sakonnet I feel the old hate well up inside. I have tried to make peace with them in my heart, have tried to understand why some people were so eager to go with the English . I can understand the ones who were put under a spell by Eliot and Gookin. I do not hate these people for they could not help themselves. Perhaps the English also cast a spell on Awashonks and Annawon and their people. The Mohegans were playing their own game, this I know, and, as Pometacomet had predicted, it backfired in their faces.

"I spend many hours sitting in the sun thinking about these things. This happens when you get too old to go out and do things. You go over your past again and again. Some days I think I should never have joined the cause, other days I feel not one drop of regret. All I know is I would do it again.

"I wear these many coup feathers with pride. Every English person I killed was replaced by two more from that place called England but maybe someday a plague will be sent to them and they will be the ones dying. I can only hope that when that day comes enough of you will remain to go back to Quansik, to Massachusetts, to Pocasset and Agawam and the homes of your ancestors.

"This is why you must remember all that we have told you this winter. You must never forget who you are. You must never forget how to walk the good native road, how to be one of the people.

"Do not be beguiled by English, Dutch or French objects. Learn your ancient ways. You must learn to hunt with the bow before you take up the gun. You must learn the names of our gods and carry them always with you in your hearts.

"I, Windwalker, have spoken."

Chapter 38
(A re-telling of how the Christian Indians were sent to Deer Island and how the neutral tribes fled west in 1676)

Konkowasco has changed during this time of remembering. Like metal cleaned in fire, he has been hardened - and purified.

"Now I will tell you what the English thought of their praying villages during the war. Soldiers rode into many of them and rounded the people up then marched them to the sea and loaded them into boats to go to the island they bought from Squaw Sachem's son Winnepurkit (George Romneymarsh).

"This island they called Deer Island. It was off the coast of their village Boston. They marched the Christian Indians there in the winter without mantles or robes or blankets. Their food was left behind for the English soldiers. On the island there was no deer, no game, nothing to eat except what the ships brought them and they did not bring food often. There were no wetus, no longhouses, nothing except bare land. The people built brush pile houses and huddled together to keep warm as the cold winds whipped across the water all around them. A great many died from disease, starvation or the cold. Some tried to swim the icy waters to escape but drowned. Many of the men volunteered to fight with the English if they would let them get off the island and send food to their families.

" I wonder how much they loved their god that winter on the island. Did he send warm robes to them? Did he feed them or give them warm houses?

"This is what the English did to their most loved indians. They told them they were keeping them safe. Safe from what?

"The praying village of Wabquasett was near the island I brought the quansik people to. Although the Wabquassets had a fort they knew they would be attacked by Mohegans so they came to us and asked for refuge and we took them in. They brought much corn with them and my people were grateful for this. The following spring they went back and planted huge cornfields then returned to our island while it grew.

"Two moons before we left Quansik a wounded brave cried to us from the bank of the river and we brought him over. He reported that the English captain Talcott had been at the praying village. He knew it was Talcott for his men always wore bright red silk banners across their chests. There was a large army of English, Mohegans, Niantics and Pequots with him. The Christian Indian said their horses had ridden through all their cornfields and trampled the tender corn then visited his praying village at Chabugakungamon.

"He had been on his way to Wabquassit and had seen this. He kept hidden as he followed them into Chabungakungamon. From the trees he watched as they charged into the peaceful village, shooting and waving their swords. The survivor told us he ran into the village to defend his family and was wounded in his side but he managed to escape before they captured him. He said they killed twelve men and seven women and children. They took the rest with them as captives - the men going west with Talcott - and the women and children were sent back south towards Norwich. Throughout the attack Black James and Joseph tried to stop them, shouting to the warriors with Talcott's men to tell them what they had done wrong.

"After they attacked and looted the village the soldiers set fire to the wetus and trampled the corn fields. He told me he heard Talcott give orders to march to Quaboag, so I ordered a party to go and spy on them to see if they were planning to attack us. Up to that point our neutrality had been respected by both sides and we had not been bothered. The attacks on the Christian villages struck fear into our hearts. If this was what they did to those they loved, what would they do to the rest of us?

"As soon as my spies told me Talcott was out of the area - his men having cut down all the corn fields between there and Hadley - I sent word to all of the sachems in Quaboag and Wabbaquaset to sit in council with me.

" I called my brothers together and told them of the raids on Wabquassit and Chabungakungamon. Some of the young warriors were haughty and said the Christians got what they deserved and that they would not have died if they had joined Pometacomet's army. I told them that was not the point.

" I said, 'A strange wind has blown across our land. It will seek us out no matter where we hide. It will find a crack in our wetus and come in and either take us away or kill us. Our corn is gone now. We have no food for the winter. We are like the wolves who sleep on the snow. We have no home. Our noses will be tucked inside our fur to keep us warm as this strange wind howls all around us. We will die or become slaves to the English if we stay here.'

"I said we had to gather all the people together and go west, into Mohawk territory, but John and Sam felt they could write a letter to the English and beg for mercy and they would treat with us. They were returning all the English they had captured so the English would look favorably upon them, they said.

"I laughed in their faces. 'Look how they treat their friends, the Christian tribes! Do you think they will treat you, who have English blood on your hands, any better?'

"Many sachems began sending their people to our island after that meeting and we waited until Talcott left Hadley for Narragansett to send the first party west. Over 200 children and young adults, many of them Wabbaquasetts, were able to escape across the quonicticut and the housatonic river into Mohawk territory.

"While Pometacomet was hiding in the swamp with John Tahattawaban and the others, I led the second party westward. My group was mostly the old women and men. There were about fifty warriors with us, carrying the old people on their backs.

"We traveled by night to a fording place on the chicopee river out of sight of the village of Springfield, to the south. We crossed at night below the great falls by cutting white birches and lashing them together into rafts so the old people could cross. As we were ferrying the last group over we were discovered and shot at but no one was injured. Once across the river we weren't chased on the other side and we walked without stopping, sucking on corn stalks we found along the way for strength.

"My heart was heavy as I looked around and saw one old person after another collapse near the banks of the oussotinoog (Housatonic) river. I knew it would not be long before the English caught up with us. If only we could get across the river!

"While they slept I accompanied the younger braves up and down the bank to find a good fording site. We returned to camp and woke the people up, forcing them onwards. By now the sun was up and we had no cover but we were so close we had to press on.

"As we reached the river bank we heard shouts and then guns as Talcot and his red-striped soldiers came over the rise and rode straight for us.

"The old people suddenly regained their strength and began scrambling into the water. Our warriors held the English back briefly and some of the people made it across but the Mohegans with Talcott had circled around on either side. I saw the old men and women dropping into the water or on the banks all around me. Their blood pooled along the riverbanks then joined the waters of the ossontonig (Housatonic).

"Something snapped inside of me then. I ran towards the English with my hand raised as if to stop the bullets. With tears streaming down my face I yelled, 'I am Konkowasco. Let my people go!'

"Oneko recognized us as the neutral band and shouted for them to stop firing and to let us cross. As he rode over to talk to Talcott, I got the rest of my people across and we disappeared into the woods on the other side, our hearts pounding as we waited to see if we would have to run or if we would be allowed to leave.

"They did not chase us any further. After many sleeps we were met by the Mohawks. They had attacked our first party. After killing a few of the younger people, they had agreed to adopt them - and us. Some stayed on with them and others, like myself, found homes in other villages. This is how those of us from Quansik came to live here in Iroquois territory.

"Most of us who survived the war wanted no more to do with the English or the Dutch or French. But some went on to fight with the Onadogonda against the French. Two winters ago some of those old warriors and their children again raised their tomahawks against the French. Such is their destiny - perhaps the destiny of all our people. Maybe we will never know peace.

"Those who fled from Quansik wanted only to find a place far away from the whites so we could live as we had before they came across the ocean. You children have never known a time when the land belonged only to us so you do not know what we wanted, what we searched for here in the land of the Iroquois. We didn't want their guns anymore, we didn't want their wool or their pork or their knives or copper kettles. These things carried too high a price.

" Some of the Quansiks returned shortly after the war and lived in the woods like animals, hiding from the English. They and their children continue to live there today and will live there tomorrow if they can find a way to become invisible.

" But for me, I like to sit on a high rock in the sun and smoke to Creator. I like to sing and beat a drum loudly so all the winds can hear. I will die just as I lived - free.

Konkowasco stands there, his eyes falling on each little brown face as he says,

"Many of the things we have told you are not new, for the Oneida live much as we did. But we have shown how it was in Quansik, for we cannot separate our memories from our home. To us, the water will always be colder and clearer at the falls on the quanicticut river and on the quinnabaug. The hills will always be greener and the sky bluer in the land of our grandfathers.

"Many of the things we have told you are not things normally shared in the open, but are private things saved for sacred initiations. However, the day is not far away when only one of you will have pure Quansik blood in your veins. We do not know who this will be so we tell all of you everything in the hope that the last Quansik will continue to tell his or her children these things, and they theirs, until the time of the seventh fire when they will return to our lands.

"We know not what terrible thing we have done to make Cautantowwit so angry with us. Every day we pray that he will again listen to his children and send a plague to wipe out the English. But he does not listen. Some say he is alseep or can't hear us over the noise of the white man. Others say the white man's medicine has driven him away. But I believe he is teaching us a lesson and we must be patient while he plays a game with the white man.

"There will come a day when Quansiks will once again walk the hills and valleys of their grandfathers. When that day comes, your children's children must remember these things. Keep them in your hearts always so the circle will not be broken and our people will not die.

"As long as the rivers in Quansik flow and the eagle flies over the waddaquadducks, the spirit of our grandfathers will live on in the land of the long hills and the long waters."

Chapter 39
(Konkowasco tells of his years after the war and his entry into the Dancing Lodge of the Dead, 1698)

The Memory and Passing ceremony is over. The Oneida villagers are at the falls, fishing. Konkowasco remains behind with his fellow midewiwin lodge members. Today there will be two ceremonies for him: he will undergo his fourth-degree initiation into the medicine lodge and perform his Last Singing.

The ceremony is preceded by a purification sweat in which his mentor tells him again that the stone in the middle of the lodge represents the rock used in the sweat bath. Many years past when Konkowasco became an initiate of the first order, he was taught the song for the ancient stone, "But it is I who am so mysterious..."

The ceremony for this day includes songs for a blue day (clear, sunny day), and a speech in which Konkowasco is told that the creator of the Midewiwin will make known his great love for him. He is told that white is the color of everlasting life and that the white shell or migis in the sacred otterskin bag will kill the parts of him that have hampered his spiritual quest.

He is led in procession to the lodge. Four times they circle inside the lodge, then make offerings and sing medicine songs. As an initiate of the fourth degree, he enters the rectangular lodgehouse at its northern door, stopping first at the Mother Earth, the center-of-the world stone, then on the blanket in the middle, facing his four medicine poles at the other end. On top of each pole, cut from living trees, is carved the owl. His first degree pole has serpent beings carved into it, his second has bear beings, his third has panther beings and his fourth has witch beings. The fourth one is squared. Its four sides are painted with the colors of the earth's four directions but the top of the pole and its arms are white with red spots representing the spiritual, or medicine strength Konkowasco has acquired during his years as an initiate. It sits west of the sacred stone.

Konkowasco is told to stand still as an elder takes the first of four sacred otterskin bags and points it like a gun at Konkowasco's chest. The powdered white shell shoots Konkowasco. This is done by four elders, each with a different bag. The fourth time, he falls down as if dead and they place all four bags on him, chanting and singing him back to life.

The ceremony then continues as he is taught mor e medicine songs. He is told the mide myths of Manabus and his dead brother Naxpatao and how Manabus told his brother's shadow (spirit) how to get to the land beyond the living. Manabus gave his brother fire so he could see the path and told him to make four plain spaces and a good trail through them marked by pretty flowers so those who would come after him could find the land. The soul would begin its journey imme - diately on this path. It would see a large boulder of strawberries and take some to eat along the way then continue until it reached a deep, swift river with a twisting, turning bridge. After crossing this bridge, if the soul looked back , it would see that the bridge was actually a large snake spanning the river. The journey would take four sleeps, then the soul would arrive in Cautanowwit's garden. Naxpatao was told to make them welcome, to give them food and drink when they arrived and to revive their spirits and bodies with medicine. There was always lots of game and food and always feasting there for new souls arrived each day.

Konkowasco is told the mide will hold a feast for his relatives after he dies. This he knows because they always look after their mide brothers.

Afterwards he addresses the group,

"During the war against my people many parents left their children with John of Packachoog. While my families were crossing the river, John surrendered to the English and turned the children over to them to be raised as servants in English homes. He was told they would be treated well and would learn the teachings of Christ.

"These children were Upacunt's grandson and Nannuntum's son Peter of Quantisit and Woomthe's boys Jabez and Joseph , Santeshes's son Tom and James Natomet's daughter from Packachoog. The Nashaway children were John W ossumpigin's neice Hester and Piambow's cousin Joseph. Nohanet's son Samuel from Chabungagungamug was given as well as Annaweakin's boys Joseph and another whose name I don't remember from Hassanamesit. The Magunkog children were William Wunnuko's sons Joshua, John and Tom. Wunnuko was one of the sachems executed in Boston after the war.

"The English executed most of the warriors who surrendered and then sold their families into slavery to pay for the cost of the war. The Christian indians were told they could only live in five places.

"The largest of these prison villages were on the island of mananticut (Braintree), oustide uncataquissit (Milton) and menchoiset (Dorchester). In these places there were 35 Punkapog braves and 140 squaws and children under the supervision of Thomas Swift. The Naticks were forced to live in four places. James Romneymarsh and his family, with five braves and 20 squaws and children, were allowed to live near the English village of Medfield.

"Ten braves and 20 squaws and children were allowed to live in the building next to Andrew Dewin's house in Natick and Tom Waban was allowed to keep 12 braves and 50 squaws and children with him near the quinobequin (Charles) river falls under the supervision of the English Captain Thomas Prentice. The English allowed 15 braves and their 60 squaws and childen to live at Nowantum hill. They let the 10 braves and 40 squaws and children of the Nashobas stay in musketaquid (Concord) and another seven braves and 33 squaws and children went to live in English houses.

"Wannalancet's people south of the Merrimac river were allowed to live in waymessick (Chelmsford). After crossing the Housatonic, I took my family to Wannalancet's lands farther north in Pigwacket.

"Later the English reduced the area we could live in to three villages: Punkapoag (Canton), Natick and Wamesit (Lowell). The Massachusetts were allowed to live with the English, but were called children of the state and were under the supervision of English.

"Fifteen years after the war, Hyems claimed chief sachemship over all the lands of lower quanebaug/quansik.

"He sold most of the lands in exchange for a five-square mile reservation at chabungagungamug pond. The sachems Waban, his son Tom Waban, Piambow, John Senior, John Jr. and Samuel Awwasamog, Samuel Bowman, Noas' brothers Anthony, Tom and Benjamin Tray (uncles to John Wompus), Jethro, Joseph Amon, Peter Ephraim, Andrew Pityme, Nehemiah, Zachary Abraham, Samuel

Neaucit, George Moonisco, Elizer Pegin, Simon Saconit, Great Jacob, Elisha Milton, and Mecnumion signed the deed with him.

"For twenty English pounds of English money, Hyems, his sons Benjamin and Simon, Sam Jaco, Wolowanonck, PePey Pegans, Papionishot, Allump's son Cotoosowk, Wabuequola and Siebqueat gave away all their land rights.

"Later most of these same sachems, plus the Maine sachem Sassowanno, John Magus of Wachuset, Tom Dubler and "Watertown" William asked the English to give them the rest of their lands back. While they were waiting many moons for a reply, John Wompus sold lands that weren't his and the deeds were challenged by Waban, Piambow, Nowanit, Jethro, William, Anthony and Tom Tray. John Wompus was not the chief sachem of these lands and had no right to sell them. He only sold them for rum.

"The English court took a year to reply but then gave them back the lands between Natick and Hassanamessit, because they felt they were useless. In exchange, the sachems deeded most of central and southern Quansick, commonly called Nipmuck, to the English.

"Two winters later the sachems again wrote to the government protesting the English purchase of the lands at Marlborough. The sachems involved were many of these previous ones plus my uncle Nassowanno, Ono Pequin, John Moqua, Old William Ahaughton, his son William, John Annoquin, Peter Mishquapooge, Anonogut, Peter Bogkotoge and Joshua Ashott. All men. No women, the rightful heirs of the land, signed any of these deeds.

"The following winter the Nipmucks asked for four square miles of Mishalisk's land at Skaucoononk (Squacoononk) in Squakheag. They told the English they wanted them 'so our posterity may not suffer want for future or want for a place to dwell in.' Signing this petition were Awoosamug, Sagamore John's son Squamog, Nassowanno, his son Edwmund, Josias Potaroo, Sunsawinno, John Robin, James Romneymarsh's son Isreal, Noas' son James Printer, Sagamore Sam's son Samuel Nawont, my brother John Nameshoot, Zachary and Joseph Abraham, Peter Ephraim's son Peter, Simon Patacomb, James Wizer, Peter Puttapog from Potipaug, Aquittimaug's son John, my uncle David's son Edward David and Piambow's son Benjamin Boho and his daughters Deborah and Sarah.

"After they got this land, Nassowanno sold the Wombessuck area to the English.

"During all this time, I and many of my people were living north in Panukkog and Natukkog on the malamake river . The Mohawks were constantly raiding our area and we knew if we didn't get help they would kill all of us. So we asked the English for protection.

"They agreed but said we had to sign a peace treaty with them. I signed our plea for protection as John Hawkins (Hogkins). Old Robin and Peter Robin signed, Simon Betogkom, Joseph Traske, King Harry, Samulinis, W apeguanat, T aguachushat, Mamonsques, Andrew, George Roddunnonukgus, Wahoush, Hopehood, John Toneh, John Canoua, John Owamossimin, Nathonill, Netambomet, sachem of Saco, Ned Higgon and Newsome signed with me.

"When they came to our villages with the peace treaty, it had been changed. They added a new provision: we were to remain as prisoners in our villages and if any wanted to leave, we had to first let the English know, otherwise we would be considered enemies.

"When the English king died a short while later, we no longer felt bound to this terrible agreement. I learned that the English were resettling on my father's lands in Quansick and decided to take action into my own hands.

"I called a war council and changed my name to Wawanwejajagtuck and, with Wahacoet and ten others, deliberately left the village. We knew this one act declared us enemies of the English. We had to travel carefully, at night, but in Casco Bay at Cape Porpus as we were making our way south to the Merrimac, an Abnaki spotted us. When he ran to tell the English we killed him with our arrows.

"We followed the Merrimac to upper Quansick, then crossed to Squakeag on foot, searchng for the four miles of land the English had 'given' us. We didn't find the settlement, but we did see English at the Quaboag Plantation fort. We needed guns to drive them away so we crossed the quonicticut and traded for them at Schagticook. Then we traveled downriver to Deerfield. A few sleeps later at a pond in Springfield we tried to get a group of braves to join us to drive the English out of Quansick, but they refused. We were afraid they would tell the English of our plans, so we killed them in their sleep.

"We went through Northfield to see if we could find any Squakeags to join us. In the English village we were stopped in the street by three English men and their women. We killed them all without blinking an eye and then went on to Quaboag. One of the braves said he recognized the young woman from the raid on Quaboag plantation during the war. We celebrated over that and said we would get all of the ones who escaped.

"Rage drove us that summer. Everywhere we went, our people were treated like the dirt the English scraped off their shoes. They lived outside their square villages, trying to look English by wearing their clothes and speaking their tongue, but they were laughed at and despised.

"We were surprised at how our lands were now filled with English. Mother Earth no longer grew our corn. Now she grew English wheat. Her waters now were being used to water English fields and English cattle and hogs.

"Walking through our lands we felt like people from another country.

"It was more than a brave could stand. We were proud of who we were - not sorry and ashamed the way the Christian indians were. My heart was filled with rage every time I met a Christian brother or sister and they couldn't look me in the eye. Their eyes were downcast. They stared at Mother Earth - but knew her not.

"We hung around the fort in Quaboag for a couple of moons while traveling to Quinebaug and Wabbiquasset to see if we could find any non-Christian people in hiding who would join us. We were unsuccessful but we couldn't return to Pigwacket for we were wanted men. While hanging around the fort, we overheard the soldiers say the French had declared war on the English and were looking for indian scouts to help them, so we went north and joined the French army.

"So for almost ten winters, I have been a warrior, fighting with the French to drive the English out of the upper lands.

"We burned and razed the English settlement at Pemaquid to the ground, driving all the English away. During the next three winters we raided so many villages that the only ones left on the eastern side of the Piscataqua River were the English towns of Wells, York and Kittery. But when the French surrendered Port Royal to the north, without even a battle, some of our sachems became uneasy, convinced that the English would be the victors against France. They switched their allegiance and signed a truce with the Boston English. This made the rest of us so angry that we didn't wait for the ice on the rivers to melt to get our revenge. We decided to attack their main town of York on the agamenticus river. For a moon, we traveled by foot, using snowshoes to cover the distance.

"When we got there, we rested on top of agamenticus mountain, planning our attack of the village below. That night we rushed down, our flintlocks booming, our warriors whooping as we killed most of the people and burned all the buildings, except the garrison house, the meeting house and the jail, which were heavily defended.

"We took many captives that night, but what I remember most was that I let one go. This I had never done before. He was only about four winters old yet he stuck out his chin and yelled at me, 'I am Jeremiah Moulton, let me go!' His lack of fear and repeated attempts to escape amused me so much that I finally let him escape into the cold winter night. There was something in his face that I felt was older than the two of us: something that said our paths were joined. I have thought about it often and still don't understand why I let him go.

"During these past years, I had a hope in my heart when I was fighting. A hope that the English would be conquered and driven back to England and that the French would give us our lands back.

"I had a hope, but now it is gone.

"While we were remembering, the English and French became friends. And now we are the common enemy once again."

Konkowasco wipes a tear from his eyes. His voice is very low and soft,

"So now I go to the Dancing Lodge of the Dead. There is no place for me now. I will sing my death song and return to Quansick in the shape of a spirit panther.

"As Spirit Panther I will never leave the lands I loved. I will walk them forever, waiting for the day when the children of Quansick return."

The End.

BIBLIOGRAPHY

This book was based on information obtained in the following books and articles. They are listed for those wishing more detailed informa-tion on a specific subject. The majority of out of print material can be referenced at the American Antiquarian Society in Worcester, Mass.

The Nipmuck Path - Nipmuck School Elders , Chief Wise Owl
The Rhythm of the Land-Debra Ostrokolowicz (unpublished article)
Sex, Seasons, Seeds and Spirits -(unpublished article) Little Turtle
A Guide to Indian Artifacts of the NorthEast -Roger Moeller, American Indian Archaeological Institute, Wash., CT
Ceremonial and Domestic Products of Aboriginal New England -Massachusetts Archaeology Society Bulletin
Classification of Stone Implements of New England -Massachusetts Archaeological Society Bulletin
The Oakholm Site: A Preliminary Report -Karl S. Dodge, Mass. Arch. Soc. Bulletin, 1966
History of Western Massachusetts, Vol. 2, Part 3 -Town of Holland
The Red Man and the White Man in North America -Dr. Ellis
The Making of New England-Samuel Adams Drake, 1898, Scribner and Sons
Handbook of Native American Crafts-Karna L. Bjorkland
Indians of New England America-Jacob Edwards Library, Sturbridge
Indians-Edwin Tunis, World Publishing Co.
Algonquins of the Eastern Woodlands -Edward S. Rogers, Royal Ontario Museum Publications
Indians of the World-George E. Hyde
Indian Reminders in Rhode Island and Connecticut-State St.Trust, Boston, '41
History of Union, Connecticut-Ellen Larned
Native American People, Places, Things -(self-pub.) Paula Mountain Spirit Whynot
Red Man and Black Lead, chapter of Sturbridge Yesterday and Today -Brian Burns, Worc. County Newspapers
The Story of My Adopted Town -(unpub. ms.) Sarah A. Chase, Holland Public Library, Holland, Mass.
Touching the Earth Through Traditional Art Forms -(unpub. ms.) Debra Ostrokolowicz-c/o Chief Wise Owl
Fort Hill Archaeological Study (photostat ms.) - Deerfield Public Library
Native American and Social History, the Confederacies of 17th Century N.E. -(college paper, 1987) Neal Salisbury, Deerfield Public Library
In the Maelstrom of Change: Indian Tribes and Colonial Policy -(Univ. microfilm ms.) Peter Allen Thomas, Deerfield Public Library
Indian Tribes of North America -John R. Swanton, Bureau of American Ethnology, Bull. # 145, 1952
The Hundredth Town - Glimpses of Life in Westborough -Hariette M. Forbes, Westborough Public Library
Lands Occupied by the Nipmuck Indians of Central New England1600-1700 -Dennis A. Connole, Massachusetts Archaeological Society, 1976
History of Windham County-Ellen Larned, Worcester, 1874
The Great Powwow-Clara Sears, Fruitlands Museum, Lancaster, MA.
New England Prospect-William Wood, 1897, Boston
The Nipmuck Path-Slide presentation, the Nipmuc Tribe, Little Turtle

America, B.C.-Barry Fell
Historical Collection of Indians in New England, Indians in New England
-Daniel Gookin, 1970 Towtaid Publishing
Other Indian Events of New England-Allen Forbes, State St.Trust, Boston,'41
The Massachusetts Language-Boston, 1822
A Key Into the Language of America
-Roger Williams, Gregory Dexter, London, 1643
A Reference Encyclopedia of American Indians
-Bernard Klein and Daniel Icolari, B. Klein & Co.
Indians of the United States-Clark Wissler, Doubleday Anchor Books
Native American Indians, Vol. 4-Rose A. Palmer, Smithsonian Series, NY
The American Indian- Dimensions of Ethnicity
-Edward H. Spicer, Belknap Press, Harvard, MA
Picture Writing of the American Indians, 2 vol.-Garrick Mallery, Dover Books
Dictionary of the American Indian
-John Stoutenburgh, jr., Philosophical Library
Indians of the Americas -Matthew Stirling, ed., National Georgraphic Society
The Patriot Chiefs -Alvin M. Josephy, jr., Penguin Books
The Last of the Mohicans -James Fennimore Cooper, Washington Square Press
Letters and Notes on the Customs and Conduct of the Native American Indians, 2 vol.
-George Catlin, Dover Books
I Have Spoken-Virginia Irving Armstrong, Swallow Press
Offering Smoke-Jordan Paper, University of Indiana Press
I Send a Voice- Evelyn Eaton, Quest Books, Theophysical Pub. House, Illinois
Breath of the Invisible-John Redtail Freesoul, Quest Books
A Short History of the Indians of the United States
- Edward H. Spicer, Robert E. Kriger Pubb. Co., Florida
The Indians Who Met The Pilgrims
-(teacher's guide), Children's Museum of Boston
Voices of the Winds-Margot Edmonds and Ella E. Clark, Facts on File Pub.
Touch the Earth
-(speeches) compiled by T.C. McLuhan, Simon and Schuster, Touchstone
Indian New England Before the Mayflower
-Howard S. Russell, University Press of New England
Iroquois Stories -Joseph Bruhac, The Crossing Press
Legends of the Iroquois -William W. Canfield, A. Wessels Co., NY
The World's Rim
-Clyde Kluckhohn, University of Nebraska Press, Bison Book
Indian Place Names of New England
-John C. Hudson, The Museum of American Indian, Heye Foundation
Cautantowwit's House (Narragansett Burial Ground)
-William Scranton Simmons, Brown University Press
Tales of the Eastern Woodlands and More Tales of the Eastern Woodlands
-(cassette tapes) Medicine Story, Story Stone Co.
Story Telling Stone -ed., introduction Susan Feldman, Dell
Indian Tales -(retold by) Joseph and Edith Raskin, Random House
Legends of the Longhouse
-Jesse J. Cornplanter, intro. Carol Cormer, Empire State Hist. Soc.
Mythology of North America-John Bierhorst, William Morrow &Co.
Handbook of American Indian Games
-Allen and Paulette MacFarlan, Dover Books
Names on the Land-George R. Stewart, Random House, Canada

The Sex Life of the American Indian-Jack Glover, Cow Puddle Press
The Ordeal of the Longhouse
-Daniel K. Richter, University of North Carolina Press
Tales of Native American Indians
-Stith Thompson, ed., Indiana University Press
Foxfire Books-Eliot Wissinton, Anchor Books
Nature's Year-John Hay, Ballentine Books
New England Rarities-John Josselyn, Mass.Historical Society
Native American Sourcebook-Barbara Robinson, Concord Museum
Native American Indians Before the Coming of the Europeans
-Philip Kopper, Smithsonian Books
New England Series: First Contact up to 1675-Bob Eaton, Mohawk Arts
The Last Indian Raids-ibid
Famous Indian Tribes-Random House
The New England Indians-Keith Wilbur, Globe Pequot Press
Search for the Purebloods-Charles Banks Wilson, Univ. of Oklahoma Press
Rooted Like the Ash Trees-Richard G. Carlson, ed., Eagle Wing Press
We're Still Here-Joan A. Lester, Children's Museum of Boston
Encyclopedia of Native American Indian Tribes-Bill Yenne, Arch Cape Press
The Smithsonian Chronicle of Native American Indians after Columbus
-Herman J. Viola, Orion Books
The Spirit of Native America-Anna Lee Walters, Chronicle Books
Indian Dances of North America
-Reginald and Gladys Laubin, University of Oklahoma Press
The Ambiguous Iroquois Empire-Francis Jennings, Norton Publishers
The Indian How Book-Arthur C. Parker, Dover Books
Wolf Dog of the Woodland Indians
-Margaret Zehmer Searcy, Univeristy of Alabama Press
Indians of the Woodlands-George E. Hyde, University of Oklahoma Books
Indians of the Americas -Edwin R. Embree, Houghton Mifflin
Native American Indian Arts-Andrew Hunter Whiteford, Golden Press
Indian Deeds of Hampden County, Mass.-Harry Wright, ed., Springfield, 1905
Book of Indian Records for their Lands-Wilbraham Public Library
The Winthrop Papers, Pinchon Records
-Eva Butler papers, The Indian and Colonial Research Center, Mystic, Ct.
Rhode Island Colony Records-Mathias Speiss
Records of Oxford-Oxford, Mass.
Mason to Talcott letter-Eva Butler papers, Indian and Colonial Research Center
Hopkin's Account-(ms.) Timothy Woodbridge
Plymouth Colony Records, Records of the Colony of Massachusetts Bay in New England and Massachusetts Senate Records
-University of Massachusetts, Amherst, research library
The Lead Mines at Tantiesque-Charlton Historical Society, 1989
The Quinebaug River-Harry E. Bock, Quinebaug Historical Soc. leaflets, 1903
The Tale of Tantiesques
-George H. Haynes, American Antiquarian Society Proceedings, 1901
The Indians of This Locality
-Mrs. George K. Dresser, Quinebaug Historical Society Leaflets, 1900
Gazetteer of Massachusetts
-John Hayward, Boston, 1846-The Rev. Elias Nason, B.B. Russell, Boston
History of Holland, Massachusetts-The Rev. Martin Lovering, 1915
Early History to 1783 (Holland)-Corinne L. Goodhall, U.S. Bicentennial , 1976

History of Palmer-Josiah Howard Temple, 1889
History of Brookfield-Josiah Howard Temple
History of Worcester County-Peter Whitney, C.F. Jewett & Co., Boston
Our County and Its People-(for the town of Monson), Dr. George E. Fuller
Narrative of the Captivity and Restoration of Mrs. Mary Rowlandson
-Mary Rowlandson 1600s
Eliot's Brief Narrative-Old South leaflets, #21, 1670
A New England Town: the First Hundred Years
-Kenneth A. Lockridge, W. W. Norton
The Changing Face of New England-Betty Flanders Thomson, MacMillan Co.
Quabaug Plantation alias Brookfield-Dr. Louis E. Roy, Heffernon Press, Worc.
Chronicles of Old Salem-Frances Diane Robotti, Bonanza Books
Old Boston in Colonial Days-Mary Caroline Crawford, The Page Co., Boston
Changing New England-Edward Elwell Whiting, The Century Co.
Puritanism in New England-Alan Simpson, University of Chicago Press
The Seventeenth Century Background-Basil Willey, Doubleday Anchor
Massachusetts Federal Writers Project-Joseph Gaer, ed., Houghton Mifflin
The First Frontier: Life in Colonial America-John C. Miller, Dell Books
Once Upon a Time in Rhode Island
-Katerine Pyle, Country Life Press, Doubleday, Page & Co.
Picture Guide to Historic Plymouth-Rose T. Brigs, ed., Pilgrim Society
Manitou and Providence-Neal Salisbury, Oxford University Press, NY
The Massachusetts Bay Colony, 2 vol.-Leo Bonfanti, Pride Publications, Inc.
Biography and Legends of the New England Indians Vol. 1-5-ibid
The American Colonies 1492-1750
-Marcus Wilson Jernegan, Fredrick Unger Pub. Co.
Rhode Island-Irving Berdine Richman, Houghton Mifflin Co.
Cotton Mather-Barrett Wendell, Dodd, Mead & Co.
Springfield Present and Prospective-James Tower, ed., Pond & Campbell Pub.
The Plymouth Adventure-Ernest Gebler, Doubleday & Co.
Labor in a New Land: Economy and Society in 17th Century Springfield
-Stephen Innes, Princeton University Press
Fur Trappers and Traders-Beatrice Siegal, Walker & Co., NY
Changes in the Land-William Cronan, Hill and Wang
Homes in the Wilderness: Pilgim Journal of Plimouth Plantation, 1620 by William Bradford and others of the Mayflower Co.
-Margaret Wise Brown, ed., Linnet Books, Hamden, Ct.
A Little Commonwealth: Family Life in Plymouth Colony
-John Demos, Oxford University Press
Of Plymouth Plantation
-William Bradford, Harvey Wish, ed., Capricorn Books, NY
Saga of the Pilgrims-John Harris, Globe Pequot Press
A Journal of the Pilgrims at Plymouth (Mourt's Relation)-Corinth Books
Puritan Village-Summer Chilton Powell, Wesleyan University Press
Founding the American Colonies 1583-1660
-John E. Pomfret with Floyd M. Shumway, Harper Torch Books
Mayflower Heritage-D. Kenelm Winslow, Funk and Wagnall Co.
The Puritan Dilemna (Story of John Winthrop)
-Edmund S. Morgan, Scott, Foresman and Co.
Boy on the Mayflower-Iris Vinton, TAB Books
The Pocumtuck Confederacy
-George Sheldon, Springfield Museum Publication

Land of the Nonotucks
-C. Keith Wilbur, Northampton Historical Society, Northampton, Mass.
King Philip's War-George W. Ellis and John E. Morris, Grafton Press, NY
The Indians of Connecticut-Mathias Spiess, Ct. Tercentenary, Yale Univ. Press
History of the Indians of Connecticut-John W. DeForest
Notes Towards a Documentary Nipmuc History
-Thomas Doughton, Nipmuc Tribal Acknowledgment Project
Notes on the Pegan Indians of Dudley-ibid
Valley of the Nipmucks-Webster Times
Biography and History of the Indians of North America, Books 2 and 3
-Samuel Drake
Wars of America, Vol 1-Robert Leckie, Bantam Books
The Enslavement of the American Indian
-Barbara Oleyey, Library Research Assoc., Monroe, NY
Flintlock and Tomahawk: New England in King Philip's War
-Douglas Edward Leach, Norton Library
Soldiers in King Philip's War-George Madison Bodge, Leominster, 1896
Dawnland Encounters
-Colin G. Calloway, ed., University Press of New England, 1991
Algonkians of New England, Past and Present
-Dublin Seminar 1991, ed. Peter Benes, Boston University Press
Pequot-Mohegan War
-Leo Bonfanti, Pride Publications, Inc.
Massasoit-Alvin G. Weeks, Plimpton Press, Norwood, Mass.
King Philip
-John S. C. Abbott, Harper and Brothers, Makers of History Series
The Skulking Way of War
-Patrick M. Malone, John Hopkins University Press
So Dreadful a Judgement: Puritan Responses to King Philip's War
-James K. Folsom, Richard Slotkin, ed., Wesleyan University Press
The New England Company-William Kellaway, Barnes and Noble
New England Frontier- Puritans and Indians, 1620-75
-Alden T. Vaughan, Little, Bron & Co.
The Pequots in Southern New England
ed. Laurance M. Hauptman and James D. Wherry, Univ. Of Okla. Press
Indians of New Jersey-M. R. Harrington, Rutgers University Press
Vermont Indians-Thomas E. Daniels, Journal Press, Poultney, VT
The Conspiracy of Pontiac-Francis Parkman, Collin Books, NY
Historic Hampshire in the Connecticut Valley
-Clifton Johnson, Northampton Historical Society, 1932
History of Oxford-George F. Daniels
Records of Oxford -Nipmuck and Huegenot-Mary deWitt Farland
The Native American in Heritage of Horizon
-Woodstock tercentenary, Kevin McBride and Mary Salisbury, 1986
An Atlas of Massachusetts River Systems
-Walter E. Bickford and Ute Janik Byman, UMass Amherst Press
Maps of Early Massachusetts-Lincoln A. Dexter (self-published)
Atlas of the Quabbin Valley and Ware River Diversion-J.R. Greene (self-pub.)
The New England Prospect, Maps, Place Names and Historic Landscapes
-Dublin Seminar for New England Folklife, Boston University
Maps of Sturbridge, May 6, 1795 &1860s-Jacob Edwards Library, Sturbridge
Tantiesques Hill Survey, 1643 for Winthrop-ibid

Sturbridge Area Survey, 1725-ibid
Headwaters of the Quinebaug River-Quinebaug Historical Society leaflets
"Sturbridge Lead Mine Named as Historic Site"
-(Article) *The News*, Jan. 1984 and May 7, 1984
Early Holland Topographical Map-Lovering, History of Holland, 1915
Old Plymouth Trails-Winthrop Packard, Winthrop Packard, Inc.
Exploring the Housatonic River and Valley
-James and Margaret Cawley, A.S. Barnes and Co., London
Great Trail of New England, Journey of John Withrop the Younger, 1645
-George C. Hughes
Great Trail of New England-Harold Ayres, Forum Publishing Co.
Early Topographical Map of Brimfield-J. Morse, Brimfield Public Library
Area Topographical Maps
-United States Geographical Survey Topographical Map Service
History of Palmer-J.H. Temple. 1889
Land of the Nipmuck and Neighboring Tribes
-James E. Atchenson P.E., 1975, Millville, MA
Trails of the Algonquian Tribes-ibid
Interpretation of Woodward and Saffrey's Map of 1642
-Quinebaug Historical Society Leaflets, Vol. 1, #7
Early Indian Trails Through Tantiesques
-Quinebaug Historical Society Leaflets, Vol. 1, #6
The Bay Path and Along the Way-Levi Badger Chase, Plimpton Press
1975 U. S. Dept. of Agriculture Study of Central Mass. Forests, Rivers, Soil
-Published 1978

Shaman's Path-Gary Doore, Shambhala, Boston and London
Native Healer-Medicine Grizzleybear Lake, Quest Books
The Sacred Path-John Bierhorst, Quill, NY
Birdstones of the American Indians
-ed. Townsend, Heiman Imported Books
Medicine Women, Curanderas and Woman Doctors
-Perrone, Storkel and Krueger, University of Oklahoma Press
Mother Earth-Sam D. Gill, University of Chicago Press
Magic, Myth and Medicine-D.T. Atkinson, M.D., Fawcett Books
Warriors of the Rainbow
-William Willoya and Vinson Brown, Naturegraph Publications, CA
The Way of the Shaman-Michael Harner, Harper, San Francisco
Manitou - The Sacred Landscape of New England Native Civilization
-James E. Mavor, jr. and Byron E. Dix, Inner Traditions, International
Native North American Spirituality of the Eastern Woodlands
-Elisabeth Tooker, ed., Paulist Press
The Practical Botanist-Rick Imes, Fireside Books, Simon and Schuseter
How Indians Use Wild Plants for Food, Medicine and Crafts
-Frances Densmore, Dover Books
The Spirit of the New England Tribes-William S. Simmons, Univ.Press of N.E.
Wildwood Wisdom-E. Jaeger, Iroqrafts
American Indian Medicine-Virgil J. Vogel, University of Oklahoma Press
Wild Edible Plants of New England-Joan Richardson, Globe Pequot Press
Earthway-Mary Summer Rain, Pocket Books
Daughters of the Earth: The Lives and Legends of American Indian Women
-Carolyn Niethammer, Collier Books

Herbal Healing for Women
-Rosemary Gladstar, Fireside Books, Simon and Schuster
A Modern Herbal, Vol. 1 & 2-Mrs. M. Grieve, Dover Books
The Compleat Herbal-Ben Charles Harris, Barre Publications, Mass.
Old N. E. Curious Customs and Cures-Robert Ellis Cahill, Old Saltbox Pub.
Herbalist and Alchemist, Inc.-Bloomsbury, New Jersey
Native American Herbal Workshop-Earthshine (Debbie Hayes), Monson, MA
David Winston and Joe Rose (Lectures)
-N.E. Native American Institute Conference, Boxborough, Mass., 1992
New England and the Medicine Men and Witch Doctor
-(Article) Hasmann and Haynes, *New England Galaxy*, Spring 1967

MISCELLANEOUS REFERENCE SOURCES

Tom Brown's Field Guide to Nature and Survival
-Tom Brown, jr., Berkley Publishing
Complete Field Guide to North American Wildlife
-Joy Ellis Ransom, Harper & Row
Spotter's Guide to Birds of North America-Dr. Philip Burton, Mayflower Book
Guide to Fishing-George S. Fichter, Phil Francis, Dr. Herbert Zim, ed., Golden
Outdoor Life's Deer Hunting Book - Jack O'Connor, Harper & Row
Wildflowers at at Glance-Julius King, Harter Publishing Co.
"Weeds and Wildflowers of New England - a Commentary"
(Article) Sarah P. Ingalls, New England Galaxy
Stars- a Guide to the Constellations, Sun, Moon, etc.
-Dr. Herbert S. Zim, Golden Nature, Simon and Schuster
American Natural History-William T. Hornaday, Charles Scribers Sons
Trees- a Guide to Familiar American Trees
-Dr. Herbert S. Zim, Golden Nature Guide, Golden Press

MISCELLANEOUS NEWSPAPER AND MAGAZINE ARTICLES

"Twilight of the Nipmucs"-Sarah Anne Swift, *The Villager,* Nov./Dec., 1973
"Savages vs. Puritans"-Geraldine R. Foty, *Worcester T&G* 11/20/83
Series of Interviews with Nipmuc Leaders
-Gene Merrit and Cindy Gormley, *The News*, 11/24/84, 12/1/84
"Nipmucs Give Thanks For Charter"-David P. Koval, *Worcester T&G*, 3/29/82
"Indian Lore and Legend"
-series by T.R.I.B.E., *The Palmer Journal*, 4/22/82 and July - Sept., 1982
"West Brookfield Was a Large Indian Village"
-Edith Holmes, *New Leader* reprint from *TriTown Weeklies*, 5/27/1938
"Bay Path - Black Lead Mine"
-Mary Anna Tarbell, *Sunday Republican*, 7/30/1922
"Private Group Preserves Resources"-*Worcester T&G* 3/5/1967
"Tantiesques Reservation"-Andrew Howarth, *Evening News*, 9/5/1973
"Leadmine"-Andrew Howarth, *Shoppng News*, 9/12/1973
"Green Bean Thanksgiving Ceremony"-Barbara Davis, *Journal Bulletin*, 7/92
"Discovery of Campsite Hidden Behind Wall of Secrecy"
-Frederick A. Smock, *Worcester Telegram and Gazette*, 1/12/86
"Glimpses of Indian Hill"-Anna Tarbell, *Springfield Union*, 10/18/1933
"Brimfield Indian Relics- Lectures of Professor Brown"
-Anna Tarbell, *Springfield Union*, 9/22/1912 and 6/20/1912
"Indians Families Who Lived in This Vicinity"
-Mrs. Joseph Woods, *Warren Herald*, 6/18/1897

"Palmer Indian Trails"-*Union News*, 2/5/1907
"When Indians Lived in Palmer"
-O.P. Allen, paper read to Palmer Historical Society, early 1900s
"Indian Pride"-Pat Cahill, *Sunday Republican*, 10/10/1993
"Local Native American Finds Roots in Area History"
-Carol Campbell, *On the Common*, 9/5/1990

INTERVIEWS, LECTURES

Lecture Series on the Nashaways -Mary Ann McCloud, Sterling, Mass., 1991

Interviews about aspects of Native American culture:
Nipmuc Chief Wise Owl, Nipmuc Medicine Man Little Turtle, Paul White (Gentle Moose), D.J. McBride (White Thunder), Princess Winona, Arrowmaker, Peter Silva, Eagle Strong Sun Heart, Joe Rose, David Winston, Rudy Martin, Joe Salzano and Alan Leveilee.

Interviews about local Native American history:
the Freeman family, Brimfield, Richard Cox, Brimfield, Richard Sullivan, Brimfield, Ada Merchant and David Worth, Wales (and many others too numerous to list).

INDEX IS ARRANGED AS FOLLOWS:

NATIVE AMERICAN WORDS

PLANETS/ SEASONS

NATIVE AMERICAN LIFE

NATIVE AMERICAN PERSONAL NAMES

* indicates fictional character, some with historic names

NATIVE AMERICAN PLACE NAMES

NATIVE AMERICAN PLANT USES FOR FOOD AND MEDICINE

Medicinals:

N. E. NATIVE AMERICAN TRIBES

ENGLISH NAMES - PERSONAL, ETC.

ENGLISH TOWN NAMES

See page 357 for Index layout information

ORDER FORM

PANTHER PUBLISHING
P.O. Box 181
Wales, MA 01081
(413) 245-6655

Please send ( ) copies of the book **The Pond Dwellers** by Kelly Savage to:

Name______________________________

Street______________________________

City or Town__________________________

State______________ Zip ___________

For each book ordered, include a check or money order made out to Panther Publishing for: $16.95 plus 5.0 percent sales tax (Mass. residents) and $2 for shipping. Allow 4-6 weeks for delivery.

Thank you for your order.